XANTHIPPIC DIALOGUES

Other books by
Roger Scruton
include

NON-FICTION

Art and Imagination
The Aesthetics of Architecture
The Meaning of Conservatism
Sexual Desire
The Philosopher on Dover Beach

FICTION

Fortnight's Anger
Francesca
A Dove Descending

XANTHIPPIC DIALOGUES

comprising: *Xanthippe's Republic; Perictione's Parmenides;*
and *Xanthippe's Laws;*
together with a version, probably spurious, of
Phryne's Symposium

Edited by
Roger Scruton

SINCLAIR-STEVENSON

First published in Great Britain 1993 by
Sinclair-Stevenson Limited
an imprint of Reed Consumer Books Limited
Michelin House, 81 Fulham Road, London SW3 6 RB
and Auckland, Melbourne, Singapore and Toronto

British Library Cataloguing in Publication Data
A CIP catalogue record for this book is available from the British Library.

ISBN 1 85619 281 4

Typeset by Wilmaset Ltd, Birkenhead, Wirral
Printed in England by Clays Ltd, St Ives plc

Contents

Editor's Preface	1
A Note of Scholarship	8
Xanthippe's Republic	9
Perictione's Parmenides	41
Xanthippe's Laws	99
Phryne's Symposium	173
Index	271

Editor's Preface

When I left university, thirty years ago, my only friend was Plato, and I travelled with him to the Cyclades. The tourist trade had not yet robbed the islands of their beauty, nor the people of their innocence, and as I roamed the quiet ports, sleeping now in whitewashed cottages, now beneath the stars, it seemed only a matter of days before I would be visited by some divine inspiration – perhaps by the *daimonion* of Socrates himself. The book that I projected was to cancel all those centuries of weary scholarship, and to show the Plato whom the Greeks had known.

The days turned to weeks, the weeks to months, and one morning, when the ship on which I travelled entered the oily roadways of Piraeus, I acknowledged failure. My senses longed for the fecund dreariness of home; while my mind, far from taking wing in that pure air, had stayed perched amid its old possessions. I stood at the rail, and watched the porters as they chattered on the quay: enough remained of my mother's legacy to settle me in London, and in a few hours I could be flying home, with all this throng of careless life behind me.

The packboat that sailed each week for Alexandria was docked beside us, and I turned to watch the travellers who boarded it: a few official-looking men, with scarcely any luggage, moving slowly and silently as though under orders. Suddenly my gypsy companion gave me a sharp punch in the ribs.

'Egypt,' she cried. 'That's where you'll make your discovery! And there's your boat!'

I pressed her to explain herself, but she, pocketing my fifty drachmas (a decent sum, considering she had taken two hundred more when she thought I was sleeping), laughed in an animal way, and ran down the gangway to the quay. Her bare feet slapped on the briny planking and her long skirts danced at her knees. I watched her until, without another glance in my direction, she met a group of her fellows, was absorbed without a greeting, and swept irrevocably away. The pang of sadness turned into a decision, and I resolved to take my gypsy girl's advice: it was the only real idea that Greece had offered me.

Rococo hotels crowded the shore of Alexandria, their Hollywood opulence comic in decay. Billboards and posters disfigured the façades, where families clustered in open windows, and bearded sheikhs smoked hookahs in the doorways, spitting sideways on to the dirt-encrusted marble. The white-hot sky throbbed above the town: it seemed as though a myriad spotlights had been mounted there, each concentrated on some sizzling fragment below. Along the sea-front cars went hooting and buses roared, while people jostled on the pavements. Many were soldiers, who moved side by side, half marching, half dancing, with little fingers locked in friendship. Wrinkled boys chanted suras over empty begging bowls; their faces were blank and ageless, like tombstones worn away by the desert wind. Thin-faced men in jellabas shouted their wares, while throngs of adolescents drifted by the kiosks, snatching paper cones of chick-peas and salty pickles, or pausing over a plate of pullets' eggs, baked brown and crumbled on a bed of beans.

From time to time a short-sleeved clerk, symbol of the new socialist order, would hurry out of a side street, clutching a plastic briefcase, and looking fixedly before him, as though determined to show that he, at least, had a destination. But soon he would be lost in the amorphous crowd, his body carried by the stream which poured through tin-covered cinemas and soda fountains, along oil-smeared sands and dusty alleyways, to lose itself in rubbishy whirlpools, which slopped into the darkened doorways and ran backwards to the sun. As the waves of people washed across the city, eroding its crust of elegance, and thronging the marble halls with a life for which they were never intended, a multitudinous noise arose, the voice of an Arab crowd, ringing like a metal hammer against the gong of the sky.

This was a great city, where Europe placed a foot in Africa. And still here and there – in the lonely eye of a caryatid, in a broken stretch of ornamental railing, in the stone façade of a warehouse that was once a church – I could catch a glimpse of Europe's luxuriant decay. But it quickly vanished beneath the human tide. Alexandria's elegy had been sung by Cavafy and again by Lawrence Durrell; its ageing denizens had now been chased from their *garçonnières* by Gamal Abdul Nasser.

2

Scarcely a resident could recall the epoch of nostalgia, still less feel any ripple of the city's ancient greatness, long since vanished under the encroaching sea. Alexandrian life was anarchic, pitiless, corrosive as the desert wind which blew its sand-filled streamers through the alleyways. I fled to the empty cafés on the promontory, to the *quartier grec*, where abandoned villas sank beneath their rampant gardens, to Pastroudis' restaurant, in which a few departing foreigners spent what they could of their worthless currency, and to the bar of Cecil's hotel, where I sat, the only customer, waited on by silent figures as a lonely sheep is waited on by crows. My thoughts turned once more to England, and I was about to enquire at the one remaining travel agent – the Tourist Board of the United Arab Republic of Egypt and Syria – when I made the discovery which the gypsy girl had prophesied.

West from the waterfront, past the old suburbs of stone, with their shadowy windows and streets smelling of urine, stood the unfinished tenements, where uncountable families clambered through the concrete skeletons, their radios competing in the stifling air. There, not far from the stinking waters of the Mareotic Lake, stood a Coptic shrine, dedicated to the blessed Nawal, a holy woman of local fame. I like to think that it stands there still, its single palm-tree drooping in the windless courtyard, and behind it the old house of brick, with imported Parisian window-frames, wrought-iron veranda, roof of corrugated sheeting caked with camel-dung, and a notice hanging between the upstairs windows, announcing the House of Hind. I like to think that beans, kebabs and hummus, mint tea and Coca-Cola still are promised there, and that more interesting wares are still to be obtained.

In *Bait Hind* the air was cool, and many were they who entered from the streetless wastes outside: carriers and bricklayers, electricians and repairmen, vendors of radios, water, dried figs and camel hide – the drifting tide of the half employed, who would wander from place to place in search of a few piastres, and who formed the social undertow of Egypt. They came together on terms of strict equality, since all must queue for service at the marble counter, and none could sit until money had changed hands. People came for rest and refreshment, and not for chatter. Once installed, however, you could sit all day. You could read without being pitied for your loneliness. And from time to time you would meet women who looked you in the face, and who had access to the rooms upstairs.

Hind herself was about forty, with a grey burnous wrapped always around her handsome features. Day and night she stood at the counter, shouting to the men who came, and sometimes singing, in long, breathy phrases, of the hopeless pain of love. Her eyes were a dreamy olive-green, her skin pale from years of sunlessness. And her expression, as she kept steady vigil at the sparsely furnished counter, was one of quiet cunning, as though secretly planning an event that would shake the world.

I had been coming to *Bait Hind* for a week before she spoke to me. It was midday, we were alone together, and I had just returned to my studies after a pneumatic drill, which had been squealing all morning like an importunate child, suddenly hissed and died.

'*Ya sayyidi*,' she volunteered; 'I feel sorry for your mother.'

'My mother,' I replied, 'is dead.'

'May all her health be yours,' said she politely.

There was a silence during which Hind stared fixedly out of the doorway, and I pondered her words. After a minute she spoke again.

'It is not surprising that your mother is dead.'

'How so?'

'She grieved to see you reading.'

'Is it a crime to read?' I asked.

Hind ducked beneath the marble counter and surfaced with a bottle from which she poured *araq* into two thick glasses. By convention she never left the counter except to the hidden rooms behind; I rose, therefore, and we drank together standing.

'*Ahlan wa sahlan*,' said she, lifting her glass.

'*Nakh biki.*'

I raised my glass in turn.

'It's a crime to read when you do nothing else.'

'I walk here each day from the city. That's something else.'

She smiled, showing a cluster of gold teeth.

'Have it your own way. And do you read these old things too?'

'What old things?'

She took from the drawer behind the counter a stiff yellow folio, which had crumbled a little at the edges. It was unmistakably a papyrus. Both sides were covered in black script, with editorial signs – diple, obelus, cereaunium, dotted anti-sigma – showing that some scholiast had been to work on it. I studiously contained my excitement while Hind wiped the counter with her sleeve, and carefully laid the papyrus down on it.

'Where did you find it?'

'Can you read it?' she asked.

'I could try.'

'It was my mother's. And her mother's before her. And they say – I do not know how truly – that it once belonged to the woman of the shrine.'

'To the Blessed Nawal?'

'The same. Who had it from Zubaida grand-daughter of Fatima, sister of Hakim the wise, Imam of the Prophet, may the blessing and peace of Allah be upon him. And Hakim's second wife had obtained it from a Coptic monk in the desert, who had inherited it from a saint.'

'And how had the saint obtained it?'

'They say it came to him from the holy Alexandra, she who washed the feet of St Anthony, may Christ grant him eternal joy.'

'And you believe this?'

Hind shrugged her shoulders.

'I neither believe nor disbelieve.'

'And from whom did Alexandra receive it?'

'They say from a Roman woman who befriended her, who had it from Ankhe, great grand-daughter of Ptolemy, priest of Osiris, who himself had borrowed it from some library which burned down before he could return it – you see the library's stamp there.'

She pointed to a mark at the top of the papyrus, printed in Gothic script: *Ex Libris Charlotte Schüler* and, written beside it, *1 Januar 1881, von meiner Mutter.*

'You may be right!' I exclaimed. 'How do you know so much about Hakim the wise, St Anthony and the cult of Isis? Do I suspect you of reading?'

'Ah, once I read. But then the foreigners left, trade went to the dogs and – well, *tamusratu*, I went Egyptian.'

'And can you read this?'

'Alas no; it is in English, for the English had charge of Egypt then. Maybe you could tell me what it says.'

A palimpsestic hand had colonized the folio and the black squads of lettering fought each other across the page. In a clearer space at the bottom I read: 'Pisces: II lib. Pan: III Or. Flam: IV min. Sal. IX. ex vill. apud occ.'

'It's a shopping list.'

'Is it worth anything?'

'Possibly.'

'Then take it,' she said, pushing the papyrus towards me.

'What?'

'Take it for your mother's sake.'

'*Sayiddati* Hind, I could not possibly.'

'Take it, read it, and let me know what it says. *Insh Allah*, you may be surprised. And when you have finished, bring it back to me, and I shall let you have another.'

I need not say how eagerly I returned to the sparsely furnished room in the Hotel al-Dajajah, where my books and papers were spread across the marble table. For once the honking of cars and buses, the screaming of hawkers, the cooing of whores in the nearby windows, the wailing of radios, even the plopping and scraping of cockroaches, as they fell from the ceiling or scuttled about the floor, did not disturb my thoughts. By the cool hours of morning I had extracted from the papyrus not only the Roman shopping list which occupied its lower left-hand corner, and the pornographic graffiti, no doubt the work of one of Hind's clients, which disfigured the upper part, but also the beginning of a Socratic dialogue, composed in Attic Greek, and written out in the meticulous hand of some Alexandrian scholar. I was at once convinced that I had before me the opening fragment of the lost *Xanthippe's Republic*, a dialogue which was certainly in existence in the fourth century BC, and which is indeed obscurely referred to in several ancient sources. (For example, Pamphila, *Memorabilia*, 26, i; Arete, *On Sophistical Weaving*, 509D; Sosipatra (concerning whom, *vide* Eunapius, *Lives of the Philosophers*, 469), *On Notorious Women*, 359E.)

I transcribed the sheet, and, having slept but two hours, returned to *Bait Hind* to obtain its successor. After the usual exchange of compliments, and having looked about her to ascertain that no one was privy to our conversation, Hind asked me what I thought of the piece of cardboard.

'The papyrus? Oh yes, the one you lent me yesterday. I have it here somewhere.' I took it from my bag and placed it on the counter. 'Not very interesting, I am afraid. A shopping list, as I suspected.'

'A shame, *sayyidi*. Then you will not require to see any more?'

'I didn't say that. You never know, there is always a chance of finding some scrap of useful information.'

'Then,' she said, with a friendly smile, 'you would be willing perhaps to pay five dollars – I ask for so small a sum, you understand, for your poor mother's sake.'

'Five dollars? For another shopping list?'

'The German gentleman who came this morning offered ten.'

'German gentleman? What German gentleman?'

'He did not leave a name. But stay till the sun goes down, and *insh Allah* you will meet him.'

Of course, I had no such intention. Hind had her five dollars; and the ten dollars she asked on the next day, and the twenty dollars on the day thereafter. When I discovered, in addition to *Xanthippe's Republic*, two further dialogues, nowhere mentioned in the literature (unless the obscure remark of Plotinus, at *Enn.* XII. 3 [62] 14. 10–12, should be, as I suspect, a reference to *Perictione's Parmenides*), I realized that I must accept the terms that Hind dictated, lest the world of scholarship be deprived of one of the greatest discoveries since the Rosetta stone. I only regret that, in order to obtain each folio, I was obliged to return its predecessor, so that the papyrus remained in private hands, awaiting the next lonely scholar whom the need for female company should bring to *Bait Hind*.

In England my discoveries were treated with scorn. Mortified, I put the dialogues aside, drank what remained of my mother's legacy, and entered on an academic career. Lately however, prompted by unexpected developments in the world of scholarship, I have begun to ponder again that brief encounter in the slums of Alexandria. If Jacques Derrida is a philosopher, Michel Foucault a historian, and Martin Bernal a classical scholar, could it not be that Hind is an archaeologist, and Xanthippe a real Greek? I therefore decided, before retiring completely from the academic profession, to translate the dialogues and offer them to the world.

A Note of Scholarship

According to Aristotle (Fragment 72 Rose), the art of the Socratic dialogue, brought to such perfection by Plato, was invented by Alexamenus of Teos. Aeschines, pupil of Socrates and rival of Plato, is said to have written Socratic dialogues remarkable for the realism with which Socrates was portrayed. It is even said (Athenaeus, *Deipnosophistae*, 13, 611D) that Aeschines obtained his material from Xanthippe, Socrates' wife – a rumour which is obliquely confirmed by the fact that his dialogues contained female characters: there was an *Aspasia*, dominated by the famous woman of that name, mistress of Pericles; and also a dialogue (possibly the same one) between Aspasia, Xenophon and his wife (Cicero, *On Invention*, 51–3). Unfortunately only fragments of the dialogues survive, the Aeschines whose works have come down to us being a later orator. Aspasia is also recalled in the *Menexenus*, a dialogue generally attributed to the middle-aged Plato, and probably written under the influence of Xanthippe. (See *Xanthippe's Laws*.)

I incline to the view that the Xanthippic dialogues are the work of the Cyrenaic school, founded by Arete, daughter of Aristippus (435–350 BC), a pupil of Socrates. They may even be the work of Arete herself. The position of Cyrene, inland from the Libyan port of Apollonia, would have certainly led to great interest in her works among the women of nearby Alexandria, when that city was founded during Arete's old age. Unfortunately, although Pamphila of Epidauros wrote a synopsis of Arete in her *Memorabilia*, this has not come down to us, and even the hermaphrodite Favorinus, summarizing Pamphila, chose to delete all reference to the Xanthippic corpus: a fact which, like her masculine name, shows that she preferred, in the end, to be counted among the men.[1]

---

[1] Favorinus is described by Philostratus, *Lives of the Sophists*, 489–92, and is mentioned by several other ancient writers. For Polemo's account (which seems to imply that Favorinus carried her masculine disguise to the limits of sexual subterfuge) see L. Holford-Strevens, *Aulus Gellius*, London, 1988, pp. 72–3.

XANTHIPPE'S REPUBLIC

Socrates to Critobulus:
'Are there any men to whom you entrust more matters of importance, or with whom you have less conversation, than with your wife?'

Xenophon, *Oeconomicus*, iii, 12

Xanthippe's Republic was first performed on 28 June 1990 at the Royal Court Theatre, London, with the following cast:

SOCRATES: Bernard Horsfall
XANTHIPPE: Patti Love

The producer was Bill Alexander.

XANTHIPPE'S REPUBLIC

Characters:
SOCRATES, an Athenian philosopher, about 65
XANTHIPPE, his wife, about 30

In the *Republic* we find, expressed through the mouth of Socrates, the two most famous of Plato's theories: that of the just state, ruled over by a class of guardians, in which the philosophers are kings; and that of the forms – the abstract and eternal essences which are the true reality behind the world of appearance. Modern scholarship tends to the view that the second of these theories never crossed the mind of the historic Socrates, and that the whole episode so brilliantly described in the *Republic* is an invention of Plato's. The following dialogue seems to confirm the view that Socrates really believed the theories attributed to him by Plato. It also suggests that he defended them on that historic occasion (405 BC, according to the chronology implied in *Perictione's Parmenides*) in a manner not unlike the one recorded (though admittedly with many embellishments) in the *Republic*.

Until the discovery of these dialogues, little was known of Xanthippe, besides the fact that she had two, possibly three, sons by Socrates. Antisthenes, in Xenophon's *Symposium* (2, 10), describes her as 'the most troublesome woman of all time,' a remark that illustrates the jealousy of Socrates' male disciples, who could not bear to think that a woman might be closer to their master than they were. (See *Xanthippe's Laws.*) Socrates' eldest son Lamprocles is also recorded by Xenophon as having complained of his mother's ill-humour (*Memorabilia*, II, ii, 1); but again the complaint may be dismissed, since it certainly refers to a former wife, Myrto: in any case Lamprocles is rewarded with a strong rebuke from Socrates.

Xanthippe is described in Plato's *Phaedo* as carrying one of her sons as a babe-in-arms to visit the seventy-year-old philosopher, who has been condemned to drink hemlock on charges of impiety and 'corrupting the youth'. She must therefore have been considerably younger than her husband. And if Xanthippe was as she appears in the following dialogue, it is not surprising that Socrates chose to behave in public as though she hardly existed. Of all the ancient accounts of her, that given fleetingly by John Chrysostom (*Homily on I Corinthians* 4, 26, 8) probably comes nearest to the truth. Xanthippe, he writes, was 'difficult, talkative and tipsy', while Socrates, when questioned, said that he put up with her because she provided 'a practice-ground for philosophy at home'. Socrates' hearers assumed that he meant a practice-ground for the philosophical virtues of patience and self-control. In fact, as this dialogue shows, Socrates meant what he said.

Socrates' mother was a midwife, and he described himself as a 'midwife' to others' ideas. (Plato, *Theaetetus*, 149ff.) It was his famous maxim that 'the unexamined life is not a life for a human being': a belief which conveniently excused the enormous amount of time that he spent in conversation. It now seems that one person saw through this piece of humbug, and was prepared – in private, at least (and what woman in ancient Athens could speak in public?[2]) – not only to defend the unexamined life, but also to warn against the political consequences of the Socratic philosophy.

[2] Readers interested in the Athenian 'Woman question' should consult John Gould, 'Law, custom and myth: aspects of the social position of women in classical Athens', *Journal of Hellenic Studies*, vol. 100, 1980, pp. 38–51, and Roger Just's survey, *Women in Athenian Law and Life*, London and New York, 1989.

XANTHIPPE'S REPUBLIC

(Scene: the interior of Socrates' house; Xanthippe, a young woman in her early thirties, is arranging the table for the evening meal. Socrates, a large man with bare feet, a wispy beard, and a disorderly robe that gives him an unkempt and tramp-like appearance, enters left. He is about sixty-five, and stares about him in a manner that is slightly shifty and insecure. Xanthippe smiles, and goes back to her work.)

SOCRATES: I can stand just so much.

XANTHIPPE: Yes, Socks.[3]

SOCRATES: I am patient, I think, just, generous, even to a fault.

XANTHIPPE: Yes, Socks.

SOCRATES *(sits down at the table)*: I don't ask much of others; I don't expect them to put up with me for longer than is strictly required by common decency. And if, despite my defects, young men seek my company and affect to relish my words, am I to blame? To be brutally frank, I'd rather spend my time with old Aspasia. Hello, what's this?

XANTHIPPE: Your supper, Socks.

SOCRATES: Do stop calling mc Socks!

XANTHIPPE: Yes, dear.

SOCRATES: Today, for instance, that Plato – how he gets on my nerves, with his sycophantic manners and his snobbish ways. No sooner had I sat down because of my weary bones in the Palaestra after a neat game of dice with Aristonymus, when the little creep catches sight of me, and comes mincing across with Timaeus and Cleitophon (who I must admit is rather charming), oh yes, and the winsome Themocrates as well. And seeing him, they all begin to gather round: a crowd of unknown faces in which there is sure to be some tell-tale

---

[3] The expression used by Xanthippe – Σωκρατίδιον – comes from Aristophanes' earlier lampoon of Socrates, *The Clouds*, line 222. The Greeks formed such terms of belittling endearment by lengthening names, as we do by shortening them (hence my translation).

13

democrat. Then up pipes Plato in that mimsy voice of his, asking me whether there is such a thing as a just state, and if so how would I define it: right there in the Palaestra, with half of Athens listening over his shoulders. I could have been lynched. Which was perhaps his intention, so that he can weep over my tragic demise and write heroic dialogues about me, without fear of my contradicting him. Yes, I see it all: that's his scheme. To become a celebrity by killing me. The little runt!

XANTHIPPE: So what did you do?

SOCRATES: What did I do? What could I do? To say nothing would be to imply a criticism of our wonderful democracy, and maybe even a secret leaning towards Sparta. To say what I think, would be even worse. Then I thought of a brilliant wheeze. You'll like this. . . .

XANTHIPPE: What?

SOCRATES: I pretended that, the day before, when discussing the difference between a just and unjust man . . .

XANTHIPPE: Or woman . . .

SOCRATES: Between a just and unjust man, I had described the just and unjust state, but only, you understand, as allegories of the human soul. So that nobody could accuse me of talking politics. And I added a few ironical twists, so that I could always make out, you know, that this bit was a joke, that bit metaphorical, this bit allegory, and so on. By the dog, what's this stuff you've given me?

XANTHIPPE: Goat, Socrates. Goat with anchovies. Good for the rheumatism. And the goat was sacrificed to Asclepius only this morning.

SOCRATES: No wonder it's so tough. But the anchovies are good. I adore anchovies!

XANTHIPPE: I know.

SOCRATES: Do you know, or merely believe?

XANTHIPPE: I beg your pardon?

SOCRATES: Oh, nothing, just a thought. Anyway, no sooner had I begun than Plato took tablets and stylus from his handbag, and began to scribble it all down. So I packed the thing full of stories, he being a sucker for fictions. He'll never make the grade as a philosopher, you know. His mind begins to work only when there is some image rattling around inside it – the story of Gyges and the magic ring, for instance. I ask you!

XANTHIPPE: I like that story.

SOCRATES: Of course you do; you told it to me. Anyway, I made up a yarn about the party in Piraeus – the one in Cephalus' house last night.

XANTHIPPE: You were rather drunk last night.

SOCRATES: Just so. But I was rather less drunk today, and decided to tell a tale that would give that Plato something to think about. I pretended that the greatest philosophical event in the entire history of the world had happened, and he alone had not been there. His brothers had taken part – Glaucon, you know, and Adeimantus – and that made him pretty furious, because, to do him justice, he has a bit more on top than they have. And Thrasymachus too; by the dog, how that Plato hates Thrasymachus! You could see him going white with rage beneath his make-up. If he ever gets to write it all down – and you can bet your boots he will, stringing the whole pack of lies on those threads of dialectic he is so proud of, but which stick to honest fingers like spiders' webs – when as I say he writes it down, you can be sure there will be a rough part in it for poor old Thrasymachus. Not, mind you, that Thrasymachus is what you would call a subtle intellect, roaring like a bull as he does and thumping his fist on the table. And I confess, I did the old boy a disservice this morning. I attributed that foolish definition of justice to him.

XANTHIPPE: What definition?

SOCRATES: You know, justice as the interest of the stronger, a ruse to manipulate the masses, the ideology of a ruling class, as you might say – though even Thrasymachus wouldn't use quite so vulgar a phrase. Of course, it is inconceivable that anybody could believe such rubbish, and whether Plato wrote it down and took the trouble to refute it (as any fool can refute it), it won't make the slightest difference to the world. Anyway, where was I?

XANTHIPPE: You were going to talk about beds.

SOCRATES: How did you know?

XANTHIPPE: It's your favourite example: the bed, the form of the bed, that kind of thing.

SOCRATES: An argument has to start somewhere.

XANTHIPPE: And yours start with bed; and very often end there, I gather.

SOCRATES: My dear Xanthippe, let me tell you what really happened with Alcibiades.

15

XANTHIPPE: I don't want to know. Carry on with the party at Piraeus.

SOCRATES: Well, you are right. I did begin by asking them to consider a bed. The question I put to them is this: what can be known of this bed? Through the eyes, for instance: how it looks, yes, but from what angle? From one point of view it looks rectangular, from another square; in this light it is brown, in that light yellow. And so on for the other senses. To the healthy man it is soft, to the sick man it is hard. . . . In short, study the bed however you like, if you attend only to its appearance you will be lost in contradiction, and know nothing of the bed's reality.

XANTHIPPE: In which case we need philosophy, so as to catch up on our sleep.

SOCRATES: So how can we know the bed as it really is – what, in this bed, is really *real*? Not the appearance, which is a sum of contradictions. So is there some real particular bed, lying behind them, unobserved and unobservable, yet nevertheless a thing that we can know?

XANTHIPPE: Don't ask me.

SOCRATES: I'm not asking you. In any case, the answer is no. For let us consider what is knowledge, I said to them.

XANTHIPPE: To whom?

SOCRATES: To the people at Piraeus. Listen, are you interested in my story?

XANTHIPPE: Of course, Socks.

SOCRATES: Then remember to package it in inverted commas, as though you were Plato.

XANTHIPPE: Yes, Socks.

SOCRATES: Please stop calling me Socks. 'Let us consider what is knowledge,' I said. 'Is it not true that knowledge is to be contrasted with opinion?' 'Yes,' they answered. 'And that the man with knowledge is the one whom we trust and from whom we seek guidance; while the man of mere opinion is one from whom we take no advice?' 'Yes,' they answered, 'excellently said.' 'And is it not also true that to know an object is to know what it really and essentially is, whereas to have an opinion is merely to guess – or, at best, to know the appearance, but not the reality?'

XANTHIPPE: 'Yes,' they answered.

SOCRATES: 'But then,' I said, 'if a man's knowledge changes from day to day, can he be relied upon to tell us the truth about the thing he claims to know?' 'Of course not,' they answered. 'So his knowledge is not knowledge, but only opinion?' 'It seems, Socrates, that you are right.'

XANTHIPPE: This dialogue lacks opposition; you should put a woman in it.

SOCRATES: 'But consider a particular bed,' I went on. 'Does it not change from day to day: now made, now unmade; now new, now old; now broken, now mended, and doomed at last to destruction?' 'Of course, Socrates,' they said. 'In which case there is no truth about a particular bed that may not cease to be a truth?' 'No, Socrates.' 'Therefore all that we say and think about a particular bed is changeable and unreliable?' 'That would seem to be the conclusion, Socrates,' they said. 'In other words, our thoughts about a particular bed are always opinion, never knowledge?' 'It seems so, Socrates.' Here I must say, the unseemly Antiphon – who had stopped off to listen on his way to the baths – started to make some kind of protest, until darling Cleitophon gave him such a look. . . .

XANTHIPPE: There's a particular bed I'm thinking of at the moment.

SOCRATES: Wait, let me finish, I'm getting to the good bit. 'If we accept my argument,' I said, 'and I don't for the life of me think that we can really do otherwise, then it follows that there is no knowledge of particular things, but only of their essences.' 'That does indeed seem to follow,' they said. 'And furthermore, it follows that their essences are eternal, participating in the world of time and change but forever apart from it. For if they themselves were changeable, so too would be our thoughts of them.' 'Indeed you are right,' they said, with an oath. 'From which it is easy to see,' I went on, 'that the truth about a bed can never be discovered by experiment and observation, but only by philosophy, which leads us to the forms themselves – to the eternal, immutable idea of bed. . . .'

XANTHIPPE: What a lovely sleep you could have in it!

SOCRATES: Please stop interrupting. So then, I fixed that little Plato with my most penetrating expression, and addressed my remarks specifically to him. 'Let us consider,' I said, 'the work of the poet. You will admit, my dear Plato, that the bed on which you lie is a mere appearance, a copy of that transcendental bed in which only thoughts embrace but never bodies.' You should have seen him change colour.

XANTHIPPE: You disgusting old man!

SOCRATES: And what is a poem about the bed, but a copy of this copy –
a portrait in words of an appearance, twice removed from the really
real, twice steeped in falsehood, doubly deceiving, a dying flame in a
temple whence the god has fled?

XANTHIPPE: Nice; a poem. I like it.

SOCRATES: Please keep your comments to yourself – you are under-
mining the Socratic irony.

XANTHIPPE: Sorry, Socks.

SOCRATES: Where was I? Yes, poetry. The passions: there's another
great theme, and I socked that one to him as well. The way poetry
stirs us up, leads us to sympathize with feelings we would normally
be horrified to confess to, pollutes the world with illusions and
obscenities. I went further. I argued – rather originally, I think – that
all art teeters on the brink of emotional excess. And this excess, I
said, which seems to a self-intoxicated youth like Plato to be the
highest of virtues, is in fact a deep disorder of the soul, a distraction
of the intellect by means of the passions, a way of responding
wrongly and unfeelingly to all the things that count.

XANTHIPPE: Which is why it is primarily men who are sentimental,
whereas we women have the true discipline of the soul.

SOCRATES: And what is this true discipline?

XANTHIPPE: The art of feeling the right emotion, on the right
occasion, towards the right object, and in the right degree.

SOCRATES: Your ideas, my dear Xanthippe, are far in advance of your
time.[4] It is a pity you have no Plato to write them down.

XANTHIPPE: Truth, my dear Socrates, is better preserved and more
deeply effective, when embodied in an oral tradition. Write something down, and within minutes you'll find it refuted. This is why
wives are useful.

SOCRATES: Why?

XANTHIPPE: For the tales they tell.

SOCRATES: You know, I think you may have a point there. But what did
you think of my speech about poetry? Not bad, eh?

XANTHIPPE: Fine, in its way. But what does it have to do with politics?

[4] Xanthippe's ideas were later taken up by Aristotle in his *Nicomachean Ethics*. It seems
likely that Aristotle, during his years as Plato's pupil in the Academy, was in the habit
of visiting the ageing Xanthippe. See below, *Xanthippe's Laws*, and H.P. de Selby, 'The
Feline and the Feminine: *arete* and *pathos* in the *Nicomachean Ethics*', *Epithumia*, XIII,
1973, pp. 124–36.

SOCRATES: Ah well, you see, there's the subtle part. That Plato, who fancies himself as a poet, a musician, and Zeus knows what else, also imagines he is cut out for a political career, like his appalling uncles. So I thought, what better way to punish him for provoking me, and what better way to throw the bystanders off the scent, than to advocate a kind of politics in which people like Plato had no hope of succeeding?

XANTHIPPE: And in which people like you were kings?

SOCRATES: I admit, I did get rather carried away. But that's not the point. It only helped to reassure the mob that I was pulling everyone's leg, even though a part of me, I confess, was serious.

You know, Xanthippe, have you ever wondered why it is that I feel so tired these days?

XANTHIPPE: Frequently. Perhaps it is the energy you expend on doing nothing; the concentration required, in order to neglect your wife and your sons at every moment of the day and night. The incredible calculations needed, to avoid all possibility of an honest job. The sheer sweat of refusing every offer, and all the time posing as a serene philosopher, whom the gods have forbidden to dirty his hands with money. It must be exhausting; I honestly don't know how you manage it.

SOCRATES: The reason why I am so tired is that I am a slave. I might have led a quiet life like my poor old father, chiselling away at blocks of marble, making genteel little tombstones for the upper classes, inventing those soporific verses that serve to console people for the fact that their nearest and dearest have at last escaped from their clutches for ever. But there, I chose instead my mother's career: the career of midwife – I am speaking metaphorically, you understand.

XANTHIPPE: You always do when I mention money. One day, perhaps, you will favour me with a straight reply. No, please don't let me interrupt your sublime thoughts. You were saying that you are a slave.

SOCRATES: A slave, yes; a slave to philosophy. You think, of course, that I am being melodramatic.

XANTHIPPE: No, no.

SOCRATES: Yes, you do. You imagine that there is nothing easier in the world than to traipse around the Agora, searching for eternal truths, surrounded by a circle of young admirers, following Reason wherever she leads. But you are wrong, and this was the burden of what I said to Plato. You would do well to listen to it. Is there any more of that Corinthian wine?

XANTHIPPE: Only our very last amphora.

SOCRATES: Let's have some. And please don't bother me with domestic economics.

(Xanthippe goes for the wine, while Socrates muses aloud.)

SOCRATES: The stony path of truth, and the primrose path of fantasy: I could make something of that, if some other bugger doesn't get there first.

(Xanthippe returns, and mixes wine and water in a bowl, which she hands to Socrates.)

SOCRATES: Hmm. On the verge of going off; better finish it. Listen, Xanthippe, have you ever asked yourself why there is this absurd passion for democracy nowadays? Why this vaunting of equality, and resentment towards every power of man over man, every dignity, virtue, or status?

XANTHIPPE: I have indeed. Could I have some wine?

SOCRATES: And what is your answer to those questions?

XANTHIPPE: That the Athenians only pretend to love democracy, and that when they praise it, they are really praising something else. Most of the people are either slaves or metics or women, who between them do all the work. And these democratic rights of which our citizens speak are merely the privileges of a leisured class. Can I have some wine?

SOCRATES: You speak like Thrasymachus.

XANTHIPPE: Except that, unlike Thrasymachus, I know that what I say is only half the truth.

SOCRATES: And what is the other half?

XANTHIPPE: You were going to tell me.

(She helps herself to wine.)

SOCRATES: Easy on that stuff: it's the very last amphora. Our Athenians may be only sham democrats. But there is no doubt that they believe in equality – and their passion is all the greater, in that they don't know what equality means. If Xenophon is rich and Phaedrus poor, there is sure to be some scheme afoot to ensure that Xenophon is as poor as Phaedrus. If Isocrates has some talent which Meidias lacks, there will be a movement to decry the talent of Isocrates, and to prove that it runs counter to the common good.

And with this passion for equality goes a kind of snobbery, I have noticed.

XANTHIPPE: Snobbery?

SOCRATES: I mean, in everything that matters – in art and poetry and music, in morals and politics – the popular opinion is sacred, and whoever seeks to question it, or to deprive the people of their loathsome pleasures, is regarded as an outcast. Take these new fads in music: that appalling mixolydian mode, those clashing cymbals and mind-numbing rhythms, those bestial dances, and the wailing tuneless voices of the 'stars', as Plato calls them – what man of refinement can hear this stuff without a tremor of indignation? The entire younger generation has decided to prefer Marsyas to Apollo, and to throw their dignity away. Moreover, corruption in music is the root of lawlessness. Yet can you express such ideas in public? Can you say – as I said to Plato the other day, when he was drooling over his latest idol – that the mixolydian mode should be banned entirely and the dorian made compulsory in its stead?[5] Say these things, and you will be dismissed from polite society as a pariah: such is the fate of anyone who implies that one kind of man is superior to another.

---

[5] We do not know enough about the Greek modes to have a clear insight into Socrates' antipathy to all except the dorian. (The subject is taken up again in *Xanthippe's Laws*.) It seems, however, that the mixolydian was more dirge-like than dionysiac.

Plato's obsession with pop-stars is recorded in a famous poem, attributed to him by Diogenes Laertius, III, 29, and widely accepted as genuine:

> My star-gazing star, would I could become
> The heavens, so as to look on you with many eyes.

Diogenes Laertius advances the absurd story, repeated by subsequent commentators, that this poem refers to a person called Aster (star). One modern scholar has even constructed an argument purporting to show that Plato's beloved is none other than the Aster who put out one of Philip of Macedon's eyes, at the battle of Methone in 354 BC. (Walter Ludwig in *Greek, Roman and Byzantine Studies*, vol. 4, 1963, pp. 77–80.) In fact, as is evident from the Xanthippic corpus, Plato intended the term as a description, not a name. It is probable that the couplet has come down to us (one of the few to have escaped Plato's destructive rage against his adolescent poetry – see *Perictione's Parmenides*) because Plato was in the habit of copying it at each concert, and sending a slave back stage in the hope that his favourite singer of the day would respond to the implied invitation. According to Pamphila, the rubbish heap behind the Theatre of Dionysus was for many years piled high with shards of pottery bearing Plato's monotonous verses. (Pamphila, *Memorabilia*, 38, iii.) The emotional grip exerted over Plato by the word *aster* is revealed in the contrived etymology that he provides for it, at *Cratylus* 409c.

XANTHIPPE: You may be right, Socrates, but where is this leading?

SOCRATES: I'll tell you. Why do you suppose that men believe in equality?

XANTHIPPE: Women don't.

SOCRATES *(ignoring her)*: Not because the belief is true. Indeed, you have to put truth from your mind if you are to accept it. You must renounce the ways of philosophy, which will only serve to threaten your dear conviction; and you must adopt the ways of myth. Beliefs come into the mind of the ordinary man because they serve his interests, and not because he has any grounds for endorsing them. And since the mediocre majority are happier in the conviction that no one is superior to themselves, this will be their belief. Such in general are the opinions that rule in a democratic state: opinions that flatter the believer, but which have neither the truth nor the certainty that are required for knowledge.

XANTHIPPE: Yet it is precisely about these things that people – men especially – are most certain. I heard an orator say the other day, 'We hold these truths to be sacred and undeniable, that all men are created equal . . .', or some such nonsense.

SOCRATES: Really? Are the teachers of rhetoric prepared to go so far? 'Truths'; 'sacred'; 'undeniable': how disgusting! Most definitely, the world is coming to an end.

XANTHIPPE: So what is your remedy?

SOCRATES: Let me summarize my discourse of today – which, you remember, was well padded with inverted commas. People are governed well, I suggested, only when they are governed by knowledge, and not by opinion, which will infallibly lead them astray. Most of mankind, however, are without knowledge; such glimpses as they gain of the truth are distant, hazy, refracted through the clouds of sentiment that fill their souls. Unless some lucky fate take charge of them, they must certainly perish in lawlessness and civil war. And unless they are governed by some higher power, they will live in perpetual conflict and in error.

XANTHIPPE: And what is this 'higher power'?

SOCRATES: What can it be but philosophy, which is the only path to knowledge?

XANTHIPPE: As I suspected, in your ideal republic, it is the philosopher who rules.

SOCRATES: I did, I confess, entertain that idea; but partly, you understand, as a snub to Plato, and by way of showing that poets and dreamers have no right to the throne. In fact, I was a trifle more subtle than you suggest.

XANTHIPPE: I am impatient to hear you, Socrates.

SOCRATES: You will admit, I suppose, that philosophers are not given to working in the same manner, or to the same extent as artisans, say, or soldiers.

XANTHIPPE: No. They work far harder; for their labour is unceasing and at the end of each day there is nothing whatever to show for it. So that next morning they must begin all over again.

SOCRATES: But the state depends upon the work of artisans and soldiers?

XANTHIPPE: And of women.

SOCRATES: So in our state not everyone can be a philosopher?

XANTHIPPE: Nor everyone, thank Zeus, a philosopher's wife.

SOCRATES: If the state is to be ruled by knowledge, therefore, not everyone can have a part in government, but only those, the philosophers, who have set their sights on truth, and who dare to believe what truth dictates to them. The philosophers, therefore, are the natural guardians of society, entitled to rule over the artisans and soldiers – who compose, so to speak, society's bodily part.

XANTHIPPE: So far, so predictable.

SOCRATES: But do you not see a problem?

XANTHIPPE: Explain your meaning, Socks.

SOCRATES: How do we persuade the other classes to accept the philosophers as their guardians? It is not enough to say that this is reasonable, since reasonableness has weight only for philosophers. We must induce the man of mere opinion to accept the rule of the man who knows. We must therefore present him with a myth – a consoling story, a noble lie, as you might say (nice phrase, don't you think? You should have seen the greedy expression on Plato's face as he scribbled it down) – in order to persuade him to believe that it is right and fitting that he should be excluded from office. Without this myth, it is natural that the ordinary man should covet power, since power, for him, is a means to gratification. For the philosopher, I should add, power is an onerous duty, taken up with reluctance and for the common good.

XANTHIPPE: What a load of humbug.

SOCRATES: Wait, we are coming to the most beautiful part. For do you not see another problem?

XANTHIPPE: Thousands.

SOCRATES *(becoming gradually excited)*: Is it not the case that those who live by a lie, however noble, must at the same time shield themselves from the truth?

XANTHIPPE: Indeed; I know a very good instance.

SOCRATES: Consider, then, the fate of the philosopher, entitled to rule over his fellows, yet knowing that they must be forever hostile to his profession. When they discover what sort of man he is, will they not seek with all their might to destroy him, and to seize the reins of government from his hands?

XANTHIPPE: Where, if you ask my opinion, they should not have been in any case.

SOCRATES: I wasn't asking your opinion. I was summarizing my argument. And behold, at this very point, I was visited again by my *daimonion*, and the divine spirit, instead of arresting me, offered a beautiful story, a summary of my meaning, philosophy and politics in a single glowing image – a gift for Plato, and one that he would not fail to misunderstand. Imagine, the *daimonion* said, a cave, in which men are imprisoned, their legs and necks fastened so that they can look only straight ahead. Some way off, behind the prisoners and higher than them, a fire is burning, and in front of this fire is a screen like the screen of a puppet show.

XANTHIPPE: Go on.

SOCRATES: Men come and go behind this screen carrying objects above it, whose flickering shadows are cast by the flame of the fire onto the wall visible to the prisoners. And this, in brief, is the condition of the unphilosophical man, who sees not the light of day, and knows the world only by the changing shadow which it casts, from the palest of illuminations. Just such a shadow is that particular bed we were discussing earlier. Yet the unphilosophical man believes that these shadows are the whole truth of the world.

But suppose now that one of our prisoners is released from his bonds, turned away from the world of shadows, and forced step by step towards the fire, and beyond it into the blinding sunlight. At first, of course, he would be dazzled. But soon he would know the truth of his condition and laugh at the delusions of the world below. No longer would he respect the opinions of the prisoners, covet their honours, or envy their illusory powers. He would rather, as Homer says, be 'a serf in the house of some landless man',[6] than hold the opinions and lead the life that they do.

Should he now descend again into the underground darkness, however, is he not likely to offend the prisoners who reside there, with his indifference to their beliefs and customs, and his ability to know the true causes of matters whose explanation lies forever beyond their grasp? 'Of course,' they said.

XANTHIPPE: *Who* said?

SOCRATES: The people in the Palaestra, I mean at Piraeus. 'Of course,' they said, 'and he will surely be in the greatest danger should he try to govern them.' 'What, then,' I asked, 'are we to do?' 'Please tell us, Socrates.' 'Just as our artisans are to be fed on myths, so must our guardians be trained to respect those myths. They must cultivate a sublime and – if I may make so bold – religious irony, speaking pleasantly and agreeably of the illusions that grip the souls of lower mortals, and never for a moment revealing that they do not subscribe to them.' I think you will agree, my dear Xanthippe, that this is a beautiful idea. And did I not get off the hook rather cleverly, so that not one of the buggers could accuse me either of upholding the myth of democracy or of denying it? And there was that little Plato, scribbling away, his cheeks all aglow, and the smell of armpits beginning to jab its way through his veils of hyacinth![7]

---

[6] *Odyssey*, xi, 490. It is strange that Socrates should quote this line – though his use of it is confirmed in the parallel passage of Plato's *Republic*. For it is uttered by the dead Achilles, who compares his lot unfavourably with that of the meanest of the living. In fact, Socrates has been granted a premonition of the true meaning of the Cave, as this is revealed in *Xanthippe's Laws*.

[7] Plato's contemporary, and fellow pupil of Socrates, Aristippus, later exclaimed to Phaedo: 'Confound the woofters (κίναιδοι) who spoil for us the use of good perfume' (Diogenes Laertius, II, 76) – an obvious reference to Plato. Later, in his revulsion against his earlier sexual tastes, Plato too was to use the word disparagingly: *Gorgias*, 494D–E, while Demosthenes denounced Aeschines as a κίναιδος by nature (Demosthenes, 18, 242). By the mid-fourth century a κίναιδος meant any man who adopted a passive role in the homosexual act, though the fanciful etymology given by the *Etymologicum Gudianum* suggests a more active involvement. (A bird called κιναίδιον also went under the name of σεισοπυγίς: bottom-waggler, suggesting that effeminacy at least was intended by the term.) See further, for a belligerently homophiliac examination of this word, John J. Winkler, *The Constraints of Desire*, New York and London, 1990, Chapter 2. Aristippus was, incidentally, the father of Arete, and is sometimes wrongly credited with her achievement in founding the Cyrenaic school. He was also the first of Socrates' pupils to charge fees for tuition.

XANTHIPPE: Outrageous. They should have you arrested and tried!

SOCRATES *(laughing)*: Tried! For what crime, may I ask?

XANTHIPPE: We women were never allowed to study law.

SOCRATES: Is that an injustice, I wonder?

XANTHIPPE: But if there isn't a crime, they ought to invent one. A corrupter of the youth, that's what you are!

SOCRATES: Corrupter of the youth! That's rich! You should see those young devils. Corrupters of old men, all of them. Why, the other day, that Phaedrus came up to me, his face all winks and smirks, to where I was lying (half drunk, I admit) and . . .

XANTHIPPE: I am not interested.

SOCRATES: And what should be the punishment for this new crime you've invented?

XANTHIPPE: I don't know: maybe they should make you drink hemlock. Yes, that's the answer!

SOCRATES: Thanks a lot. Have some less wine.

XANTHIPPE *(softening)*: I'd miss you though.

SOCRATES: Really? Even though you don't understand a word I say?

(Xanthippe allows Socrates to hug her, and then pushes him away.)

XANTHIPPE: That's what you think. As a matter of fact, this cave idea: I think I understand it rather better than you.

SOCRATES: Perhaps you will enlighten me.

XANTHIPPE *(taking more wine)*: Certainly. Suppose a man has been strolling about in the sun, preening himself, chatting pleasantly to young admirers, noticing this and that, following things with his eyes . . .

SOCRATES: Yes, yes; come to the point.

XANTHIPPE: And suppose, being hungry or whatever, he comes out of the daylight into a house where some woman has prepared a meal for him.

SOCRATES: Well, and what then?

XANTHIPPE: 'Which of these two, the man or the woman, will see most of the interior of the house?' I asked. 'Tell us, O Xanthippe,' they said.

SOCRATES: Hey, wait a minute, that's my technique.

XANTHIPPE: The answer is obvious. The woman, of course. Her eyes are accustomed to the interior, she has made her home in it, can feel her way around every obstacle, and sees as accurately in the semi-darkness as the man saw in the daylight.

SOCRATES: So far you merely repeat my argument.

XANTHIPPE: Indeed, if the woman should choose to attack the man as he entered – not that a woman would dream of such a thing – do you not think that she would have the advantage of him? Would he not stumble about helplessly, not knowing where the blow was coming from, and unable to ward it off?

SOCRATES: True enough.

XANTHIPPE: And who do you think would be best able to arrange the affairs of the household: to set food on the table, stoke the fire, heat water for a bath, and fetch the wine? Would it be the man, who perceived these things only dimly, or the woman, to whom each was entirely visible?

SOCRATES: The woman, of course.

XANTHIPPE: Let me go further, for the story interests me. The affairs of the household are not matters of food, wine and shelter only, even if they may appear so to the casually visiting male. There must be peace in the household, and comfort; children must be cared for and educated – unless you go along with the crazy yarn you spun for Plato's sake, in which children are farmed like animals.

SOCRATES: What crazy yarn?

XANTHIPPE: I am coming to that. In any case, whichever way you look at it, there would be little comfort in a household if order were not maintained there, and if friendship – that quality of which you speak so beautifully to your young admirers – were not a part of it.

SOCRATES: You speak well, Xanthippe, and I almost suspect you of listening to your husband.

XANTHIPPE: Less irony please, and listen to a plain piece of argument. Friendship, you will admit, is of many kinds?

SOCRATES: I cannot deny it.

XANTHIPPE: Consider, then, the friendship formed in the street or the gymnasium, in the bright light of day, between those who are not bound to remain in one another's company, and who can affect a thousand smiles and greetings and then go their way regardless. Is there not a world of difference between that friendship and the other, which comes from sitting day by day in a cool interior, studying each other's smallest gestures, learning to read in the expression of a face or the glint of an eye the whole secret of the other's need; building, instead of that busy world of commerce and contract, a little haven of peace and gratitude? How am I doing?

SOCRATES: Not bad; a bit short on irony, perhaps. Have some more wine.

XANTHIPPE: Well then, if we grant that there are these two kinds of friendship – that of the market and that of the household, the outer and the inner, the light and the dark – which of our two original characters is best able to maintain a friendship of the second kind?

SOCRATES: Explain your meaning, Xanthippe.

XANTHIPPE: Let me say a little more, then, about these two kinds of friendship. The first, so open, so generous, so full of the light of day, is not necessarily the happiest or the most durable. Oh, I grant you, there is your Plato, who hangs on your every word, there are those famous pairs of lovers who are always in each other's company, and who bore the world to death with their protestations that they will die for the other's sake. But those are exceptions. And besides, the young lovers become old, cracked and ugly, and not always, dear Socrates, as wise as you.

SOCRATES: Irony, my dear wife, must be sharply distinguished from sarcasm. Proceed with the argument.

XANTHIPPE: In any case, these friendships of the marketplace may quickly die; and although we women are granted only the occasional glimpse of them, it seems to us that they are often not worth the words that are spent in forming them, and could be more profitably replaced with some kind of commercial deal.

SOCRATES: How many times must I tell you that I am not in it for the money? Really, Xanthippe . . .

XANTHIPPE: So let us consider the second kind of friendship. However dark, however mysterious, however far from the cheerful light of your man-to-man encounters, this second friendship is superior at least in its lastingness, if in no other respect. Moreover, it is to the sphere of darkness that you blessed ones, who moon about all day without an obol in your pocket, must return for the things that you require.

SOCRATES: There is a grain of truth in what you say.

XANTHIPPE: This friendship of the hearth can exist, however, only by virtue of a great work of vigilance.

SOCRATES: You mean a constant prying and nagging.

XANTHIPPE: On the contrary, I mean that quarrels must be anticipated and defused, conflicts avoided, tempers gauged, problems negotiated. For in these cramped interiors, passions might otherwise quickly boil over.

SOCRATES: You speak truly, indeed.

XANTHIPPE: And to come to the point. Who is best able to conduct this work of vigilance: the one who, living in the dark, has become accustomed to perceive its contents clearly, who can read and understand the faces and gestures of her companions; or the one who, venturing in from time to time from that sphere of light, stumbles helplessly over the threshold and gropes around for support?

SOCRATES: The former, I warrant you.

XANTHIPPE: So now you will understand the story of the cave. Those beings whom you count so fortunate, who ascend from the darkness into the sphere of light, and who fancy that nothing is visible below save the shadows of higher things – are they really capable of finding their place in the cave, without the guidance of those accustomed to seeing there?

SOCRATES: I think not, Xanthippe.

XANTHIPPE: And suppose that the mass of men are condemned to live in that cave, and to find there, not only the necessities of their short existence, but also the friendship which is their best consolation. Who is fit to govern them, the one who yearns for the sphere of light, who constantly ventures into it, and who returns from time to time in blinking confusion; or the one who patiently lives out his – or rather her – days in those lower regions, striving to observe what they contain, and to establish an order compatible with their imperfections?[8]

SOCRATES: The latter of course, dear Xanthippe. But you forget that my parable also had a philosophical meaning.

XANTHIPPE: I am coming to that. Let us just agree on one thing. If, as your parable implies, this human world is a world of imperfection, in which all light is reflected and refracted from some higher sphere, then we by no means qualify ourselves for government by aspiring to

---

[8] The prevailing view was that indoor occupations are dishonourable: see Xenophon, *Oeconomicus*, iv, 3. Pamphila argues (*Memorabilia*, 39, iii), that this was one reason for the suppression of Xanthippe's philosophy; Sosipatra (*On Notorious Women*, 240A) even adds that Xanthippe was later charged with impiety for her arguments, and made to drink hemlock – a contention strenuously denied by Hypatia, in the lost *Dipsosophistae*.

that higher sphere; on the contrary, we thereby risk the little competence that we have.

SOCRATES: In a sense you are right.

XANTHIPPE: So now you will see what a position your philosopher king will be in, as he steps from that 'higher' realm – though let me say that I do not for a moment accept that 'higher' is the right word to describe it – into the place where he is to exercise his divine right of government, and where he sees far less well than the meanest of his subjects. And if it came to a fight, who do you think is best placed for victory, the one who has just stumbled in from the light, or the one who can see his every movement in the darkness?

SOCRATES: I cannot help feeling that you have taken the parable in another sense from the one that I intended.

XANTHIPPE: But perhaps it was you who misunderstood the voice of your *daimonion*?

SOCRATES: No, no. I was absolutely sure of it. I felt like the Pythian prophetess seated on her tripod, as though a spirit had entered my body, in order to capture the hearts of the young. And there they were with gaping mouths, saying yes Socrates, quite right Socrates, just so Socrates, it is indeed as you say Socrates, and not for a moment realizing that I was as astonished and delighted by my words as they were.

XANTHIPPE: Poor Socrates! How you deceive yourself! And if this *daimonion* of yours really exists, do you not think that he would have more concern for the youth than to allow you to trot out the dangerous nonsense that you have put into Plato's head?

SOCRATES: What dangerous nonsense?

XANTHIPPE: This stuff about the rearing of children, for instance.

SOCRATES: Who told you about that?

XANTHIPPE: I have my spies.

SOCRATES: After all those lessons in virtue, it is impossible that my young men should report back to *you* – a woman, and, what is worse, my wife.

XANTHIPPE: You are certainly right that it is worse. If you really want to know, it was a woman who told me.

SOCRATES: A *woman*? Listening to my sublime discourses? Disguised, perhaps, as a man? You don't mean that Plato . . .

XANTHIPPE: No, no. Plato is a perfectly normal example of the male sex: he is only interested in boys. I am referring to Perictione.

SOCRATES: Plato's mother!

XANTHIPPE: She was here only this morning.

SOCRATES: What on earth would a descendant of the great Solon be doing in the house of a stone-mason's son?

XANTHIPPE: Perhaps she admires my mind. In any case, that poor lady has problems – you being the chief of them.

SOCRATES: Me?

XANTHIPPE: Yes. And since you are *my* chief problem as well, we spent a cosy hour or two commiserating. Besides, where do you think the wine comes from?

SOCRATES: What do you mean, Xanthippe?

XANTHIPPE: Perictione takes the view, and I agree with her, that since you refuse to accept fees from her son, the least she can do is to slip me an obol or two for household expenses.

SOCRATES: You mean you take fees on my behalf?

XANTHIPPE: We don't call them fees; merely a little something to off-set the cost of living with a philosopher.

SOCRATES: By the dog, if this gets around I'm done for. Just imagine what Protagoras and Gorgias and the other sophists will say! 'Never, never ought men of sense to allow their wives to be visited by women!'[9]

XANTHIPPE: Are you interested in what she said to me?

SOCRATES: Carry on; I can take it.

XANTHIPPE: This Plato, apparently, has been strutting up and down the house announcing that everything must be changed according to a wonderful new system invented by his teacher Socrates – that's you. Members of the household are to greet their fellows with a military salute, and in place of names they are to address one another as 'Comrade Guardian'. His uncles, who Zeus knows are already tempted enough in that direction, are to make over their wives and children to a common pool, so as to ensure that no exclusive affections will disrupt the great philosophical plan. He has even designed a kind of pen in the grounds of the house, into which all the children are to be herded under the care of specially chosen comrade guardians, and taught to goose-step up and down with philosophical expressions on their faces. The women – well, Zeus knows what obscenity he is preparing for them; no one can accuse

---

[9] Euripides, *Andromache*, 943–6.

31

Plato of being over-sensitive to the feelings of women. Nevertheless, it seems that he has already marked out a wing of the house
for the females, and into that wing, if he gets his way, they are all
to be gathered, even Perictione herself, to endure the embraces of
whichever comrade guardian should feel called upon to father
another little monster like himself.

SOCRATES: Impossible!

XANTHIPPE: On the contrary, all too probable. And the idea, he says, is
yours.

SOCRATES: Nonsense, Xanthippe! It's all completely garbled. I admit,
I have made one or two advanced proposals concerning the reform
of education. But this stuff about the women – that's pure Plato!

XANTHIPPE: I believe you. If you ask me, it is all part of his revenge
against Perictione for marrying again. That boy's got real problems.
But I can't say you've done much to help him.

SOCRATES: I do my best; but you know how it is.

XANTHIPPE: Yes, I know. You get carried away. Just as you did about
the cave. And, since there is a drop of wine left, and since you are
clearly not ready for bed, let us subject your educational theories to a
Socratic, or rather Xanthippic, examination.

SOCRATES: Must we? I wanted to talk about truth.

XANTHIPPE: *I* want to talk about truth too. But I disagree with your
habit of looking for truth in mere abstractions. That, in my view, is
where you go wrong.

SOCRATES: Explain yourself, Xanthippe.

XANTHIPPE: Willingly. Let us start with this crèche of Plato's. You
will admit that the purpose of this peculiar system is not to breed
humans as farm animals, but, quite the contrary, to renew the supply
of rational beings.

SOCRATES: That was my intention.

XANTHIPPE: So it *was* your idea!

SOCRATES: Well, I . . .

XANTHIPPE: You will also admit that, while a rational being has many
things in common with the animals – desires, for example, appetites,
a certain determination to survive and flourish – he is also distinct
from them.

SOCRATES: Indeed he is.

XANTHIPPE: And it is because of the thing which distinguishes him
that a rational being is also a free being, and a citizen?

SOCRATES: Indeed, those are but so many names for Reason itself.

XANTHIPPE: So if we wish to know how to cultivate Reason, we should enquire how to educate our children to be citizens?

SOCRATES: Exactly. That was my meaning.

XANTHIPPE: So let us enquire, my dear Socrates, into the qualities of the good citizen. Will he not be superior precisely in those respects which benefit the state – or rather, since we must not assume that the state is an unmixed good, in those respects which benefit society?

SOCRATES: Indeed he will.

XANTHIPPE: And how does an individual benefit society?

SOCRATES: You tell me, Xanthippe.

XANTHIPPE: Let us take another example. It seems to me that there are three ways in which a horse is benefited. First by those things which maintain his life; secondly by those things which restore his life when it is diseased or threatened; thirdly by those things which enable the horse to flourish according to his nature.

SOCRATES: You speak wisely for a woman, and it is clear that I did right to marry you.

XANTHIPPE: Do not rush to that conclusion, Socrates, until you have heard my argument. Society, then, is benefited by those who maintain its life, by those who restore it and by those who enhance it?

SOCRATES: Yes, by the dog.

XANTHIPPE: The first, I take it, are those who obey the laws. For what is the life of society, if not the laws which govern it?

SOCRATES: What, indeed?

XANTHIPPE: And those who obey the laws are distinguished, if I am not mistaken, by their ability to put aside their own selfish appetites, for the sake of what is lawful?

SOCRATES: You speak truly, Xanthippe.

XANTHIPPE: Our second class of citizens are those who can heal society in times of crisis: those who will defend it against its enemies, or bring peace in civil war.

SOCRATES: Indeed.

XANTHIPPE: And they too must be able to set aside their own desires. For whether in battle or in civil conflict, only the one who is capable of sacrifice is truly useful to the community.

SOCRATES: True, Xanthippe.

XANTHIPPE: And our third class of citizens, who enhance the quality of civil life, are those, are they not, with public spirit – whose who devote themselves to the common good, through works of charity, through education, and through the staging of plays and festivals: including plays like those of your friend Aristophanes, in which philosophers are cut down to size?

SOCRATES: Yes, yes; let's get to the end.

XANTHIPPE: I am nearly there. For you will concede that no virtue tends to the good of society so much as the virtue of sacrifice, and it remains only to establish how that virtue is to be learned.

SOCRATES: I am impatient to hear your theory, Xanthippe.

XANTHIPPE: Does a child learn physics by studying the latest theories, and sitting with those who debate them?

SOCRATES: By no means.

XANTHIPPE: In general, I think, a child must begin with the simplest and most immediate examples: such as that apples fall from trees?

SOCRATES: I cannot deny it.

XANTHIPPE: So a child will learn the virtue of sacrifice only if there are reasons for sacrifice which can be understood by a child?

SOCRATES: So it would seem.

XANTHIPPE: Now your Plato offers us no such reasons. Oh, I grant that the little monsters in his crèche will be beaten into a kind of discipline. But that means only that they behave well out of self-interest, being afraid of punishment, and by no means for the sake of another's good.

SOCRATES: Possibly. But I feel that you have overlooked the . . . the *beauty* of the idea.

XANTHIPPE: Indeed. But since you are opposed to beauty and I to ideas, it is quite right to ignore your objection. Let me come quickly to the point. A child finds his first motive to sacrifice through love, and through love alone. This is the thing which causes him to set the good of another above his own desires.

SOCRATES: I don't like the sound of this.

XANTHIPPE: Now what is love?

SOCRATES: An old chestnut.

XANTHIPPE: If you love Cleitophon, for example, is it some quality of Cleitophon that you love: his beauty, say, his courage or his generosity?

SOCRATES: Indeed it is.

34

XANTHIPPE: Then must you, in loving Cleitophon, love every other instance of those qualities – everyone who is beautiful, courageous and generous as he?

SOCRATES: By no means, Xanthippe. For if that were so, you might say to me, 'Do not love Cleitophon, but take Plato, for he will do just as well.' And I *hate* Plato.

XANTHIPPE: You begin to see my meaning, Socrates. For it follows, does it not, that you love the individual, and not his qualities, and that no other individual will do as well as he?

SOCRATES: It cannot be that you have refuted me. I must look into this.

XANTHIPPE: So, if a child is to learn love, he must love an individual, who has some special meaning for him, and on whose behalf a sacrifice seems right?

SOCRATES: Let us, for the sake of argument, grant the point.

XANTHIPPE: And he will strive for that individual to love him in return, and to care for him as an individual, rather than as a mere instance of a class? For who wishes to be loved as an abstraction?

SOCRATES: Perhaps there is some small difference between men and women.

XANTHIPPE: Love, then, is the first need of our future citizen, and the condition from which his virtues as a citizen derive. And the world of a child must be a world of love, in which each one is loved for the thing he is.

SOCRATES: There is a grain of truth in what you say.

XANTHIPPE: So now let us cease to beat about the bush and give a name to this world of love from which society derives, and which is the first education of the citizen. It is the family, is it not, Socrates – the hearth, the household; not the impersonal, military crèche of your misguided pupil?

SOCRATES: You could be right, and I have a mind to repeat your arguments in the gymnasium.

XANTHIPPE: Before you do so, however, I should like to draw a few conclusions. We began from your wondrous vision of a world ruled by philosophers, whose eyes would be fixed upon the abstract ideas which you so admire. And we saw that these philosophers would be quite incompetent to rule; that the best they could do would be to constrain our human feelings into their cruel geometry, and deprive us of our little happiness.

35

SOCRATES: I am not sure we *proved* the point.

XANTHIPPE: And we saw how much this love of abstraction blinds us to the *real* truth: the truth about the here and now, about life itself and our living it. Truth is not abstract but concrete. It resides in the particular. And it is this particular, in all its frailty and imperfection, that we love. Since it is from love that the great experiment in citizenship begins, the state, my dear Socrates, must be founded on a study of the particular, and not upon abstract ideas.

SOCRATES: But abstract ideas are so noble!

XANTHIPPE: And as you said, it is not philosophy which leads us to the particular, but something else.

SOCRATES: Explain your meaning, Xanthippe.

XANTHIPPE: Call it what you will – poetry, rhetoric, imitation – it is the art of appearances, of showing the world as it really *seems*. And since we too are appearances, it is poetry, and not philosophy, which gives the truth of our condition.

SOCRATES: For Apollo's sake, don't say this to Plato's mother.

XANTHIPPE: And do you not see another defect in this philosophy which you recommend to us?

SOCRATES: What do you mean?

XANTHIPPE: Suppose those people who call themselves philosophers are permitted to teach, and to spread the rumour of a 'higher' form of knowledge. What effect is this likely to have on our decent citizens, who have learned the ways of sacrifice and acquired, at no small cost to themselves, a store of moral certainties? Is it not likely that they will learn to doubt their present beliefs, while acquiring nothing to replace them? Philosophy, you tell us, involves the examination of life, the constant questioning of ancient pieties. But he who begins to examine his life may cease after a while to live it. Life depends upon faith, and faith is destroyed by philosophy. If you ask me, Socrates, the examined life is not a life for a human being.

SOCRATES: 'The examined life is not a life for a human being.' I say, that's rather good. I think I'll use it. Might need a bit of adjusting, of course.

XANTHIPPE: And now let me paint for you, my dear Socrates, a picture of your ideal state, as I envisage it. The rulers of this state are called philosophers, and to earn this title they undergo the most rigorous tests, reciting the doctrines and rehearsing the proofs of some future Socrates, whom they adopt as their master. Of course, those who remain below, in the cave reserved for citizens, do not attain enlightenment. Nor can they know that another has done so, and therefore must take it on trust that these philosophers are really entitled to their name. The philosophers are careful not to include among their number anyone who is unreliable, or who questions the sacred doctrine. The doctrine is in fact rather useful to their ambitions. It tells them not only that they are entitled to rule, but that any lie is permitted, provided it is sufficiently noble. And the proof that a lie is noble consists in its ability to justify the rulers, and to fortify their power.

After a while it may become apparent to our philosophers that even the doctrines of their master are false. Yet this will not deter them from repeating those doctrines, or from requiring the masses to parrot them. For what if the exalted status of the philosopher, as high priest of the eternal verities, is itself a noble lie? Does this disqualify the doctrine? By no means, my dear Socrates. On the contrary, it only serves to reassure our philosophers of the ultimate rightness of their government. For, as the philosophers will now say to themselves, it is not the truth of the doctrine that matters, but the fact that it serves the higher interests of the state.

And what are those higher interests? Our philosophers, you will recall, have lost the habit of observing particular things or individual people. Indeed the whole notion of the individual is anathema to them, since their power derives from abstract ideas alone. The individual, for them, is never more than a member of some kind – a representative, for example, of the working class, or the vanguard party (as I can imagine them describing themselves). And one of their noble lies is that they rule in the interests of the 'people': by which name they do not mean you and me and Cleitophon and Plato, but a peculiar, immortal and unchangeable abstraction, quite distinct from every one of us. In the name of the people, therefore, they may quite reasonably destroy whomsoever and howsoever many they chose.

Of course, real individuals will go on existing, and, through their freedom and their projects, they will pose a threat to the guardian party. The philosophers, therefore, will recruit a subordinate class of guardians, whose business it will be to watch over the common people, and ensure that none of them does anything to threaten the empire of lies. They will fear nothing so much as individuality and distinction. And they will be deeply suspicious of the customs that produce those qualities: of the home, of the love that grows in it, and of the habit of sacrifice. They will therefore do their best to eliminate those things, as signs of a benighted and reactionary state of mind. They will announce that all people are equal, and that no one is to stand apart from the crowd. There will be a law forbidding private property and private enterprise. All associations will be controlled by the guardians, and children will be removed from their parents, as Plato recommends, and nurtured as collective property. I envisage a new kind of education, in which the children are taught to march up and down, shouting the Socratic slogans, and swearing eternal vengeance on the enemies of philosophy. For you can imagine that, having so far raised the temperature, the guardians will invent the most useful and most 'noble' lie of all: the lie of an enemy who threatens everyone, and against whom there is no defence save the absolute rule of the guardian party.

And meanwhile the creatures of darkness – the ones who have loved and cared enough to make some sacrifice, who have refused to betray their family and friends, who have adhered to their trusted prejudices and spurned the enlightened doctrines of their rulers – these poor creatures will be cast out and anathematized. Or they will be herded together into one of Plato's farms, and there forced to work for the 'common good', as the ruling party will describe it, while the philosophers picnic somewhere in the citadels, enjoying the meagre fruits of the citizens' labour.

And the most wondrous thing of all is this: not one of these people who call themselves philosophers need have the slightest qualification, other than the endorsement of his fellow guardians. For only the ruling party is entitled to say who is and who is not a philosopher. And if, from time to time, the party is mistaken, who is there to correct it? Besides, what motive do these self-styled philosophers have to deserve the name? None whatsoever, I think, my dear Socrates. On the contrary, their interest is power, and their intellectual efforts are devoted to enhancing it, and to extending the network of mendacity into ever-newer regions, so that the truth – by which I mean the concrete and particular truth of human freedom – shall never be perceived.

SOCRATES: It is a frightening vision, Xanthippe. Is there more wine?

XANTHIPPE: Here, finish it. And dream of eternal rest in the form of a bed. I shall sleep in a real one.

FINIS

PERICTIONE'S
PARMENIDES

Antisthenes the Cynic, having failed to rebut Zeno's paradox about the arrow, started pacing up and down the room until the philosopher snapped:

'Keep still, for heaven's sake!'

'So,' murmured Antisthenes, 'you admit that I am moving?'

Proclus, *In Parmenidem*, I 694 23

(An impossible dialogue, in that Zeno the pre-Socratic died before the time of Antisthenes, who in turn died before the time of Zeno the Stoic.)

PERICTIONE'S PARMENIDES

Characters:
PLATO, aged about 18
PERICTIONE, his mother, a youthful 50

Plato's dialogues testify to a lifelong interest in the thought of Parmenides of Elea, founder of the Eleatic school, and teacher of Zeno. The Eleatics specialized in the refutation of empirical methods and did much to establish the reputation of philosophy as the highest form of knowledge. Parmenides' thought survives in the fragments of an obscure poem. In it he invokes the Way of Truth, which is set before us by philosophy, and the Way of Opinion, along which the mass of mankind stumbles into darkness. The Way of Truth leads us to Being, which is changeless, indivisible, continuous, uncreated and in all probability spherical. The Being of Parmenides reappears many times in the history of philosophy, kicked like a football down the centuries, headed off by empiricist spoil-sports but always bouncing back into the field, until dribbled into goal at last by Heidegger. Sometimes it seems vast and radiant like the universe itself (as in Plato, *Timaeus* 33B–C, 62D); sometimes like a pumpkin head, ghostly and satirical. Perhaps it is the earth, or an atom; perhaps it is some moral or spiritual thing: the apple of discord, say, promised to the fairest among the goddesses, or the apple which Eve took from the tree of knowledge, to the everlasting sorrow of mankind. The best things, it seems, are spherical; but so are the worst.

In a famous and impenetrable Platonic dialogue, Socrates recalls a youthful encounter with the ageing Parmenides, who had come on a visit to Athens with Zeno. No work of Plato's has puzzled commentators more than the *Parmenides*. The thought and style are almost wilfully obscure, and the character of Socrates recedes totally into the background, as though the *elenctic* method had nothing to add to the torrent of metaphysics that pours from the old man's mouth. And strangely, when searching for the requisite number of inverted commas, Plato gives a prominent role to his half brother Antiphon (not to be confused with Antiphon the sophist, who in turn should probably not be confused with Antiphon the orator).

Some light is cast on these matters by the following dialogue, in which another and more plausible account is given of that original meeting. We discover that it was not Socrates to whom Parmenides unburdened himself, but a person yet closer to Plato – so close, indeed, that he was never able, in later years, to confess to her influence. Plato's only hint of her place in his emotions lies in the ironical prominence that he accords in the *Parmenides* to Antiphon, offspring and symbol of their mother's transgression.

PARODOS[1]

(Perictione's drawing room. A couch left, another right, with a stool before it. In the background a marble monument, on which the urns containing the ashes of Perictione's ancestors are assembled. Perictione is lying on the couch right, giving orders over her shoulder to an invisible slave.)

PERICTIONE: Two large octopuses for Charmides, and a basket of flat fish for the children. And don't forget the Cretan cheeses and the oil of walnuts. When you pass the temple of the winds please offer a special prayer to Boreas and mention my estates at Thebes, which I mean to visit just as soon as this wretched war is over.[2] Say that I shall come myself to sacrifice as soon as I can, but that meanwhile a bit of rain would be appreciated. You might offer a prayer to Demeter too if you go that way. And don't talk to strange men. The last slave-girl I sent to the fish market never came home. Three weeks later I discovered her in the house of young Xenophon, tarted up in the costume of a favourite and so cocksure of herself I thought the hussy was going to wink at me! She did not, I should add, escape her punishment, Xenophon's fancies being so short-lived. Talented he may be, but a sticker he certainly is not!

(She turns back to the room.)

Mind you, one can hardly blame the girl. It's not much fun in this house since the boys took up philosophy.

PLATO *(entering in great agitation)*: Mother! How could you!

(He flings himself onto the other couch.)

---

[1] The division of the dialogue into three sections – *parodos*, *agon* and *parabasis* – refers to the three principal 'movements' of an Attic comedy. It is clearly the idea of the scholiast.

[2] Internal evidence would suggest that the conversation recorded in this dialogue took place in 405 BC, the year after the victory at Arginusae, when Athens was briefly hopeful of a speedy and successful conclusion to the Peloponnesian war. It would have been impossible for Perictione to visit her estates in the region of Thebes, on account of the Spartan garrison at Decelea, built eight years earlier on the treacherous advice of Alcibiades. The dire situation of the Athenians seems to have made little impact on their philosophical discourse. In this dialogue, as in many of the dialogues of Plato set in the darkest years of war, almost no mention is made of the prevailing danger. The question how Perictione, an Athenian, came to *possess* estates at Thebes is an intriguing one, to which recorded history offers no answers.

PERICTIONE: My dear boy, what *have* I done?

PLATO: What have you done? What have you not done, by the dog!

PERICTIONE: Must you use that vulgar expression? Can you not swear by the gods, as civilized people do?

PLATO: For Zeus' sake!

PERICTIONE: That's better. So what have I done? What in particular, I mean?

PLATO: This, on top of everything! I could die!

PERICTIONE: Exaggeration is bad style. Can you not speak in a way that would make it rewarding to listen to you?

PLATO: As though you hadn't destroyed enough of me! And now, of all times, at the very outset of my career as a philosopher – this, this betrayal!

PERICTIONE: Oh, do stop playing the chorus! I want to hear the plot. Which particular betrayal do you have in mind?

PLATO: *Your* betrayal! Of *me*!

PERICTIONE: But you have already accused me of twenty treasons this week. It would help to propel the dialogue if you were to be a trifle more precise.

PLATO: Those treasons were nothing compared with this one: for now you have put everything at risk – my hopes, my love, my self-esteem, my *very existence*!

PERICTIONE: You are beginning to bore me.

PLATO: Admit it! Admit that you told Socrates about my – about my Great Design!

PERICTIONE: Listen, I hardly know Socrates, thank Demeter. To which Great Design are you referring? Do you mean the machine for writing philosophical dialogues, using every permutation of the first ten lines of Hesiod? Or the scheme for attacking the Spartan navy with burning carrier pigeons? Or was it the one about the apple pips. . . .

PLATO: Mother! You know what I mean, for Zeus' sake! I mean the Great Design in the Garden. The New Republic. The Philosophical Kingdom. The Socratic Phalanstery.

PERICTIONE: The Socratic what?

PLATO: He said he heard about it through you! Everything, every little detail! Even about the women! I could have died of shame! And the way he looked at me, so full of belittling reproach, as though to say, 'my poor dear Plato, how could you be so naïve, so unsophisticated, so unphilosophical, so devoid of irony, as to take my suggestion seriously?' I shall never be able to look him in the face again. Never! Socrates! The only man I admire, the only one I love! My whole life in ruins! How could you do this to me?

PERICTIONE: There, there. You'll get over it.

PLATO: The fact is he knows: and it was through you, he said, that the information came. Through you, Mother!

PERICTIONE: I admit, I did mention it to Xanthippe. But is that so very wrong? Cannot women discuss their children's problems together?

PLATO: Xanthippe? That ill-bred little shrew? Mother, how could you – a descendant of Solon the wise, related one way or another to all the great men of Athens, past and present – how could you talk to that creature, that wicked persecutor of the most noble man in Hellas? Why, only the other day, I am reliably informed, she tipped a bucket of slops over his dignified old head, as though she would wash it off his shoulders!

PERICTIONE: As a matter of fact, Xanthippe is a virtuous, long-suffering woman, who merely happens to lack our social advantages. I should be sorry to think that my station as a public figure prevented me from visiting her.

PLATO: All right, go and speak to your Xanthippe, if you will. Tittle-tattle to your heart's content. Pour scorn if you like on the greatest man in all creation. But do you have to mention me? Do you have to prise away my mask for the benefit of gossips, and expose the poor trembling creature that lies beneath? Do you have to? Do you?

PERICTIONE: Now let's try to get to the bottom of this. What exactly do you object to? The fact that Socrates has discovered your little secret? Or the fact, as you suppose, that I am responsible for revealing it?

PLATO: Both. But most of all – yes, it's you I object to. Your way of standing on the path of all my little endeavours, waiting in ambush to send me screaming back home. In everything I do or try, whatever it might be, always you are there to undermine it!

PERICTIONE: I say, this *is* interesting. I had always assumed our relationship was rather a routine affair. Hang on while I get a drink.

(She claps her hands, and, reaching behind her off stage, receives from an unseen slave the regular bowl of wine, flavoured with aniseed. She drinks.)

Yum, yum!

(A pause, while Plato looks at her.)

Well, I'm waiting. You were going to talk about Pyrilampes.

PLATO: Pyrilampes! What do I care about Pyrilampes, that flat-headed, wooden-tongued Aegisthus whom you happen to have invited into your bed![3]

PERICTIONE: Well, that sounds like caring.

PLATO: Rubbish! It's not him I mind! I've got used to the old creep. It's everything else!

PERICTIONE: Do be more precise.

PLATO: It's your arrogance, Mother, your beastly self-assurance, your ability – Zeus knows where you take it from – to get away with every kind of social outrage, and to shrug off the shame of it! You think I am referring to Pyrilampes, when in fact I don't care a damn about that second-rate bore whom you chose to marry for reasons that all Athens has striven in vain to understand. In fact I am talking about an unending sequence of disasters and humiliations.

PERICTIONE: For instance?

PLATO: For instance, your barging into my room, as you did last night, at the very moment when I am writing my diary, and snatching the stylus away! And thereafter treating me to a tipsy description of the party at Euryptolemus' house, and the great strokes of wit with which you refuted and embarrassed your hosts. For instance, your eavesdropping on me and Cleinias the other day, when you alone knew that I had been able to detach him from the feast and take him into the *exedra* so as to pour out my heart. For instance, your decision to abandon me at the tenderest age to that hideous nurse Castallax who smelt of dung and who scolded me perpetually on account of my delicate digestion. For instance, your appalling taste in clothes, which leads you to wear saffron silk to the feast of Artemis, and kinky black leather at weddings. For instance, your decision to have even more sons by that oaf Pyrilampes – so that, having been cheated by Glaucon of the rights of the eldest, I find myself without the special consoling love which is lavished on the last-born, on Antiphon of all people! And there is your habit of borrowing my make-up, of walking off for whole days with my handbag, so that I hardly dare go to the gymnasium, I look such a

---

[3] In the *Charmides* – a dialogue devoted to the virtue of self-control – Plato (speaking in the persona of Socrates) praises his stepfather Pyrilampes in such exaggerated terms, as to confirm the underlying hostility. (See *Charmides*, 158A.) As always Plato tries to dramatize a virtue, in the very dialogue that discusses it.

fright. And then those friends of yours with affected names like Deianeira and Iole and Briseis and Nausicaa – precious antiques, imagining they need trace their ancestors only a couple of steps in order to come across a god or two. I could go on.

PERICTIONE: Yes, but the style is appalling, I don't think I could bear it.

PLATO: And that too: your constant denigration of my talents, your pretence that – had you the time which your duties as the most attractive woman in Athens deny you – you could effortlessly improve on everything I write or say. No sooner do I begin to recite, and you collapse in shrieks of theatrical laughter. 'Would Homer have written that?' you say; or 'How's that for bathos!' or 'How it limps and totters!' As though literature ended with Aeschylus. As though there were no place left for innovation! Of course, Mother: I know I'm no good. But do you have to remind me always? Do you have to let me know, with those sarcastic looks and gestures, what a disappointment I am to you, with my puny body and my mixed-up emotions? Is it a wonder that I spend my days elsewhere, at the foot of the only good man in Athens? But of course, knowing this, you decide to spoil my relations with him as well, spreading rumours to discredit me, and poisoning the only pure affection which it has been my fortune to enjoy. Honestly, Mother, if I were to kill myself, I could hardly be blamed!

PERICTIONE: Finished?

PLATO: Yes, I think so.

PERICTIONE (*after a pause*): Are you very busy at the moment, darling?

PLATO: And your habit of calling me darling,[4] as though I were some kind of lover, and not your despised and neglected child, condemned to hang on your every word, in the vain hope of being comforted. Zeus! No, I am not very busy; why do you ask?

PERICTIONE: I just wondered whether you had time for a tutorial?

PLATO: A tutorial! She wants to give me a tutorial!

PERICTIONE: Yes. For as a matter of fact, I feel a little guilty in your regard.

PLATO: Thanks. She feels guilty! Maybe I'm supposed to be grateful. Guilty about what?

---

[4] μέλημα: a lovers' word, often used in comedy, but applied by Electra to her brother Orestes, at line 235 of Aeschylus, *The Libation Bearers*.

PERICTIONE: About your education. I've let your language run to seed. And I've given no guidance at all, I now perceive, in the crucial matter of your emotions. I suppose it is this which has caused you to sit at the feet of that wretched old fraud, soaking up philosophy.

PLATO: Please don't blaspheme against the only god you have left me!

PERICTIONE: Socrates may be exceptional, but surely he is not a god?

PLATO: I mean philosophy, Mother, not Socrates.

PERICTIONE: As for that, I am quite prepared to admit that philosophy is divine, like love and war and the smallpox. But it is definitely *not* the way to self-knowledge.

PLATO: If that is the theme of your tutorial, I don't want to hear it.

PERICTIONE: There you are, you see; philosophy has closed your mind. It tells you to question everything except itself.

PLATO: To question the question is also part of philosophy.

PERICTIONE: That is why philosophy is the enemy of self-knowledge.

PLATO: What do you mean?

PERICTIONE: Self-knowledge is an art, a skill, a spontaneous certainty in the things that matter.

PLATO: And what are they?

PERICTIONE: The passions. We must learn, as Xanthippe argued the other day, the right emotions, towards the right objects, on the right occasions and in the right degree. Only then do we obey the command of Loxias: which incidentally ought to be attributed to my ancestor Solon.[5]

PLATO: And how do we learn this strange thing?

PERICTIONE: As we learn everything else: by imitation. And the highest form of imitation is art. Nothing, therefore, is more important than style.

PLATO: Not even truth?

PERICTIONE: I am talking of another and higher knowledge: not the fumbling after truth, but the certainty of the heart. That is our goal in life, and it is beauty, not truth, that leads us there. That is why I say that no gift of the gods is greater than style.

PLATO: Still greater, it seems to me, would be a loving parent. Or even two loving parents.

PERICTIONE: Love too is a matter of style. Which is why, my dear, you

---

[5] Loxias was the name assumed by the Delphic Apollo. The command to which Perictione refers – 'know thyself' – is also an aphorism of the Seven Sages, one of whom was Solon the Wise, poet, statesman, and chief artificer of the Athenian *polis*.

are so hopeless at it. But come here, and let me prove that I love you, less perhaps than a mother should, but as much as I can, and maybe as much as you deserve.

PLATO: And how will you do that?

PERICTIONE: By imparting my wisdom.

PLATO: You know I can resist anything except wisdom.

PERICTIONE: My dear Aristocles![6]

PLATO: How many times must I ask you? I am no longer called Aristocles! Aristocles is no longer my *name*! My name is Plato!

PERICTIONE: Sorry, dear. Plato, of course. On account of your broad shoulders.

PLATO: Very funny. Ha, ha. I *know* I have the puniest body this side of Marathon.

PERICTIONE: Sorry, Plato. I just wonder why I have to use this ridiculous name.

PLATO: Shan't tell you. It's a secret. So there!

PERICTIONE: All right, I won't ask. Let's kiss and make up, shall we? Then I'll give you a nice tutorial.

PLATO: OK, Mother; but don't think I didn't mean what I said. I did. Every word of it.

PERICTIONE: But that's where you're wrong, you see. You didn't mean a single word of it. Oh, I grant that you made a certain impression on yourself; but making an impression on yourself is not the same as meaning something.

---

[6] Plato was called Aristocles by his parents. Πλατύς means 'broad', and some commentators explain Plato's adoption of this nickname by referring to his supposedly broad shoulders. A more plausible explanation can be deduced from this dialogue, however. It is clear from what follows that Plato had access to the texts of the comedies which were to be shown that year at the Lenaean festival – one of them being Aristophanes' *Frogs*, which won the prize. Plato must therefore have been intimate with some of the actors, and perhaps with the playwrights themselves – a fact which is consonant with his own poetic ambitions. One of Aristophanes' competitors in the contest was Plato the dramatist, who entered a political comedy called *Cleophon*. It is not implausible to suppose that Plato the future philosopher was infatuated with this playwright, and therefore took his name. This too would explain why he will not reveal his secret to his mother. On the other hand, 'Plato' was a fairly common name, with no less than thirty-one known Athenian instances, not all of whom, it must be assumed, were in love with Plato the dramatist: and besides how did *he* get his name? (See J. A. Notopoulos, 'The Name of Plato', *Classical Philology*, 1939, 135–45.) It seems, from a note in Pamphila's *Memorabilia*, that the relations between Plato the philosopher and Plato the dramatist were touched on in *Phryne's Symposium*, a Xanthippic dialogue, now unfortunately lost.

PLATO: Of course not, for that involves making an impression on *you* – something I have never succeeded in doing.

PERICTIONE: Oh no, you have succeeded. But there is such a disparity between the impression you make, and the one you intend, that interpretation is quite out of the question. And where there is no interpretation, there is no meaning either. An emotion, you must realize, exists only through its expression, and its expression must be clear, dramatic, objective if it is to touch the heart. It must take the form of a dance – rhythmical, exact, working naturally towards its climax, but at the same time with a tincture of surprise. It was a nice touch of yours, actually, to introduce the complaint about the handbag. Nothing reveals another's soul – or, rather, nothing creates another's soul – so much as an unexpected word or gesture. And you were right to keep off the topic of your father: it is an elementary rule that the *real* object of anger should be just out of view, revealed in the language and imagery of the protest, but sensed rather than seen, like an animal watching from the under-growth. But the whole speech was incoherent, jumping from the tragic to the farcical and back again like a hare caught in a hunting net. It was impossible to attach any meaning to it. The complaints came in any order, the words were imprecise and without rhythm, and the audience could create no image of their target.

PLATO: Their target?

PERICTIONE: I mean me, Perictione, the silent player in the dialogue.

PLATO: Silent! I like that!

PERICTIONE: Silent, I mean, while you were speaking, dutifully awaiting my cue, understanding, as I do, the therapeutic value of utterance.

PLATO: I'm really grateful, Mother. No, honestly.

PERICTIONE: But you see, my dear Plato, that even as therapy, the value of your words would increase a hundredfold, if only you could find the appropriate style.

PLATO: And what is the appropriate style?

PERICTIONE: The objective style, the style which gives form and reality to the passions, by detaching them from the self. I do not, as you suppose, think all literature ended with Aeschylus. But there began then a decline in the language of poetry, and also in its inner purpose. This Euripides, for instance, who died last year.

PLATO: Euripides! Give me Xenocles or Pythangelus any day![7]

PERICTIONE: Let's stay with Euripides, since he has been such an influence on your master, Socrates – if it wasn't the other way round, which I rather doubt.[8] How far he is from the clarity, the marmoreal objectivity of Aeschylus. Instead of archetypes he gives us characters; in place of the human condition, mere bewildered specimens, who strive to endow every paltry fragment of their experience with some weight of melodrama, and as a result can only leave us cold. Real emotion is precise, guided like an arrow to its target; false emotion is vague, uncertain, full of irrelevances like a kleptomaniac's shopping-bag. Consider that dreadful Medea, for instance.

PLATO: Dreadful indeed, like every woman who makes a sacrifice of her children.

PERICTIONE: I grant she has her enviable side. But I am more interested, you will not be surprised to learn, in her relations with men. Let us take her answer to Jason, when he says, 'Though you hate me, never can I bear malice against you'[9] – which I must say is not a bad summary of the generous feelings that men entertain towards women whom they are abandoning. Instead of piercing his heart with a dart of irony, which is the correct feminine response, off she goes at once, quite over the top, crying, 'Oh, you sum of all evils' or some such thing, explaining herself, if I remember, at vast and superfluous length:

> I shall relieve my feelings
> By describing your evil soul, and you will hear me grieving.
> So first things first I utter them:
> I saved you, as every Hellene knows
> Who stepped with you aboard your ship, the Argo. . . .
> The dragon, guardian of the Golden Fleece
> Who coiled about it sleeplessly

[7] Minor playwrights whose works (no doubt on account of their paltriness) have not come down to us. (However, Xenocles is said to have defeated Euripides at a festival in 415 BC.)

[8] There is a story, deriving from the lost writings of Mnesimachus, and repeated by Diogenes Laertius (II, 18), that Socrates helped to compose the plays of Euripides. Other ancient writers (e.g. Callias and Teleclides) also repeat the tale.

[9] Euripides, *Medea*, lines 463–4. Perictione goes on to quote (with excisions) from lines 473–87.

I killed; and raised the flame which saved you.
My father and my home I left for you;
I came with you to Iolcos,
More passionate than wise;
And Pelias too I killed. . . .

A catalogue of grievances, all in the first person, self-pitying as any speech of yours. How true to life, we are supposed to say, and wouldn't she express herself in just such a way, when the woman clearly hasn't taken the first steps towards feeling anything at all. She is uninterested in the world outside herself, and therefore uninteresting to us: a mere atom of humanity, whose words are lost on the winds of time like the cries of a chimaera.

PLATO: I feel you are describing me and not Medea.

PERICTIONE: There you are, you see! By imitating these dreadful characters you become as self-indulgent as they. You imagine that every remark is really, in some secret way, about yourself: that you, the mere dispensable Plato, are not dispensable at all, but the very centre of the universe. There you have the essence of bad style.

PLATO: Very impressive, Mother. But scarcely a criticism of Euripides. Indeed, it says something for the reality of his characters, that they can have such an influence on Aristocles – I mean on Plato.

PERICTIONE: On the contrary. Such characters, who seem to have stepped into the theatre out of the auditorium – where of course real women would hardly wish to be seen[10] – are no part of the action, but a disruption to it, like irritating breakwaters amid a smooth flow of waves. In my view they are so alien to the stage that they ought not to be wearing masks at all.

PLATO: But how is a person less real for not wearing a mask? Are not the frozen features of a mask the very opposite of real emotion?

PERICTIONE *(laughs)*: My dear Plato, how exquisitely naïve you are! The true mask is not frozen at all; on the contrary, it wears the most mobile of all expressions, infinitely ambiguous in its illusory stillness, responding to every nuance of the actor's words. The mask is the final perfection of the true individual, the thing which brings his face and his words into harmony, by making the face the product

[10] Were women actually *allowed* in the theatre? Jeffrey Henderson ('Women and the Athenian Dramatic Festivals', *Transactions of the American Philological Association* 121 (1991) 133–147), says yes, and proves it.

of the words. What we see in the mask we see because of the words
we hear. And that is why the true mask is a lifetime's work in the
making – as you learn from the mask of Oedipus which my dear
friend Calliope made during the long years of her husband's
absence, and which she finally perfected on the day that he came
home. On which day she began the second mask – with the eyes
stabbed out. They were used last year, I am told, to great effect.

PLATO: All this is a long way from Euripides, Mother. And since, as you
say, real women would scarcely set foot in the theatre, it is the words,
not the masks, that are most important so far as you are concerned.

PERICTIONE: True, Plato. Which is why I criticize your words, and
not your facial expressions, which are, if I may say so, a topic in
themselves.

PLATO: You may say what you like. *I* don't care. Let's get back to the
tutorial. What you say reminds me of a comedy I was reading
yesterday, in which Aeschylus and Euripides vie with each other in
the tragic art, and their words were weighed in scales by the chorus.
Here, if I remember rightly, is what Aeschylus says in his defence:

> Look then at the characters I made:
> Noble, public-spirited and tall!
> Not knaves or rogues or loiterers as now
> But breathing spear and lance, their helmets plumed
> With white, their legs and breasts well-plated
> And with the hearts of seven bulls![11]

'Breathing spear and lance'! I ask you, Mother, is that what you mean
by style? Is that the way to make feelings objective, to give an
archetype and a lesson? Don't you think that Euripides has a point,
when he says in reply that the way to set an example is not to indulge in
this high-flown Parnassian jargon, but to speak like a human being?

PERICTIONE: I don't know this comedy you refer to, and I admit that
'breathing spear and lance' is not very good – certainly nothing that
the real Aeschylus would have written. But you confuse realism with
reality. The stage, my dear Plato, focuses on reality through the lens
of convention. You do not make a sculpture of a dog by casting a real

[11] Aristophanes, *Frogs*, lines 1013–7. The phrase to which Plato takes exception is
Πλέοντας δόρυ καὶ λόγχας. *Frogs* was performed in 405 BC, though it is probable
(see note 6, above) that Plato had obtained a copy in advance, perhaps from one of the
actors.

dog in gypsum. You work towards your result, chiselling your dog from the resisting medium of stone. And just as the sculptor probes the block of marble with his chisel, discovering the god-like image that lies hidden inside it, so does Aeschylus probe our language with his sharp intelligence, until the shards have fallen away from some form within. It is in creating life that we discover it. And errors of taste are errors of being: they divorce us from reality, and make us uninteresting to the world. Alas, however, as Cleobulina said, 'It is bad taste that reigns most widely among mortals, and excess of words.'[12]

PLATO: But what I expressed in my outburst was real, Mother. Sort of real, anyway.

PERICTIONE: There you have it: *sort of* real. But not really real: for neither you nor I could grasp it, and the feeling vanished from our conception like the ghost of Odysseus' mother as he strives to embrace her. You think you give reality to your feelings by pouring them out. But this is to make a sculpture by throwing gypsum on a dog. It is as though one were to show on the stage the dire scenes of murder which are the core of tragedy. Consider, my dear Plato, the great scene in the *Agamemnon* of Aeschylus: you cannot deny that you know it, since the scroll has been missing from the library for two weeks now, and must be holed up somewhere in that fetid room of yours, along with the pictures of singers and the ghastly soiled laundry which the slaves refuse to touch. Remember how, at the moment when Clytaemnestra is to murder her husband, both victim and executioner disappear from view, and words issue at last from the pent-up soul of Cassandra, strange words of prophecy, not describing but suggesting the scene. Were we to witness the murder, it would repel us. Evoking it in this way, however, makes both pity and terror bearable. That which is bearable, we are free to feel. So now you see how the emotions are educated by tragedy, and why tact is the essence of the tragic art.

PLATO: Are you saying, Mother, that we educate the emotions only by concealing our feelings in verse? Are we to suppose that no man has

---

[12] The saying is attributed by Diogenes Laertius (I, 91) to the sixth-century poet Cleobulus, whom he has confused with the fifth-century poetess, contemporary of Praxilla, to whom Perictione refers. The word for 'bad taste' – ἀμουσεία – survives in modern German *Anmusigkeit*. Cleobulina is also mentioned in Eusebius, *Chronicle*, 82,2.

ever been truly angry or pitying or joyful or jealous until he has learned to distinguish ionics from anapests, or discovered when to utter choriambic dimeters, and when on the contrary it would be better to unburden himself in catalectic trochaic trimeters with a glyconic and pherecratean to finish?

PERICTIONE: By no means, dear; life merely imitates art, it does not copy it. But I see you have been studying the forms of dramatic poetry. It cannot be that you are writing a play!

PLATO: Well I, no I, well yes, I, sort of.

PERICTIONE: Don't tell me: about a young man of noble household, whose father has died and whose mother has married again, and whose mind is burdened by a deep suspicion . . .

PLATO: Please, Mother, not this time! No sarcasm!

PERICTIONE: I am far from being sarcastic. On the contrary, work really hard at it, and I shall be spared those appalling speeches of yours; who knows, I may even be able to respond to you with feeling, as Clytaemnestra does to Orestes. On the other hand, I do not advise you to take Aeschylus as your model.

PLATO: Why not? You were just beginning to persuade me.

PERICTIONE: I refer you to far greater authors, who wrote before this barbarous habit of separating the actors from the text had arisen, authors for whom the drama was one continuous ballet, with a single chorus singing every part and also dancing it.

PLATO: To whom are you referring, Mother?

PERICTIONE: First of all to Corinna, her of Thebes: how the sound of her verse recalls me. Thebes my mother![13]

---

[13] Corinna was a Theban poetess, usually supposed to be a contemporary of Pindar, who both advised him and competed against him (while criticizing others for daring to do so).

'Thebes my mother' (θήβα μᾶτερ εμά): these famous words are Pindar's. Both Pindar and Perictione were lying. The former came from Cynoscephalae (although he resided in Thebes), while the latter's social position could be enjoyed only by someone of pure Athenian descent. We know that Perictione had estates at Thebes, but she was also proud of her Athenian ancestors: in referring to herself as Theban she probably intended to lay claim to the Aeolian culture of Thebes – the culture which had its roots in Lesbos, and which had formed such great women as Sappho and Aspasia.

It has recently been argued by Martin West that the ancient authorities who make Corinna a contemporary of Pindar were misled, and that, on grounds both literary and linguistic, she should be dated somewhere in the third century BC. (See M. I. West, *Greek Metre*, 1982, p. 141, and 'Dating Corinna', *Classical Quarterly*, vol. XL no. 2, 1990, pp. 553–7.) Perictione, who certainly knew what she was talking about, takes the customary view. Professor West's argument must therefore be treated with caution.

PLATO: But Corinna never wrote a tragedy.

PERICTIONE: Didn't she now? That's just where you're wrong; she wrote a beautiful, seamless Oresteia, modelled on that of Stesichorus. The only problem is that no one will publish it.

PLATO: Do we have a manuscript?

PERICTIONE: Do I have a manuscript, you mean? Certainly not.

PLATO: Then what's the use of referring to it?

PERICTIONE: It's all part of your education, my dear. So let us take Stesichorus instead – Stesichorus whose Oresteia is simpler, grander and more subtle by far than that of Aeschylus.[14] I would particularly recommend, before you pour out any more of your complaints before your disbelieving mother, that you make a study of Orestes' speech to Clytaemnestra in the *Libation Bearers*: so measured, so exact, and offering an archetype that would clarify your inner turmoil. For as you know, this is the most intense occasion in all drama: the son has returned, obedient to the law of vengeance. His murdered father's ghost comes from the tomb each night to trouble him. His house is in ruins – the 'remnants of the Atreidae in their helplessness', as Stesichorus puts it.[15] And then suddenly the murderer is there, at the gate of the Palace, and has recognized him. Just at the moment when you, Plato, would come out with some ghastly speech saying how she had ruined your life

---

[14] Stesichorus of Himera (*c.* 630–*c.* 555 BC); his *Oresteia* in two books was sung at a spring festival in Sparta, and was perhaps the model upon which Aeschylus drew. It is now clear that Stesichorus' narrative and dramatic poems were probably too long (over 1000 lines) to have been recited in unison by a chorus, as was previously supposed. The picture given by Perictione is of a chorus from which individual actors separate so as to re-create the events of the drama, without, however, breaking the seamless flow of the chant. This is no doubt the right picture.

Perictione's description of the poem is of immense historical importance, containing as it does not only another new fragment of Stesichorus' writing, but also an indication of the poet's standing in the eyes of Periclean Athens. As the *Phaedrus* shows, Plato acquired his mother's trick of attributing what he secretly wished to say to Stesichorus.

[15] The phrase may occur in Stesichorus. However, it is also used by Aeschylus, *The Libation Bearers*, line 407:

'Ατρειδᾶν τὰ λοιπ' 'αμηχάνως
ἔχοντα . . .

Since the metre and language do not match the simple dactylo-epitrites displayed in other Stesichorean fragments, it is safe to assume that Perictione suffers here from a lapse of memory.

and killed your father and stolen your handbag and made a frightful mess of your education, Orestes turns to hide his face in silence. 'Not Orestes?' she says. And then comes his simple reply:

> The remnants of your son am I,
> No more Orestes, but a bag of limbs
> Brought home for burial.[16]

And then, as Clytaemnestra stretches out a hand to him, the sublime words of rejection:

> Take back this hand which loosed my father's limbs
> And brought such shame upon your children!

No tedious catalogue of woes, no list of trivial sufferings, nothing about slights and diaries, eavesdroppings and handbags: just one all-comprehending image of the dismembered son, in which the entire emotion lives by implication. We sense the irresolution, the mind lost in irrelevance, the will and the body destroyed, and the subtle implication that Orestes has become one with his father, dismembered by the very blow which put paid to Agamemnon.[17] This, my dear Plato, is the kind of utterance which you should imitate. How clear things would then be between us. So, tell me about this tragedy of yours.

PLATO: I – I – must I?

PERICTIONE: Only if you want to, dear. I won't laugh.

PLATO: Promise?

PERICTIONE: Promise.

PLATO: Well then, I'm stuck. I have written the first few scenes many times, and then I get to the crucial speech, and I – well, I think of Socrates and philosophy, and the whole thing goes up in smoke.

PERICTIONE: I am impatient to hear you, my dear Plato.

PLATO: Well, you see, you've got to put aside your Aeschylus and your

---

[16] This curious passage is of immense scholarly interest, not the least for the extraordinary and shocking image of the bag of limbs – μελοθύλακος. This may contain a pun. For it is possible that the term was also used to denote a kind of bagpipe played at Mycaenean funerals (μέλος meaning not only 'limb' but also 'song'). This could of course enhance the sinister impact of Orestes' speech.

[17] Victims of murder were habitually dismembered, lest their ghosts should retain the power to pursue the murderer. The fact is explicitly mentioned in Agamemnon's connection by Sophocles, *Electra*, 445.

Stesichorus: put aside even your Euripides, and imagine a wholly new kind of character, one in which the idea of heroism is quite dead. Oh I grant, he has done his military service, killed a Spartan or two, and been debauched in the camp at Piraeus. But he doesn't have – what is it? – the kind of *certainty* in his own existence, the weddedness to being, which you see in Orestes or Electra or Agamemnon. This new kind of character is you and me, Mum, for we live in an age of decline, an age of doubt and anxiety and hesitation.

PERICTIONE: Speak for yourself, Plato.

PLATO: I *am* speaking for myself. It's the only thing I know how to do. The task is to compose a tragedy in which the troubles of this anti-hero are given an 'objective correlative', so to say.

PERICTIONE: Nice phrase, Plato. And so far, I see, you are going along with my argument.

PLATO: Here is what happens. A young man of noble household has lost his father, and . . .

PERICTIONE: . . . his mother has married again . . .

PLATO: Yes, and he naturally has his suspicions . . .

PERICTIONE: . . . the new husband having been around for some time, and perhaps a relation of the first one . . .

PLATO: . . . and his mother being so wrapped up in her new marriage, so – how shall I put it? – out of reach and dreamy . . .

PERICTIONE: . . . and he all the while a little jealous, no doubt, of his mother's happiness, and fearful that he will lose his place in her affections . . .

PLATO: . . . and of course, probably doomed to be displaced by some new offspring, a half brother, a minotaur . . .

PERICTIONE: . . . and meanwhile struggling to understand himself, seeking for his own soul, now in poetry, now in that ghastly music, now in philosophy . . .

PLATO: . . . until, lo and behold, he is visited by his father's ghost . . .

PERICTIONE: . . . who wrongly accuses his mother. If only you had known Ariston as well as I did, Plato, you would not trust a *word* he says.[18]

---

[18] Perictione would have been, like every Athenian woman of her class, the victim of an arranged marriage. An obscure passage in Diogenes Laertius (III, 2) implies that she did not take to Ariston – or certainly not at first – and that he had to force her to yield to his embraces. However, the passage also seems to imply that he afterwards felt some remorse.

PLATO: But in the play, you see, the central character is told by the ghost to play a heroic role – the role of Orestes. And this for him is the crux: not whether it is right or wrong to do it – the easy question of heroes. But whether he is rightly cast, so to speak, whether he can even understand the dilemma, or have the will to act on it. He stands at the edge of that hesitating world he lives in and stares back across a chasm to the world of heroes. How can he recuperate their certainties? How can he measure himself against their more than real reality? Thinking of what is asked of him, he hopes to melt away, to cease to exist, to dissolve and run into the crevices of the earth, there to be lost beyond recovery. And in his torment, because of course there is no one he can talk to . . .

PERICTIONE: . . . having grievously insulted the woman who bore him with lewd accusations and self-indulgent claims on her emotions . . .

PLATO: . . . he begins to lose all sense of who he is. Under the influence of his mother, or some other demonic force, he comes to think of himself as a character in a play, experimenting with words so as to endow himself with real emotions, but discovering that his emotions are mere experiments. The play contains another – because you see, Mother, this new kind of character lives his life in inverted commas; he is a quotation from a book whose title he cannot recall, and which was probably written by his enemy. The play within the play shows the war of Troy, the death of Priam, and the grief of Hecuba. And on this grief our hero meditates.

PERICTIONE: What is the name of this 'hero', as you call him?

PLATO: There's no name for him as yet. I refer to him as 'the one who strives to assert himself' (*hamileter*).[19] As I was saying, he meditates upon the drama of Troy. Is it not monstrous, he thinks, that this actor, grieving for Hecuba, tears in his eyes, distraction in his aspect, should achieve so great a presence, while the one who strives to assert

---

[19] Greek: ὁ ἀμιλλητήρ. The whole passage concerning Plato's play is of considerable interest. Diogenes Laertius (III, 5) recounts that, on hearing Socrates speak, Plato burned a tragedy that he had composed. Aelian, *Varia Historia*, ii, 30, claims that there was not one play but a tetralogy, the parts of which Plato had already distributed to the actors when the thunderbolt of Socrates struck. The passage also testifies to the influence on Greek literature of Shakespeare. It should not surprise us that the effect of a great writer can spread backwards in time: witness the influence exerted by Virgil over Homer, Dante over Virgil and Milton over Dante (and especially, of course, over Cary's translation of Dante). References to Shakespeare abound in the plays of

himself cannot react to the real death that he must avenge? Actually, Mum, I envisage the whole thing as proceeding in this way, plays within plays, until the great moment, when the principal character, striving to assert himself, comes face to face with his failure. There comes before his mind a strange image – the image of existence itself: am I, or am I not? What is Being anyway? And there, in the depth of his despair, having separated himself entirely from the world of sense and action, he discovers the universal question . . .

PERICTIONE: Which is?

PLATO: I suppose you could call it the question of existence. This is the theme of his great speech, delivered alone to the chorus, the first line of which I have actually composed already, Mum. . . .

PERICTIONE: Let's have it.

PLATO: Promise you won't mock?

PERICTIONE: Promise.

PLATO: OK, then. *(Clears his throat, and recites)*:
'Being or not-being: that defines the problematic.'

PERICTIONE: 'Being or not-being; that defines the problematic.' Hmm. Promising. Metre could be polished up a bit, I suppose. Still, no, it's got something. Yes. In the hands of a skilled poet it would make rather an impressive line. So, what then?

PLATO: That's it. I'm stuck. All the same, I've found the only path that is open out of my character's predicament.

PERICTIONE: What path?

PLATO: The path of philosophy, the meditation on existence itself, the final negation of all these anxieties and doubts, the exodus into the really real.

Sophocles, and also in such dialogues as *Xanthippe's Republic*, above. Compare too *3 Henry VI*, V, vi, lines 13–14:

> The bird that hath been limed in a bush
> With trembling wings misdoubteth every bush . . .

with Aeschylus, *Agamemnon*, line 1316:

> οὔτοι δυσοίζω θάμνον ὡς ὄρνις φόβῳ
> ἄλλως . . .

('Not with vain fear do I shrink, as a bird that misdoubteth bush.')
And note the evident reference to Hamlet (I, v, 40) in Euripides, *Andromache*, 1, 1073:

> αἰαῖ - πρόμαντις θυμὸς . . .

('Oh my prophetic soul . . .')

PERICTIONE *(sighs)*: There are more things in heaven and earth, Plato, than are dreamt of in your philosophy. Really, this Socrates has a lot to answer for, if he inspires such a muddled tragedy as the one you have just described.

PLATO: No, Mother! On the contrary, it is *because* of Socrates that I am stuck. What I want to say, I cannot say in verse or drama. I need a new language, the language of ideas: that is what I shall learn from him, if you haven't spoiled our relations for ever.

PERICTIONE: And you know I haven't, you wicked boy.

PLATO *(suddenly confiding)*: Sometimes, Mother, as I listen to him and his divine words caress my mind like summer breezes filling the woods with light and movement, I awaken to a new vision of things – no, you mustn't laugh, I'm not saying this for effect. I'll admit that all my usual outpourings are bombastic, gross, implausible – but please allow my feelings for Socrates, Mother. They are the real thing.

PERICTIONE: I allow you everything, my dear. But it was not I who invented the rules. Nor indeed were they invented by anyone mortal.

PLATO: A plague on the rules. This vision that comes through the divine words of Socrates is something that only the lovers of philosophy can know. It is a vision of peace and reconciliation and friendship, a vision of homecoming – yes, that's it, of having wandered far from home in that world where only heroes are noticeable, of having returned after many sufferings and all the pain of separation, after hungering and thirsting in a strange land, after receiving blows and insults when one begged for the necessities of life – a sensation of being suddenly protected, utterly safe. This, at last, is home – only with one difference . . .

PERICTIONE: Don't tell me: there's a new man in Mummy's bed.

PLATO: You promised not to mock.

PERICTIONE: Sorry, darling. But you are faintly ridiculous, you know.

PLATO: I don't *care* whether I'm ridiculous now – not at this moment, can't you see? For it's the truth that prompts me.

PERICTIONE: Please go on. You were saying that listening to the divine Socrates is like coming home, only – only what?

PLATO: Only that, you know the place for the first time. Heraclitus says somewhere that the way up is the same as the way down. But after the journey has been made both ways, down into earthly things, and back to the realm of being whence we came – back in thought, I

63

mean – we see at last clearly. Having previously longed for departure, we now return with open arms, knowing that this is wholeness, destiny and the infinite good.

PERICTIONE: What is?

PLATO: The thing that philosophy shows us, towards which it leads us.

PERICTIONE: And what is this thing?

PLATO: Well, I mean, sort of like, well yes, 'being'.

PERICTIONE: And what is 'being'?

PLATO: Where we truly are, where things – I don't know – come together in us and us in them.

PERICTIONE: And does Socrates teach you this?

PLATO: Well no, not exactly. That is to say, he leads us to see that nothing else will quite *do*. And that we must seek in this world for the paths that lead out of it, towards – towards being itself.

PERICTIONE: And one of these is the barracks – sorry, the Socratic what-do-you-call-it?

PLATO: Oh Mother! It was a failure, I admit. But don't you see that, on the right scale and with proper planning, we could achieve this harmony here and now, in our own world? We need only tear down the rotten things, the customs and laws that divide us and which threaten to bring disorder and servitude into our souls. Then we could re-create the world according to the divine commands of Reason – we could make a world of unity, in which, yes, being is here and now, dwelling in the souls of men.

PERICTIONE: And women too?

PLATO: Yes, and women too.

PERICTIONE: Do you know, you remind me of someone I once met.

PLATO: Could it be Ariston, my father?

PERICTIONE: As a matter of fact, Ariston might have something to do with it. Or rather, not him, but what you lost in losing him. But it was not of Ariston that I was thinking. No. A man I once encountered when I was quite a young girl.

PLATO: Please, Mother. I don't *want* to know about your past.

PERICTIONE: That's where you're wrong. You are itching with curiosity, and would go to any length not to show it. Never mind, though. There is another reason for listening to what I have to say about this man.

PLATO: Impossible! Can a person be interesting for some other reason than his relation to you?

PERICTIONE: At about the time I met him he also met your master and father-substitute, the divine Socrates, upon whom, I gather, he had a considerable influence.

PLATO: Nonsense! Nobody mortal has had a considerable influence on Socrates.[20]

PERICTIONE: Suit yourself. Only you might ask Socrates, when you next see him, whether he remembers Parmenides.

PLATO: Parmenides? What kind of a name is that?

PERICTIONE: A very respectable name in fact, and from a very respectable family in Elea. And in his day he was one of the most famous and sought-after philosophers in Greece.

PLATO: Zeus! There's so much to read. Wait while I get my tablets. . . .

AGON

PERICTIONE: Parmenides was already quite old when I met him, and had come to Athens on some kind of embassy, or maybe it was for the Great Panathenaea. In any case, he was staying at the house of Pythodorus, with his young friend Zeno, and holding court to all the most distinguished Athenians. . . .

PLATO: Of which you, of course, were one.

PERICTIONE: If you must know, yes, I was, although a mere sixteen at the time. My dancing, if I may say so, was exquisite, and I had mastered something of the art of conversation – enough to permit me to go with my father to the better households and discourse with the more respectable of their inhabitants – which is how I met Ariston, incidentally.

PLATO: Tell me about Ariston.

PERICTIONE: No, I want to talk about Parmenides. But you must remember, my dear Plato, that the circumstances of a dialogue may be just as important as the words. Fully to interpret what

---

[20] The depth of Plato's error here will be immediately apparent to readers of *Xanthippe's Republic*. Moreover, even Plato ought by now to have heard of Aspasia, in whose salon the young Socrates picked up his smattering of culture. The relation between Socrates and Aspasia is finally acknowledged in Plato's own rather feeble attempt at a Xanthippic dialogue, the *Menexenus*.

Parmenides said, it may be necessary to bear in mind that it was spoken to a young and, if I may say so, stunningly attractive girl, who had just danced before him.

PLATO: Danced before him!

PERICTIONE: Oh, we were not so prudish in those days. Young girls of the best families would be brought in to sing the paean after dinner, and those who could dance would invariably be invited to perform for the company, provided of course they were veiled.[21] As I say, the circumstances of a true dialogue are part of its meaning. And if, one day, you improve on your talents sufficiently to be able to write down the words of wisdom which you spend your days collecting, you would do well to remember your mother's counsel.

PLATO: Yes, yes. Tell me about Parmenides.

PERICTIONE: As I said, he was holding court in the house of Pythodorus, and it was naturally assumed that a beautiful young descendant of Solon the wise should be brought to display her talents to him.

PLATO: Naturally assumed by whom?

PERICTIONE: 'Naturally assumed' is a way of expressing a highly complex and unspoken piece of social discourse. Really, Plato! The problem with adolescents is that they seek to make everything explicit, to subject the whole of life to a relentless interrogation, to measure all things against an impossible ideal, and – what is worse – to seek out the one who is to blame for the world's imperfection. You are too exasperating!

PLATO: Sorry, Mother. Please go on. You were saying about your talents.

---

[21] That virgin daughters of noble parents would be brought in to sing the paean is confirmed by a reference to Iphigenia doing just this, in the *Agamemnon* of Aeschylus, line 245. The suggestion that such a girl might also dance before strangers is likely to be greeted in scholarly circles with disbelief. However, it is worth pointing out that, although dancing girls were commonly prostitutes, there was a more solemn and religious tradition of female dancing in Hellas, in which respectable girls certainly joined. The principal evidence is Aeolian: the choral songs for girls (of which Sappho wrote many). See the classic study by Claude Calame, *Les Choeurs des jeunes filles en Grèce archaïque*, two vols., Rome, 1977. J. M. Edmonds appended to *Lyra Graeca*, vol. III (Loeb edition) a long discourse on this theme. Since Edgar Lobel's review in *Classical Review*, 1922, poor Edmonds has been treated dismissively by the scholars: nevertheless his flights of fancy are immensely stimulating while they last, and may have exerted as great an influence over Perictione as Shakespeare (see note 19) exerted over her son.

PERICTIONE: Ah yes, my talents! In those days I could dance – and what dances! Your generation has no knowledge of dancing. Thanks to that phrygian mode, those clashing cymbals and excruciating crooners who turn you all into corybants, you have entirely lost sight of the educative effects of music. A true melody has character, dignity, feeling, a kind of moral point of view. And to dance to it skilfully is to form your character according to the melody's movement. I learned to dance not so as to release myself but so as to become myself – to fill my body with the dignity, the order, the grace, the poise, the subtlety, in short the *truth* of Perictione.

PLATO: When are we getting to the point of this?

PERICTIONE: At any moment. I was trying to make you understand why it was thought appropriate, in those more civilized days, for a young girl to dance before a philosopher. For dancing and philosophy had, as we conceived them, a common goal which was, to put it briefly, the care of the soul.

PLATO: 'The care of the soul.' I say, Mother, that's rather good. Do you mind if I repeat it to Socrates?

PERICTIONE: Go ahead. Well: I was brought before the great man, who sat on a kind of throne in the *aula*, surrounded by slaves who waited on his every wish, while next to him, on another and smaller throne, sat this rather dishy man in the prime of life, with lovely brown eyes and a gentle smile, who I soon learned was Zeno. And I can't tell you how shy I felt, as they pushed me forward, the flute girl throwing sweet garlands of sound across the air, the lyre-player's fingers cascading over the strings, and the soft thrum of the tambourine stirring the souls of the assembly. . . .

PLATO: Revolting!

PERICTIONE: No sooner had I begun to dance, my arms raised and the veil pulled tight across my features, than I noticed a kind of agitation pass over the philosopher's face. He leaned forward slightly on his throne, and his hands gripped the arms of it as though some sharp pain pierced his body. His beard shook, and his rather eerie green eyes fixed themselves on me with a look that was both tender and indignant, as though my dancing wounded him. I hoped that he could not see my face through the veil, though it seemed to me, in my alarm, that he was doing his best to meet my eyes, which I therefore directed towards the far more agreeable glances that sped in my direction from Zeno.

PLATO: Thank Zeus I wasn't there!

PERICTIONE: But you might thank Zeus I was so skilled a dancer, Plato, since it was this which won your father's heart: if heart is the word for it.

PLATO: Will you *please* stick to the point, Mother? I don't want to hear your beastly confessions!

PERICTIONE: That's where you are wrong, Plato. You are consumed with a passionate interest in my 'beastly confessions', as you call them, and this philosophy is nothing but a diversionary tactic. However, I am coming to that. No, don't go – I really do think you might benefit from hearing about the great Parmenides.

PLATO: So far I have heard nothing about the great Parmenides, except for the effect upon him of the great Perictione.

PERICTIONE: Well then, let me proceed. I was, as I say, a very young woman at the time, but not so young that I did not have an inkling of the old man's emotions, as I went through my paces, trying out, for Zeno's benefit, my two favourite dances – the one representing Achilles, a *pyrrhike*[22] in six iambic measures, expressing concentrated power yet moving hardly at all, and the other, a stately *emmeleia* in slow marching anapests, describing a tortoise. And Zeno, dear man, became lost in thought as he studied me. Where was I? Ah yes: Parmenides. When I had finished dancing, with some rather fetching *schemata* I had just learned from Pasariste daughter of Harmon, the old philosopher beckoned to my father and bade him bring me to the throne, there to receive the benefit of philosophical instruction, of which, it seemed, I stood in pressing need.

I bowed low before his virtuous form, being careful not to sit next to it, however, although he beckoned me most urgently to do so. It seemed to me best to stand slightly to one side and fix my eyes on Zeno.

PLATO: Why on Zeno?

PERICTIONE: Because it becomes a rational being to pay tribute with

---

[22] A *pyrrhike* is a war-like dance; an *emmeleia* is stately and decorous: see Plato, *The Laws*, 814E–815A, evidence that Plato listened attentively to his mother's remarks about dancing. *Schemata* were the gestures learned by professional dancers: Pasariste must have been a courtesan.

her eyes to beauty. Provided that her eyes are unseen. So now I have given you, I think, a sufficient description of the circumstances from which our dialogue grew. Let me then tell you what the philosopher said.

PLATO: I am all ears, Mother.

PERICTIONE: 'Divine descendant of the most divine Solon,' he began, 'hear my words.' 'I hear you,' I answered through my veil. 'Ssh!' said my father, 'don't answer back!' and 'Let her speak,' put in Zeno, in the sweetest voice. 'Yes, let her speak.' Parmenides went on, 'Since how can wisdom prevail, unless by dialogue?' 'I know not, master,' I replied, with a demure genuflection, and caught another of Zeno's delicious glances. You know, Plato, I do sometimes think it is a great pity that my father gave me to Ariston before I could meet Zeno again. Not only would I have saved the dear man from a most dreadful death, I too would have been spared much unhappiness. Where was I? Yes, the dancing.

'You imagine,' said Parmenides, in a voice that was a trifle hoarse, 'that you have moved me. You imagine that you too have moved.'

Well, I was rather taken aback by this. 'I don't imagine, master,' I replied, 'I know. That I have moved, I mean. For what is dancing, if not movement?' 'And suppose,' he answered, 'that I were to prove that movement is impossible, and that the world is sublimely still, serene and unchanging, as I am?' 'Then,' I said, 'I should be most interested in your reasoning, but I should still be inclined to dance.'

He reached towards me a hand that visibly trembled, and said, in a voice that was far from gentle, 'I would gladly undertake to change your life, were it not the case, as I shall infallibly prove to you, that change is impossible.'

It was fortunate that I was wearing a veil, you know, because, hearing these words, Zeno gave me the naughtiest wink, and I was able to gain relief from my feelings by invisibly winking back at him. When I had a little recovered my composure – an art which I mastered from the earliest age and in the practice of which, my dear Plato, I am sorry to find you so deficient – I bid the philosopher favour me with his reasoning, while my father, ever the officious chaperone, commanded the slaves to bring cushions and stools for us to sit on. This we duly did, though out of reach, I should emphasize, of the old man's far from prepossessing feet. Why is it, by the way, that philosophers always go around barefoot? It is so affected! I bowed my head in a becoming manner, and prepared myself to say 'yes' to every question – which is what the philosophical notion of a dialogue consists in, as I am sure you have discovered. 'You will admit,' he said, 'that you dance?' and his voice trembled again. 'Yes,' I replied. 'And therefore that there is dancing?' 'Indeed.' 'And therefore that dancing *is*?' 'I cannot deny it,' I responded with a sigh.

PLATO: How is it, Mother, that you are always the central character in everything that happens to you?

PERICTIONE: You mistake me, my dear. I am merely the central character in everything that happens to you. Incidentally, that is why you will do your best in future years never to mention me, for fear of the emotions that I arouse. On this occasion, however, it was Zeno who dominated my thoughts – and Zeno, therefore, to whom I shall least refer. Where was I?

PLATO: The statement that dancing *is*.

PERICTIONE: Ah yes. Beware, my dear Plato, of the verb 'to be'. Beware of its magic, its all-pervasiveness, its ability to command the void, to flourish without subject or object, to float free of grammar and become the word – the *logos* – itself. Well I never! Where did that come from? Yes, the verb 'to be'. In agreeing to the innocent proposition of Parmenides I was, of course, falling into a trap. For here is what the crafty old casuist went on to say.

'If dancing *is*,' he argued, 'then it must be identical with something. Is it identical with the dancer? Or with the dance? For I can see no further possibility.'

'How can you tell,' I asked, 'the dancer from the dance?'

At this Parmenides turned to my father.

'Is this girl facetious, or merely ahead of her time?'

'Time,' put in Zeno, 'is not the sort of thing you can be ahead of.'

Parmenides stroked his beard in vexation. 'Well,' he continued at last, 'suppose it is identical with the dancer: it follows that dancing also is not, since the dancer is sometimes dancing, sometimes at rest. Or suppose it is identical with the dance. Then this very same dance – the Tortoise, say – is danced not only here, but also elsewhere, in the Stoa (Zeus forbid), or on the beaches of Heraklion. But what is elsewhere is not here: and here, therefore, it is not. In this case too, therefore, dancing is not. So we have conclusively proved that dancing both is and is not.'

He looked round with a self-satisfied smile. His audience had grown by now to include the whole household and all the visitors, who were staring in a stunned manner as though struck by a thunderbolt. I find that nothing is more productive of wonder than incomprehensible words uttered with total conviction.

'Or let us consider the matter from another angle,' Parmenides went on, his voice calmer now, as though he were half way to vanquishing my influence. 'Dancing, you will admit, divine descendant of Solon, is a form of motion.'

'How could I deny it?'

'And motion is a form of change?'

'Indeed,' I answered.

'Or should we rather say that change is motion?'

'Perhaps,' I replied, 'we should rather say that.'

'But the thing which moves,' he said, 'is first in a place, and then not in that place?'

'Indeed.'

'And similarly for every change. The thing which changes first is in some respect, and then is not.'

'Is it?' I asked.

'Of course it is!' he cried; 'or is not, as the case may be.'

'So be it,' I answered. Parmenides looked at me with a curious beseeching expression.

'Well then,' he continued, with a sigh, 'whatever changes, and whatever is in motion, both is and is not; in which case, surely, there is nothing that it is, except the thing which is not?'

'Of course,' I said; 'or of course not, as the case may be.'

'Perictione!' exclaimed my father.

'Sorry; I only meant to say that I agree.'

Parmenides looked nervously in my direction.

'So,' he said, 'there is nothing that changes except the thing which is not, as I argued. To assume otherwise is to fall at once into contradiction.'

'And that would never do.'

There was a faint commotion in the *aula*.

'I mean,' I added, correcting myself, 'that you are right, Parmenides.'

The poor dear seemed reassured, and began to smile at me.

'But please explain to me one thing,' I went on. 'If there is no

71

movement, no change, what is there? And how do we come to believe that change exists?'

'I see that you are a ready pupil,' he answered with a smile, 'and a worthy descendant of your ancestor.'

'It is not I who deserve praise,' I continued, 'for it is only the supreme force of your reasoning that has changed my mind. And yet, as you say, change is impossible.'

I should add, Plato, that I was an early practitioner of elenctic irony.

PLATO: Of what, Mother?

PERICTIONE: Elenctic irony.

PLATO *(writing)*: Zeus! How do you spell 'elenctic'?

PERICTIONE: Epsilon, lambda, epsilon – forget it, I'll write it for you later. I'm just getting to the juicy bit. So, here is what Parmenides said to me: 'As for your first question, child, let me tell you what is. To be is to be one, is it not?'

'Yes,' I answered.

'And, as we have shown that change is impossible in the thing that is, we must conclude that the one does not change.'

'By no means can it do so,' I said.

'Nor can the one have parts – for then it would not be one but many.'

'True,' I replied.

'Nor can it be in any place: for then there would be a place where it is not, and to say of what is that it is not is to speak falsely.'

'Wow,' I said.

'Likewise for time: there is no time which is the time of the one, for that would imply the existence of some other time at which the one is not.'

'I believe I follow your reasoning,' I said, for you know, of all the arts of society, there is none that I value so highly as hypocrisy, which I mastered at the earliest age.

'And if we are to say of the one that it is not – say, because we wish to speak roughly and in the language of the vulgar – we must know that the one which is not, if it is to maintain itself in opposition to the one that is, must also at the same time be.'

'You speak well, oh Parmenides,' I said, and he responded with a sentence which you may like to make a note of, my dear Plato, for use in your maturer years.

PLATO: Hang on, I'm running out of tablets: where did I put my handbag?

PERICTIONE: Don't worry, I'll dictate it later. The sentence Parmenides uttered, and which left the whole assembly, with the exception of the serenely smiling Zeno, breathless with admiration, was this:

'Then the one which is not, if it is to maintain itself, must have the being of not-being as the bond of not-being, just as being must have as a bond the not-being of not-being in order to perfect its own being; for the truest assertion of the being of being and the not-being of not-being is when being partakes of the being of being, and not of the being of not-being – that is, the perfection of being; and when not-being does not partake of the not-being of not-being but of the being of not-being – that is the perfection of not-being.'[23]

PLATO: By Zeus and all the gods, Mother, that's brilliant! 'The being of not-being and not-being being a not-being of perfection of the partaking . . .' how does it go? Sublime! Zeus! So much finer than that wretched speech of mine. 'Being or not-being', indeed! Give me the not-being of being any day. That's it, Mum – no more poetry, no more theatricals. I'm going to be a philosopher! Darling Mum, I could kiss you to death!

PERICTIONE: Wait a minute. I haven't finished my story. Having delivered himself of this weighty utterance, and feigning now hardly to notice me, Parmenides looked around at the assembly and began again.

'So we see that the thing which is, is one, eternal and perfect in its being, unmoved and unmoving, the one reality to which, in thought, we may still be joined. But let us address the child's second question: the question of change. Clearly change does not belong to the one that is.'

'Indeed not, Parmenides,' they said.

'But to the one that is not, therefore,' he went on, and they agreed.

'Change then, and motion, are forms of not-being. To put the

---

[23] If proof is needed of the authenticity of *Perictione's Parmenides*, it surely lies here. For this very sentence recurs, word for word, in Plato's re-hash, at *Parmenides*, 162A–B. In Alexandrian society it became a standard accomplishment of well-bred ladies to be able to recite this sentence without the faintest suggestion of a smile, and afterwards to give a commentary, relating it to the issues of the day. See Sosipatra, *On Notorious Women*, 391A, and Hypatia, *Dipsosophistae*, 33, xi. For the sake of style, rather than scholarly accuracy, I have used Jowett's translation.

matter more simply, they are illusions, in which we believe just so long as we are under the spell of them, but which we may come to recognize for what they are, once we listen to the voice of divine philosophy.'

'Therefore,' I put in, 'I was not really dancing.'

The philosopher, who had raised his murky green eyes heavenward as though receiving inspiration from the gods, suddenly noticed me again.

'You what?' he asked. 'Oh yes, dancing. Emphatically not, my child – a smoke of not-being briefly veiled our minds, that was all. It was indeed a nothing. I am sorry to disappoint you.'

So I said to him, 'When I danced, did you see nothing there?'

And he replied, 'Nothing at all; yet all that there was I saw.'

PLATO: Mother! that's a line from my play! You've been reading it! Oh you beast! You've been going through my tablets, I know it, giggling at my paltry efforts and my scratchings-out, and . . . I can't bear it!

PERICTIONE: I don't know *what* you're talking about, Plato. Those are the very words he used.

PLATO: Promise you've not been snooping?

PERICTIONE: Would I go snooping in that nasty sty of yours?

PLATO: 'Nasty sty' – wait a minute, that rings a bell too.

PERICTIONE: I said *filthy* sty. For Zeus' sake, Plato, you *know* you hide the tablets beneath the laundry. Would I brave such defences? I *promise* you that I treat your tablets, and your laundry, with a religious veneration. Promise! Can I go on with the story?

PLATO: Well, all right. I'll believe you.

PERICTIONE: 'I repeat,' Parmenides said, 'that nothing happened. For if there is a happening, then, as I have shown, the thing which happens both is and is not, and is therefore maintained by the one that is not, and the one that is not, under the form of a happening, negates itself before our minds.'

And, so saying, the curious old man rose as if to leave, beckoning Zeno to accompany him. Not wishing, however, to be so soon deprived of Zeno's company, I spoke again.

'Parmenides,' I said, 'your reverence; tell me one thing.'

'I am at your service,' he replied.

'This one – the one that is, I mean. Why is it, as you imply, so perfect, and what advantage is it to a girl to become acquainted with it?'

He turned, and again his voice lost some of its Olympian calm.

'Oh most perfect descendant of the all-wise Solon,' he asked . . .

PLATO: Yes, yes, we've heard all that.

PERICTIONE: 'What is evil?'

'Evil,' I replied, 'is many things: impiety, dishonour to parents, neglect of children, intemperance, cowardice, lechery . . .'

'Yes,' he said, 'but do we not recognize in all these things a single strand, a warning as it were, which bids us not to approach them, and which ensures that, having touched them, we cease thereafter to be wholly well?'

Naturally, he was referring to my dancing, and its effect on him.

'No,' I replied, 'I cannot for the life of me see what it is that warns us against all those things. For what is evil in one of them may not be evil in another. Impiety, to my unpractised thinking, is a kind of *hubris*. Lechery, on the other hand, is not *hubris* at all, but a grovelling loss of dignity, which in an old man is most distressing to see.'

Had it not been for Zeno, who encouraged me with another friendly wink, I should scarcely have had the courage to remain where I was.

'Ah, but there you are wrong!' Parmenides cried angrily. 'And because you are so much in need of instruction, I shall endeavour to enlighten you.'

'You greatly favour me, oh Parmenides,' I said.

'Then listen carefully,' he went on. 'Evil is the perfection of not-being and the negation of being, whose perfection is good. The perfection of being is identical with being, and consists in its oneness, wholeness and harmony. It follows that evil is fragmentation, rupture, discord.'

'Those are grand words, Master,' I said, 'and, if I may express an opinion, rather empty words.'

'Eh?' he said.

'Perictione!' my father cried, seizing me by the elbow. 'Forgive me, O Master. The girl is very young, and has yet to learn the perfection of manners that would fit her for the company of so great a philosopher.'

'Let her explain herself,' said Zeno; 'the old boy can take it.'

'I mean,' I went on, quite melted by Zeno's chivalry, 'that the noble philosopher's words would benefit from some kind of illustration – some instance in the here and now.'

'By Zeus she's right,' Parmenides said, 'and we have surely an instance right here before us.'

'Enlighten us, O master,' they said.

'Indeed I will. But before giving my illustration, I must speak of geometry.'

We listened eagerly at this, for geometry was the passion of Athenian society in those days, and no man would take a wife or mistress without first examining her for her mathematical proficiency.

'Consider a cube,' he said. 'Lay it on any of its six sides and it is at rest, is it not?'

'Indeed it is,' we answered.

'But if it is tilted even the smallest fraction from one of those six positions, it will remain at rest only if subjected to a force, which keeps it uneasily in this new disposition.'

'Indeed.'

'And always it will tend of its own accord to fall back to the place of rest whence it was forcibly sundered.'

'By Zeus you are right, Parmenides,' they cried, although I must say I was unhappy about several of the old man's assumptions.

'It seems, then, that of all the infinite positions that a cube may occupy, in only six is it at rest with itself, contented, as we may put it, in its being, and not striving to be other and elsewhere?'

'How beautifully you express the point.'

'And something similar can be proved, I imagine, concerning a triangle, a rhomboid, a hexagram, or indeed any other figure, save those of one special kind.'

'Explain your meaning, O Parmenides,' they asked.

'I mean that all figures, whether symmetrical or asymmetrical, are at rest only in some positions, and indeed that the majority of them have only a finite number of resting places, if I may so express myself, in an infinite field of chance.'

PLATO: I say, Mother, this is terrific stuff, almost like Socrates. 'A finite number of resting places, in an infinite field of chance.'

PERICTIONE: I'm so glad you find it amusing, dear. I was beginning to fear I might be boring you.

PLATO: Boring me! By the gods, no! You bore me only when you talk about yourself.

PERICTIONE: Fortunately I don't believe you. In any case, listen to the philosopher's conclusion.

'All figures are thus, save those which partake of the circle: the cone, for instance, or the cylinder. For these may rest in an infinite number of positions.'

'You speak truly,' they said.

'But because they partake of other figures too – of the straight line, for instance, and the triangle – there are infinitely many positions in which they are not at rest, but from which they strive to depart with all the violence of an infant torn from the breast.'

'That also is true,' they answered.

'But there is one figure, which is at rest in every position, and which moves only when subjected to a force external to itself.'

'And which figure is that?' they asked.

'Can you not guess?' he asked, with a smile of triumph.

'Of course they can,' I said, 'but who would want to spoil your punch-line?'

'I mean the sphere,' Parmenides went on with a little frown, 'which partakes only of the circle, and therefore is always whole, closed on itself, and satisfied.'

'By Zeus you are right,' they cried.

'And by virtue of what is this possible?' he asked. 'I shall tell you. By virtue of the fact that no place on a perfect sphere can be distinguished from any other place, save by reference to something external. Each point on the surface of a sphere is equidistant from the centre, and each is related in the same way as any other to the places which it is not. Indeed the sphere has only one surface, and no part of this surface acquires any distinguishing identity, except by relation to something which the sphere is not.'

'By Zeus you are right,' they said.

'And in this we can see the perfection of the sphere: that no part of it is foreign to any other part, but each is joined inseparably and indistinguishably in a single unity. And from this divine unity and wholeness flows the perfect equilibrium upon which we have remarked. The sphere, being an inseparable unity, is also perfectly at rest, and never desires to be elsewhere and other than it is.'

PLATO: By the gods, he's right, Mother.

PERICTIONE: 'So now,' the old fraud went on, 'let me return to my real illustration – my example in the here and now, as this misguided child expressed it. Let us imagine a mind in perfect repose, equidistant from all its thoughts as the centre of a sphere is equidistant from every point on its perimeter. Nothing internal can move it, since it has reached the perfect unity from which no being can desire to depart. Its thought is not of this or that particular, but of Being itself – a thought in which all things are equally included. No particular has power to exclude another from its thoughts, nor to distract it from its inner calm. Its study is the whole of things, and it too is whole. Is this not a state of blessedness?'

'If you say so,' I put in, 'though I doubt it.'

'And then imagine that some point on this perfect sphere of intellect should suddenly become prominent, attracting the attention that was previously spread over the whole. At once the sphere loses its equilibrium: it is no longer at rest but must roll about until it finds the single point of balance, where it stays rocking uneasily and at war with itself.'

'And what could have such a dire effect?' they asked in alarm.

'An image of change and movement,' he replied; 'a young girl dancing, let us say. The observer desires to follow her movement with his eyes, to pass before his thoughts the inconstant nothingness which charms and attracts him and which he can never make part of himself. In such a case, a blemish has appeared in the translucent sphere of consciousness, and the blemish grows until . . .'

'Until what?' I asked.

'Until he falls, as the sphere falls towards its deformity. For now the mind desires to be elsewhere and outside itself – desires to unite with that which it is not, and to destroy its wholeness, integrity and calm. I, who am of course immune to such perturbations, can yet observe them in others – in Zeno here, for instance, who tortures himself with the thought of moving things, and with young girls especially – and so have come to understand the nature of evil, and the peculiar form that evil takes in the human soul.'

'And what is this form?' I asked.

'Since evil is that which tends away from perfection, and since perfection of being lies in wholeness and indivisibility, it follows that evil is whatever sunders the soul and subjects it to a power outside itself. This alienating force is what we mean by desire *(epithumia)*.

Desire is a tendency towards something outside the soul, without which it cannot be satisfied; it therefore destroys both the unity of the soul and the soul's self-sufficiency. And of all desires none, it seems to me, detracts from the mind's perfection so much as the desire for moving things. For not only is the object of such a desire outside the self; it is also a not-being, so that to fulfil the desire is yet worse than to suffer it. And although it is always possible to reach that spherical perfection which is Being itself, desire, which is the voice of not-being, tempts us deviously away. This, indeed, is our tragedy. That not-being lies coiled in the heart of Being like a worm.'[24]

PLATO: Zeus, Mother, this is the stuff! More, more!

PERICTIONE: Actually, that was the end of his speech. Or almost. He looked at me for a moment in silence, and then said, 'There you have it. Evil is the fall from Being into not-being, and the form of this fall is desire. And what,' he asked, 'is the way back to perfection? What is the task that we mortals must undertake, if we are to attain once again the unity of Being from which we have been sundered? Such, I know, is the question that is before your mind.'

'Quite wrong,' I interjected. 'I have absolutely no desire to know.'

'Then I shall tell you,' he went on, as my father pinched my elbow in a most painful manner. 'The way back to perfection is through philosophy, which shows us Being and unites us with it.'

'And how much do you charge?' I asked.

By now, however, my father was bustling me away, and although Zeno said something about five obols an hour, and even graciously mentioned that he might be visiting Pheidias' studio on the morrow,[25] the old philosopher had stormed from the room and my father was calling out in a fury for my chariot.

---

[24] This strange image can also be found in Sartre's *L'Être et le néant* – one of Being's last public appearances. The origin of the image is probably the Hindu goddess Kundalini (an avatar of Kali), represented as a serpent lying 'coiled in the heart of being'.

[25] The meaning of this passage is obscure. Plutarch (*Pericles*, XIII, 9) refers to a scandal spread against Pheidias, that he allowed Pericles to seduce free-born women who came to his studio to see the sculptures of the Parthenon, upon which Pheidias was working. However, this would have been some five or more years before Parmenides' visit to Athens. Perhaps reference to this scandal had become a kind of code, like 'how's your father?' or 'let's discuss Uganda'. In that case, however, one cannot avoid the conclusion that Zeno's remark is in rather poor taste. The mention of

PARABASIS

PLATO: Zeus! Why didn't you tell me this before? It's got the makings of something really great: all of metaphysics, all of morality in a single wonderful idea. Being, wholeness, unity, self-sufficiency. That's it, Mother! That's what it's all about! And yet . . .

PERICTIONE: Yet what?

PLATO: Why were you so unmoved by it? Why didn't it just *change your life*? Why did you, for instance, go on dancing?

PERICTIONE: Because my father wished me to acquire a husband, you fool. It wasn't Parmenides who stopped me dancing, but Ariston.

PLATO: So my father was greater than Parmenides?

PERICTIONE: No. Just more brutal.

PLATO: And weren't you impressed by the argument? Did you not immediately wish for the unity of Being, and strive to overcome in yourself the misery of this dreadful fate that Parmenides so beautifully described to you?

PERICTIONE: Darling Plato, you are so sweet. And what, do you suppose, did Parmenides mean, by this promise of sphericality?

PLATO: What do you mean, what did he mean?

PERICTIONE: Let me then explain. I do not propose to demolish Parmenides' arguments: I will leave this task for your maturity, should you ever reach it, and merely repeat my counsel to look thoroughly at the verb 'to be'. The fact is, however, that when such philosophers step into the arena of life, and invite us to leave desire and follow 'reason' instead – to prefer the unchanging to the fleeting and the eternal to the temporal, to seek ultimate reality rather than conditional appearance, to join with them in some intellectual journey, at five obols an hour, which has truth and wholeness and unity as its goal – that they are not appealing to rational argument at all, that this 'reason' of theirs is no more than an 'appearance' of reason. For what guides them in their quest is the very thing they denounce – *epithumia* – and it is by touching our passions that they capture their callow following.

---

five obols an hour suggests a special rate for young girls. For Zeno's private lessons were notoriously expensive. According to the pseudo-Platonic *Alcibiades I* (119A), the complete course cost 150 *minas*, the price of a small plot of land.

PLATO *(laughs)*: As though this had anything to do with Socrates!

PERICTIONE: Oh, I grant you, Socrates is the great exception, and answers to no emotional need whatever. But do you not notice a similarity between your Socratic escapades in the garden and the Being of Parmenides?

PLATO: What on earth are you getting at?

PERICTIONE: I mean that the same form can be discovered in both, and that it is the form, not the matter, which appeals to you.

PLATO: But the phalanstery isn't spherical. It's more like a square, only with knobbly bits, and a kind of cylinder where the watchtower sticks up.

PERICTIONE: I wasn't talking about geometry, my poor boy. What is it, I ask myself, that the followers of Parmenides really understand, when they hear his divine philosophy? Let me venture a theory of my own. In each of us is planted a seed of longing – the longing to return to the state we once knew when we lay on the breast and nestled against its spherical perfection. Those years of milk-white innocence, when the world was good and entirely part of us, remain forever in our feelings. When, in later life, we seek refuge and solace from the blows of fortune, we make for ourselves an image of peace and reconciliation, and invariably this image is modelled on that first experience of harmony. In that primeval state, the self and the world were one. And in a sense Parmenides was right to use the word 'being' to describe this state. For there is no other word so fitting to the bliss of the infant: no word so general and all-embracing, so soothing of conflict, and at the same time so affirmative of the self. The infant at the breast drinks from the pure fount of Being, in an experience where self and world are totally united. He has only one fear – that something will occur to destroy the harmony in which he is enveloped. Hence we find the Parmenidean concept of evil, as a negation, a separation, a fragmentation. And what is the root of this evil? Parmenides tells us that it is desire. But if you do as I advise, and set his speech in its dramatic context, you will see what he meant by desire. Not the desire for an apple, or a cup of wine; not even the desire for mother's breast: no, the desire for a woman – one who is rational, resistant and free.

PLATO: You are not telling me that philosophers are prone to such loathsome emotions?

PERICTIONE: Parmenides and Zeno were, I admit, abnormal.[26] But by desiring members of their own inferior sex, other philosophers do not escape the trouble to which Parmenides referred. For men, like women, are free, rational, and outside the control of those who covet them.

And I will tell you why this desire is so threatening. Unlike the desires for food and drink and warmth, *eros* points beyond myself, to another who is like me but also independent of me, whose consent must be won, and whose opinion must be minutely cultivated. In reaching out to her, I come to see myself through her eyes. All at once I am sundered from the world, disunited from my satisfactions, which depend now on another's self and therefore seem to lie infinitely out of reach. And thence come the dreadful troubles of which the poets speak, as

> Eros shakes my soul, like the wind
> Which wrestles down the mountain oaks.[27]

The torments of jealousy, in which 'a subtle fire races under the skin, the eyes see nothing, the ears ring, sweat pours forth and all the body is seized with trembling', as the divine Sappho expresses it, referring, of course, to *eros* in its very highest form, unattainable by you, my dear Plato, unless you succeed in changing sex, and loving a woman with a woman's love.

Now this reaching out towards another is the primal loss of innocence, the fall. It spells the end of childhood and its easy comforts, and the beginning of risk – by which I mean the risk of one's existence. On this primal experience of separation all others are modelled: it is our archetype of the self in danger.

PLATO: Come off it, Mother. You should have been with the fleet in Arginusae.

---

[26] In his *Parmenides*, Plato decides to imply that Parmenides and Zeno were lovers, thus giving rise to the enduring myth that Parmenides was homosexual. It is fortunate that Perictione's dialogue has been recovered, if only because it shows how truly original Zeno was, in this matter as in everything else.

[27] Sappho, Fr. 40, also quoted by the sophist Maximus of Tyre in his *Lectures*, of about 150 BC. Maximus cites the passage in connection with Socrates, who, he says, excited Phaedrus to madness when he spoke of love.

PERICTIONE: I am not talking of physical danger, but of a risk far deeper and stranger – one that lies at the heart of our moral nature. And in order to make this danger bearable, is it surprising that we tell ourselves comforting stories?

PLATO: Socrates says that ordinary, unphilosophical people must be fed on – what does he call them – noble lies.

PERICTIONE: Is that so? He may be right: except that we should not feed *lies* to people. Rather we should do our best to safeguard the stories that arise spontaneously among them.

PLATO: What do you mean, Mother?

PERICTIONE: I mean this. Women, you will admit, are social beings?

PLATO: And men too.

PERICTIONE: And the easiest of all social relations, if what I say is correct, is that between infant and nurse – the original unity, so to say.

PLATO: Easy from the infant's point of view. But, as the nurse might put it:

> . . . this witless thing must be reared
> Like an animal – how else? – according to its whim.[28]

PERICTIONE: I *knew* you had borrowed that scroll! I want it back tonight! Do you hear? In any case, it is the infant who concerns me, and her subsequent development. For, in comparison with this blissful unity, all later relationships are fraught with difficulty, and none more so, you will admit, than those whose hidden sovereign is Eros?

PLATO: You tell me, Mother; I don't think I ever got that far.

PERICTIONE: I *am* telling you; but you should remember the literary virtues of dialogue.

PLATO: How could I ever forget them?

PERICTIONE: As she enters these new relations and becomes lost in them as in a labyrinth, it is natural, is it not, that a rational being should regret the state of wholeness and completion that she left behind, and should yearn, so to speak, for the thread of Ariadne that would guide her back to it?

PLATO: Not bad, Mother; but I'm reserving judgement on the argument.

---

[28] Aeschylus, *The Libation Bearers*, lines 753–4.

PERICTIONE: Being rational, however, she will know that the past is irrecoverable, that there is no going back, but only a going forward into the unknown.

PLATO: That seems OK.

PERICTIONE: If she is to recuperate the state of blessedness, therefore, it can only be by proceeding onwards, to some future harmony which lies, as it were, at the end of suffering, a reward for her labours?

PLATO: If there should be such a thing.

PERICTIONE: If indeed. But now you see that a rational being, by virtue of the very reason that guides her, has a motive to believe something quite irrational.

PLATO: How typical of women!

PERICTIONE: The rational being will be driven to believe – if he is to maintain the hope without which life under the sun of reason cannot be borne – that the labyrinth of separation leads at last to a final harmony.

PLATO: The breast beyond the grave, you mean – that kind of thing?

PERICTIONE: I mean that the rational being will strive to view the period of anxiety and wandering as the necessary means to a great reward – a reward that could have been obtained in no other way. Hence the final unity will be painted always as a higher state and one more valuable by far than that from which we begin – the goal of life's pilgrimage, which we can reach only through the labyrinth of separation.

PLATO: By Zeus, Mother, I am beginning to see some sense in this theory of yours.

PERICTIONE: It's not mine, actually, but Xanthippe's.

PLATO: What?

PERICTIONE: That is to say, we worked it out together. In any case, the rational being, who needs to think of his condition in the way I described, will stumble across myths and stories which, while differing in detail, have a common structure. These stories tell him that man's earthly existence is a journey, which begins from wholeness, passes through alienation, only to arrive at last at some higher and more glorious form of the original innocence. And because it is a need of reason to believe these quite unreasonable things, the goal will also be a vindication of the rational striving that precedes it. The final unity will be described as a kind of supreme consciousness of things – a knowing acceptance, a reconciliation with that which was hitherto only dimly understood and wrongly resented.

PLATO: This reminds me of Heraclitus.

PERICTIONE: And so it is, my dear Plato, that rational beings spontaneously attach themselves to myths – calling them beautiful, consoling, sublime, holy – even though, in some part of themselves, they know how few grounds they have for believing these stories. I mean the stories of salvation, of Elysium, of a final return, a *nostos*, like that of Odysseus to Ithaca, but a return in which a man's ancestors gather to welcome him, his transgressions atoned for, his debts paid, his sufferings rewarded. Or stories, like that of Demeter and her holy daughter Persephone, of a final triumph over death, a reward in which we may all join by virtue of the mysteries.[29] And indeed, it is just this sequence of events – innocence, transgression and redemption – that the hierophant celebrates before the altar of Demeter on the twenty-first night, when he takes the sacred bread and the chalice from the *kistai*, summons the holy twain[30] and whispers . . .

PLATO: Mother!

PERICTIONE: Whoops! I got carried away. You didn't hear that. What a bore. I shall now have to get you initiated. Holy Artemis! The festival will never be the same, with you standing there in the congregation, croaking the hymns and fidgeting about like a chicken.

PLATO: Please, Mother! I promise I won't fidget.

PERICTIONE: We'll see about it. Where was I? Ah yes, the myths. This

---

[29] The mysteries of Eleusis were revealed only to initiates, and anyone who retailed them to an outsider was punishable by death. Aristophanes, who recounted the first part of the mysteries in *Frogs* (324ff), escaped punishment. But Aeschylus, suspected of revealing the second part of the mysteries (here touched on by Perictione), barely escaped with his life, while the poet Diagoras of Melos was sentenced to death and had to flee Athens.

Perictione's indiscretion in this passage is without parallel in Athenian literature, and enables us to answer several important questions. The sacred things (*hiera*), carried to the ceremony in their special boxes (*kistai*), are not elsewhere described. The presence among them of bread (the mysteries were a celebration of Demeter, goddess of corn), and a chalice, recalls the Holy Eucharist of the Christian Church.

[30] i.e. Demeter and her daughter Kore (Persephone), whom she rescues from the kingdom of the dead. For the use of this invocation, see also Aristophanes, *Thesmophoriazusai*.

explains, too, the stories of man's fall, such as the one related by the Pythagoreans.

PLATO: What is that, Mother?

PERICTIONE: Don't you know it? The Pythagoreans pretend that the soul, by attaining to a vision of the truth, may raise itself from its terrestrial condition and reach the blessed sphere of the gods, there to circle eternally free from hurt. Due to errors and transgressions, however, a soul may lose its wings and plummet earthwards, entering a human form and suffering the penalty of incarnation, from which it can redeem itself only by the goodness of its conduct as it flits from life to life. And the soul which three times successively chooses the life of the philosopher regains its wings, and ascends to the blessed region whence it fell.

PLATO: What a beautiful idea!

PERICTIONE: Beautiful indeed, and especially when combined with that story of the sphere and its perfection. Which reminds me of another old man, sweeter by far than Parmenides. It was Empedocles who expressed the form of all these stories most perfectly, describing that first world, where 'every animal was tame and familiar with men, both beasts and birds, and mutual love prevailed'; and introducing then unholy discord, which casts us down through the 'bitter paths of becoming, doomed without rest to change', until we rise again to that unity with the sphere which is our final end and salvation.

PLATO: Empedocles: philosopher, statesman, healer and poet, all in one! What a career!

PERICTIONE: But is it not the first duty of the philosopher to pursue the truth?

PLATO: Indeed it is, Mother.

PERICTIONE: And may not poetry lead us in the contrary direction? For 'beauty, which is the author of all things sweet to mortals, makes myth acceptable, and the incredible believed. . . .'[31] And the philosophy, so called, of old Empedocles was nothing more than myth, and no more true than a story I have heard the people of Canaan and Phoenicia tell, of man and woman alone in Elysium, from where they are expelled into the condition of mortality, on account of their primal disobedience to Zeus.

---

[31] Pindar, *Olympian Odes*, no. 1, 30–31.

PLATO: What primal disobedience?

PERICTIONE: The usual.

PLATO: Not *eros* again?

PERICTIONE: No, that came later. I mean criminal damage to the perfect sphere of Being. In fact, they ate it.

PLATO: Ate it!

PERICTIONE: Yes, and all the woman's doing, they say. But now, let me come to the point. What is it, do you suppose, that we seek through these holy stories?

PLATO: I am not sure that we are seeking *anything*, Mother.

PERICTIONE: Certainly, it is not truth or the desire for truth that leads people to believe things for which there can be no evidence, but which nevertheless they accept instinctively when they encounter them, as though welcoming a long-lost friend.

PLATO: No, it is not the desire for truth: for that is philosophy.

PERICTIONE: It is hope, is it not, my dear Plato, that draws us – but hope for what? I shall tell you. Hope for the unity with others, for the primal togetherness which we once knew at the breast and then lost in falling from it. We wish to belong again, to be accepted into a whole, and to live with our kind in harmony. And to live with them thus eternally, united with our ancestors, immortal as they. And that explains two peculiar features of the stories.

PLATO: What do you have in mind?

PERICTIONE: I mean, first, that to each myth there corresponds a community of believers, who join together in celebration, and devise rituals and ceremonies whereby to perpetuate the myth and renew its power. Such ceremonies are ours at Eleusis, from which you, thank Demeter, are still excluded. And I mean, secondly, that those who have taken the plunge, so to speak, who have joined the community and mixed their lot with the others who belong there, find that the belief which attracted them has become a matter of duty, something that they owe to the gods, and from which it is sinful to deviate. For the myths define the community; the one who rejects them is severed from the one who accepts, and must be cast out and anathematized. What is meant, after all, by the 'higher' unity to which our believers aspire? I will tell you: a communion with the dead and the unborn, to which belief alone provides the key. The gods, you might say, have an interest in our belief, and take charge of enforcing it.

PLATO: In which case, Mother, these lies are far from noble.

PERICTIONE: On the contrary, my dear Plato. For consider what follows when rational beings reject them.

PLATO: I am all ears, Mother.

PERICTIONE: Men, as I said, are social beings. But their social nature does not come to them by accident, as do the customs and costumes that divide them into tribes. It belongs to their essence.

PLATO: Hang on, let me get this down. Accident and essence – I think I understand. You mean that in some respects men may change, but that in other respects they may change only by ceasing to be men?

PERICTIONE: How clever you are, Plato. I had no idea that I meant anything so precise. But it is not so much their nature as men that I had in mind, as their nature as rational beings – the nature that they share with the gods. Now the form of reason is language, I think you will admit, and language grows only in communities.

PLATO: Could there not be a private language?

PERICTIONE: I think not, Plato. For language can function only by means of rules, and rules – the most glorious gift that the gods have bestowed on us – are social phenomena.

PLATO: By Zeus, I believe you may be right.

PERICTIONE: It follows that the rational being exists only by virtue of the community. He is by nature subject to the passions which tie him to his fellows, and which make him able, when necessary, to sacrifice himself on their behalf. And if I am right, these group emotions, however they may differ in content and doctrine, will all be alike in form. They will arise from the experience of loneliness and separation, and will aspire towards the final union with our kind which is also a union with the divine and a vindication of our earthly pilgrimage.

PLATO: A bit over the top, Mother, if I may say so.

PERICTIONE: I'll tone it down later. These passions will have their way – *must* have their way – whatever reason demands. For without them, there would be no lasting community, and therefore no reason. From which it can be seen that the triumph of reason in this world can only be short-lived and local.

PLATO: So, come to the point.

PERICTIONE: Well, at last I am there, if you have followed me so far.

PLATO: Indeed I have. But I shall reserve my objections until you have finished.

PERICTIONE: Here, then, is my conclusion. If, as I argue, it lies in human nature to feel these group emotions, then we must encourage them to take the form that prevents their becoming harmful and which gives the greatest chance to happiness.

PLATO: I will go along with that.

PERICTIONE: Now here, it seems, we find the true function of myth. The irrational belief in fall and redemption directs our feelings to another and better condition. It sets our world in the context of a cosmic drama, and deters us from altering what we must in any case learn to endure. The mystical community which is the promise of the sacred doctrine comes through a discipline of the soul, and the myths describe this life as a journey, a pilgrimage, whose goal is elsewhere and elsewhen. By believing them, we are freed from futile resentments against our earthly state. And by being freed, we become more reasonable, able to accept our life of separation, and the imperfections of our kind. This, you might say, is the 'cunning of reason': that it thrives through irrationality.

But suppose, my dear Plato, that some philosopher should come to destroy the myths, while faintly praising them for their 'nobility'. He can no more abolish the feelings from which they spring than he can turn back the tides or reverse the circle of the moon. Our feelings will find another outlet. New myths will come in place of the old. But the new myths, prompted by the sceptical philosopher, will disguise themselves as science. They will pretend to describe this world of phenomena, rather than that higher sphere of the spirit which was promised by the old gods, when they sat untroubled on their thrones. The new myths will tell us that we can overcome our alienation, and achieve perfect blessedness here below. If only the old ways are abolished, the old institutions and customs and laws overthrown, we can confront one another as we truly are: then will our alienation find its remedy, and a new community be born. Of course to achieve this glorious aim is far from easy. We shall have to devise new forms of education. The old institutions will have to be cast down and trampled upon. And at the same time, as an interim measure, a rigid discipline will be imposed on all of us, a training for the millennium, designed to anticipate that final state of harmony – when all laws and institutions will wither away, and men will live together in mutual love and uniform abundance – which differs from the love and the abundance of the breast only in being a state of consciousness and knowledge.

And there you see, my dear Plato, the origin of this Socratic what's-it in the garden, which you pretend to be the harbinger of Reason. It is not reason that provoked this monstrous thing, but the old irrational longing, in its most destructive form. This is my message to you: that, when it comes to the emotions on which society depends, there is no escaping from the irrational. Sometimes, the irrational is the friend of reason, as were the pieties that bid us to serve the gods. At other times, however, the irrational is the enemy of reason, and never more so than when it pretends to be Reason itself.

PLATO: Before I refute you, Mother, I should like to know what all this has to do with Parmenides.

PERICTIONE: Parmenides? Ah yes, well, you see, I feel the connection much better than I can argue for it. But I shall try, nevertheless. As a woman, I am the friend of reason – up to a point.

PLATO: Up to what point?

PERICTIONE: The point where it ceases to be reasonable. Indeed, it seems to me that it is the philosophers who are reason's chief antagonists. For once we put their arguments, as we must, in their dramatic context, and so discover what they *really* mean, we find something similar to what I observed in that old man when I danced before him. Of course, I do not know your Socrates well. Nevertheless, I am half persuaded, from what I hear of him, that his views are rather similar to those of Parmenides, and that they can likewise be explained as intellectual fantasies of the breast.

PLATO: This is outrageous, Mother! You should be lynched.[32]

PERICTIONE: But first I must finish my argument. Imagine, then, a new Parmenides, more ingenious by far than that lecherous old simpleton, who argues that reason has the form of our primal passions. He rewrites the whole of logic in the language of myth, and calls it dialectic.

---

[32] Plato is right to be outraged by his mother's suggestion. In Perictione's defence, however, it is worth mentioning a curious detail in the Life of Plotinus (the most famous advocate of Being in the Roman world): 'up to the age of eight, though he was already attending school, he used to keep going up to his nurse and baring her breasts and wanting to suck; but when someone once told him that he was a little pest, he was ashamed and stopped.' Porphyry, *Life of Plotinus*, 3, 1–5.

PLATO: I don't like the sound of this.

PERICTIONE: All thought, our new Parmenides will tell us, is an exploration of being; hence all thought begins from the unsundered unity which is Being itself. Out of this unity, however, springs opposition and discord. Being conjures not-being, which springs forth like a serpent from the primeval egg. We should not lament this fact, our new Parmenides tells us: for the opposition between Being and not-being can be overcome, transcended, lifted into a higher synthesis. And because this new Parmenides has designs on the world in which we live, the world of time, movement and change, he will tell us that this higher unity is not Being but 'Becoming'. This movement of thought, he argues, is repeated in every endeavour. In all the works of reason we find first unity, then alienation, and at last a restored and 'higher' harmony in which consciousness triumphs over otherness. Reason itself, the dialectic, has the form dictated by our passions: it begins in one-ness, wanders thereafter in the desert of alienation, and arrives at last in the place for which it yearns: the absolute totality in which all is inseparably and eternally one.

PLATO: I wish I could meet this new Parmenides. Will he be, do you think, a lover of young men?

PERICTIONE: Perhaps, but I doubt it. More likely he will be a womanizer, a sower of wild oats and breaker of homes.[33] But he will certainly have disciples, even if he has no lovers. Indeed, this is what frightens me. I imagine a disciple, besotted with a theory whose only ground is emotional necessity, believing that the world of appearances must obey the laws of reason, and that the kingdom of the dialectic must therefore be inaugurated here and now. This future Plato invents a philosophy of change. He proposes an original world of innocence, a golden but primitive age, when men lived peacefully together and from which they were sundered and alienated by the

---

[33] Hegel was the first modern philosopher to display any marked sexual appetite, fathering at least one illegitimate child before settling into marriage. Indeed the three modern exponents of the philosophy of Being – Hegel, Sartre and Heidegger – probably clocked up between them more women than all the other great philosophers put together, Bertrand Russell not excepted. It is worth pointing out that Hegel's dialectic, while it has some affinity with the thoughts of Parmenides, is more akin to that of Empedocles, and still closer to Pythagoras, for whom all creation, and all creative thought, was organized in terms of the sequence: *apeiron* – *peras* – *peperasmenon* (the indeterminate, the limit, and the limited).

inevitable course of events. All that permits them to live together in competition, all the institutions whereby individuals acknowledge and accept their separation, he denounces as signs of their present alienation. Property, law, religion, the market – those spontaneous networks of agreement between strangers – become expressions and symbols of the Fall, to be overcome, if need be, by violence. And he proposes a future age, when man will be 'restored to himself', to his 'species being', in full consciousness at last of his one-ness. The hope of this, and the belief that it will be realized here below, inspire in his followers an all-consuming hatred of everything that impedes their designs. In their desire for a world without conflict, they destroy the institutions that make conflict bearable. In this way, Plato, the disciples of Reason will abolish all that is merely reasonable, and lead us, at last, to the Socratic thingamejig in the garden.

PLATO: Oh, do stop referring to that!

PERICTIONE: Sorry. But you know, I do believe that these ideas come naturally to you – those of the old Parmenides, and those of the new – and I sometimes wonder what I did, that you should have turned out to be so – so alarming!

PLATO: At last you have come to the point, Mother.

PERICTIONE: What do you mean?

PLATO: You know what I mean. So let me protest against your argument – or rather, your lack of argument.

PERICTIONE: I hope you can refute me. I should hate to think there is any truth in what I said.

PLATO: I can't *refute* you. But I can raise a point of method.

PERICTIONE: Method?

PLATO: It's all the rage in the Agora: you should see Prodicus and Chaerephon raising points of method one against the other! It's a scream!

PERICTIONE: Show me.

PLATO: Well, let's see. We are to suppose that you are, as you say, a friend of reason. You will admit therefore that reason does not recommend just any form of argument about any matter. It is not content, for example, simply to awaken the passions, but must proceed according to its own principles, and regardless of where they lead.

PERICTIONE: I think I can grant that much.

PLATO: Now, Socrates says that you can answer an argument only with an argument, and that your argument must run counter to the one you are attacking. So imagine that I am Perictione, descendant of the divine Solon, etc., and that I have been asked to dance before Pythagoras, who afterwards engages me in conversation.

PERICTIONE: What about?

PLATO: About geometry. For in addition to that beautiful story you told me concerning the soul and its fall, Pythagoras, I am told, is famous for proving that the square on the hypotenuse of a right-angled triangle is equal to the sum of the squares on the other two sides.

PERICTIONE: Actually, it was his wife who proved it.

PLATO: Impossible! He had no wife![34]

PERICTIONE: Want to bet?

PLATO: I just *know* he had no wife.

PERICTIONE: Have it your own way. Carry on with the story.

PLATO: Well, then, having pranced and preened in front of the great man until he is beside himself with boredom, I allow him to expound his theorem for my benefit. And then, like the petulant girl I am, I begin to dispute the point. 'There is in the human breast,' I say (frequent mention of the breast being one of my stylistic peculiarities), 'there is in the human breast a deep emotional need, which, you will understand, O revered Pythagoras, is particularly symbolized by triangles.'

'Indeed?' he asks. 'How fascinating.'

'Yes,' I go on, 'and I propose now to enlighten you.'

'O most delicious descendant of the divine Solon,' he says, 'how you captivate my heart.'

'Well then,' I say. 'You will admit that we are influenced in our lives by no one more than our parents?'

'Who could deny it?' he replies.

'And indeed that our parents seem to us like two great forces, striving forever against each other, but nevertheless united in a certain point, at the apex which is marriage.'

---

[34] According to ancient sources, Pythagoras did have a wife, called Theano, herself a philosopher, whose writings were extant when Diogenes Laertius wrote (VIII, 42). It is possible, however, that Theano was not the wife of Pythagoras, but a philosopher-disciple, described as his wife in order to cancel the embarrassing fact of her independence.

'How beautifully you express the idea,' he says.

'So a rational being naturally tends to see herself as – how shall I put it? – drawn across these contending vectors, acted on by both of them, but identical with neither.'

'By Zeus, how charming!' he replies.

'In short, she sees herself, in a way, as the hypotenuse of a triangle.'

'Why, so she does,' he says, with a sweet smile.

PERICTIONE: And you say he had no wife?

PLATO: He was a master of – what do you call it? – elenctic irony.

'You will admit,' I go on, after executing a few rather fetching *schemata* from the dance of the Spider . . .

PERICTIONE: What dance is that?[35]

PLATO: Do stop interrupting.

PERICTIONE: Sorry.

PLATO: 'You will admit,' I say, 'that two lines cannot diverge more sharply than when they are set at right angles each to each.'

'Indeed,' he replies, 'how very bright you are.'

'And since our parents offer us our primal vision of conflict, we imagine these two vectors, the male and the female, as diverging like the sides of a square.'

'What a stunning image,' he says.

'Yes,' I reply, 'that is the general opinion of me.'

'I mean, the image of the square.'

'Oh I see,' I answer with a pert little frown. 'So, as I was arguing, a rational being will see herself, will she not, as the hypotenuse of a right-angled triangle?'

'I cannot for the life of me see,' he replies, 'how she could have any other opinion.'

'And it is for this reason,' I go on, 'that she wishes to settle, in her feelings, how the hypotenuse is related to the other two sides.'

'Yes,' he says, 'if there were female geometers, that would probably be the explanation.'

'Well then,' I triumphantly conclude, 'is it not obvious what conclusion she will draw from her deliberations?'

'Explain your meaning, O divine descendant of the etc.'

---

[35] Presumably the Tarantella, named after the place (Tarentum) where the Pythagoreans settled.

'She will conclude, will she not, that she is the sum, the reconciliation, the resolution of the two conflicting forces upon which she is balanced?'

'By Zeus,' he replies, 'I don't doubt that she would!'

'And hence she will incline to accept the story – the *muthos* – that the square on the hypotenuse is equal to the sum of the squares on the other two sides. Only this will answer to her deep emotional need.'

'By Zeus, you are right,' he replies, 'how stunningly brilliant, how indescribably charming and delicious. I could eat you up.'

'I know,' I reply, with a modest inclination of the head, 'but what do you think of my argument?'

'What argument?'

'Haven't I definitively proved to you that your theorem is nothing more than the expression of an emotional need, and that our only grounds for accepting it are that we must, if we are to live in equilibrium, think in some such way?'

'No,' he replies, 'you have proved nothing of the sort.'

'I am most astonished,' I say, 'at your obtuseness. Could you possibly favour me with an explanation?'

'Meet me tomorrow,' he answers, 'in the studio of Pheidias, and I will go through the arguments.'

PERICTIONE: But Pheidias hadn't even been born in Pythagoras' day!

PLATO: Nor, Mother, had you.

PERICTIONE (*with a sigh*): Sometimes I think I have lived for ever and that all the great men – Homer and Hesiod, Heraclitus and Anaxagoras, Theognis and Alcman and Simonides and Stesichorus – have wearied me with their vain attentions, only to see me thrown away at last on Ariston. Tragic! But there, can't be helped. And I *do* see the point of your story, darling. You are trying to say that explanation is one thing, and justification another.

PLATO: Not exactly, Mother. I want to say that in geometry it is the geometrical method that must be followed; in politics, the political method; and so on. For all you have said, Parmenides might have been right about Being and not-being, and the new Parmenides may also be right about the dialectic. And I might be right in establishing the Socratic phalanstery. These things may answer to some emotional need. But that says nothing about their intrinsic validity.

PERICTIONE: Yes, dear. But something is missing from the arguments

95

of philosophy. And if I try to provide this missing thing, by reflecting on the emotions of philosophers, it is perhaps because some god is guiding me.

PLATO: Undoubtedly you are right, Mother. But if you will allow me, I too have a contribution to make, in the matter of 'emotional needs'.

PERICTIONE: Not another of your speeches!

PLATO: No, Mother. I'm quite calm now. I just would like to take up the argument, at the point where you abandoned it.

PERICTIONE: Please do.

PLATO: Well then; suppose it is true that normal people, who enjoy the benefits of that primal unity to which you refer, yearn always thereafter to return to it. And suppose this causes them, as you say, to accept the consoling myths that promise their redemption. Is it not true that this pattern emerges only because normal people enjoy the benefits of family life and can recall, in their darkest hours, the comfort and love from which they began? These normal people have no doubt or hesitation: even in suffering they are fully themselves, knowing what they want and planning to obtain it.

But what now about the abnormal person, the un-hero of my tragedy, the 'one who strives to assert himself'? He can recall no comforting image of home. For him, there is no point of rest or stability, no 'primal unity' upon which to model his hopes. Is it surprising if he comes to view the world with disgust, and regards with indifference those instruments of compromise by which he finds himself surrounded?

PERICTIONE: Such people are, I admit, rather tiresome.

PLATO: But you see, Mother, I am one of them. I admit, not an extreme instance. But the fact is that I have never known the 'original unity' to which you refer. Or maybe very briefly, when I groped my unthinking way around the surface of the breast – though I should point out that it was not your breast, which at the time had far more pressing concerns, but the breast of my nurse Alcmene, soon to be replaced by the foul-smelling Castallax. What a start in life, Mum! And no sooner had I got habituated to this far from satisfactory arrangement than the great catastrophe was upon me: Father spirited away, and a flat-headed lump of a stranger wallowing in Mother's bed! I ask you! No, I'm not making one of my speeches. I forgave you years ago, you know very well that I did. What I want to say does not concern myself.

PERICTIONE: Well I never!

PLATO: No. It concerns the future – the very time, perhaps, when the new Parmenides and his grim disciple have seized the imagination of the literary élite. I envisage a world without families. Men and women couple and depart with all the light-heartedness of animals, and the offspring are passed from parent to parent, and from parent's lover to parent's lover, like pieces of useless furniture that nobody can bring themselves to throw out. This new generation knows nothing of the family – nothing of its all-embracing love and unshakeable stability.

PERICTIONE: I think you exaggerate your problems, darling.

PLATO: On the contrary, they exaggerate me. That is why I see the future so clearly.

PERICTIONE: Wow! And what else do you see?

PLATO: I see a new society, quite unlike anything we have known, a society in which all children are orphans, or else unwillingly attached to the remnants of families that have long since fallen apart. The experience of home is no longer available. Nor is the hope of final bliss which – if you are right – derives from it. The gods, therefore, are no longer worshipped. People live together in mutual antagonism, but with no desire to renounce the slightest pleasure, still less to lay down their property or their lives for another's sake. They do not view their alienation as a stage on the way from harmony to harmony, but as a permanent condition. And yet, as you wisely say, Mother, they are rational beings, whose primary need is for society, and hence for the kind of government which, in these dire circumstances, may still hold society together.

PERICTIONE: By Zeus, let us strive to prevent this new society.

PLATO: Let us strive, rather, to govern it.

PERICTIONE: But how can people be governed, whose only thought is for themselves?

PLATO: You provided the answer yourself, Mother.

PERICTIONE: What do you mean?

PLATO: These new people can't be governed by their hopes, for they have none, nor by their affections, which are too short-lived to be dependable. They must therefore be governed by the rules.

PERICTIONE: But what rules, my dear Plato, and who is to devise them?

PLATO: Well, here I do perceive a role for myself. For I start from every conceivable disadvantage: a shattered experience of home and emotional disabilities that beggar description. I also seem to be entirely unattractive to members of my own sex. Since my poetic efforts have come to nothing, therefore, I shall put my disadvantages to the best of use, and become a philosopher. I shall devise the rules for this future world, and teach people to follow them. And I shall be loved and esteemed, as the greatest benefactor of the human race.

PERICTIONE: In this brave new world of yours, however, neither love nor esteem will exist.

PLATO: Oh Mother! Why do you want to spoil everything? I'm going out!

(Plato exits left. Perictione looks after him, sighs, and then picks up his handbag from the floor.)

PERICTIONE: Darling! You've forgotten your handbag!

FINIS

XANTHIPPE'S
LAWS

'Why, my husband,' I asked, 'have you men decreed so
    stupidly?'
And, looking at me straight, as though to say 'Where is your
    warp and shuttle?'
He shouted: 'War is the business of men!'

Aristophanes, Lysistrata, 518–20 (quoting Iliad, vi, 318)

XANTHIPPE'S LAWS

Characters:
XANTHIPPE, about 65
PLATO, about 55
ARISTOTLE, about 15
GHOST OF SOCRATES
The action takes place around 375 BC.

In the dialogue which bears his name Phaedo describes the execution of Socrates. Plato, by his own admission, was not present at the event, nor, he claims, was Xanthippe, sent home by Socrates on account of her uncontrolled emotions. After the death of his master, Plato retired to Megara, there to stay for a while with Euclides, another disciple of Socrates. Soon, however, he began to roam the world, seeking out Pythagoreans in Sicily, magicians in Egypt (if Diogenes Laertius is to be believed), and men of wisdom everywhere. Out of friendship for Dion, brother-in-law of the tyrant Dionysius I of Syracuse, he settled for a while in that city, perhaps seeing an opportunity to establish the ideal Socratic republic. He returned disillusioned to Athens (having been sold into slavery according to Plutarch (*Life of Dion*, 5) by Dionysius and redeemed by a Cyrenian well-wisher). In Athens he founded the Academy, named after the grove, dedicated to the hero Hecademus, in which it was situated.

Plato was twice again called to Sicily, first by Dion and secondly by Dionysius II, whom Plato had vainly been grooming as a philosopher king. In his seventh epistle, usually thought to be genuine, he explained his conviction, derived from his Sicilian experience, that political reform is impossible without a rule of law. The chronology of all these events is uncertain, as are the details of Plato's life in his mature years. However, all commentators agree that Plato's style and manner, in his later writings, undergo a radical transformation. This is particularly evident in those works – *The Statesman* and *The Laws* –

which deal with politics. In the first we find a long, intricate and irrelevant discussion of weaving; in the second, a dogmatic and occasionally cantankerous description of the 'second-best' republic, which Plato proposes to establish in the Cretan town of Magnesia. The emphasis on law and order now takes precedence over the pursuit of the ideal, and the whole vision is clouded by a sense of Plato's isolation, as though the error of his views had been perceptively explained to him but, remembering only fragments of the counter-argument, he had decided to go on repeating what he knew to be wrong.

The following dialogue casts some light on the philosopher's predicament in those later years. Unfortunately, it tells us little about his private life: a fact which must cause us even more deeply to regret the loss of *Phryne's Symposium*, in which – according to the *Memorabilia* of Pamphila – Plato's sexual adventures were ruthlessly anatomized.

XANTHIPPE'S LAWS

(The tomb of Socrates, in a suburban grove of Athens. Next to the tomb on which the philosopher's head is carved above an inscription, is a small hut, in front of which is an upright loom where Xanthippe sits weaving. She is intent on her work, and does not notice Plato – an awkward man, somewhat younger in appearance than his fifty-five years, who minces uncomfortably across to the tomb, and reads the inscription. He glances swiftly around him, fails to discover Xanthippe, and then goes down on his knees, carefully lifting his tunic clear of the dust. He looks up silently at Socrates, holding out his hands in a suppliant gesture. Xanthippe catches sight of him.)

XANTHIPPE: Who on earth are you?

PLATO: Bugger!

XANTHIPPE: I beg your pardon?

PLATO *(getting up)*: Frightfully embarrassing. Thought no one was here. Must be on my way.

XANTHIPPE: You haven't answered my question. Who are you?

PLATO: Well, actually, I'm – if you must know, I'm Plato, son of Ariston.

XANTHIPPE: Plato! Son of Perictione! So we meet at last!

PLATO: What do you mean, 'at last'?

XANTHIPPE: Don't you know who I am?

PLATO: You're – you're the woman who looks after the tombs, the – what do you call her? . . .

XANTHIPPE: Plato! My poor dear Plato!

PLATO *(aside)*: Zeus! I don't like the sound of this. *(To Xanthippe)*: Easy now. I'll just slip quietly away, if you don't mind.

XANTHIPPE: Did Socrates not tell you about his wife?

PLATO: He never mentioned women.

XANTHIPPE: Liar!

PLATO: Now look here. I haven't had the honour of being introduced to you, but you ought to know that I come from one of the most distinguished families in Athens. I should be thankful if you could watch your tongue.

XANTHIPPE: Most noble liar!

PLATO: Are you trying to insult me?

XANTHIPPE: No, by Artemis. Socrates was a great advocate of the noble lie.

PLATO: I see you have heard a little about him.

XANTHIPPE: A little. Actually, I was married to him.

PLATO: Nonsense; you are far too young.

XANTHIPPE: A trifle older than you, I should say.

PLATO: You don't mean – you're not the notorious Xanthippe?

XANTHIPPE: Notorious to whom?

PLATO: Well, to all of us. I mean, Apollodorus, and Glaucon, and Phaedo and Euclides and . . . well, the whole gang.

XANTHIPPE: And for what am I notorious?

PLATO: Well, I . . . I hardly dare say. But do I *need* to say it, after all? You must *know* what a shrew you were.

XANTHIPPE: Really?

PLATO: Yes, really. For instance – yes, there's the time you refused to allow him to go to the theatre with Alcibiades, even though it was a gala performance in his honour. There was the way you wouldn't mend his sandals, so he had to go around barefoot. The way you wouldn't get supper ready on time, so he always had to hang around the houses of his friends until someone offered him a scrap of food. And the time you poured that bucket of slops over his venerable head . . . Actually, I'm surprised at myself, that I stand here talking to you.

XANTHIPPE: And you believe all those stories?

PLATO: Well, I . . .

XANTHIPPE: And if you believe them, do you *know* them to be true?

PLATO: I am of course aware of the distinction between belief and knowledge.

XANTHIPPE: It seems to me, young man, that, in the matter of slanderous stories, there is no place for the distinction.

PLATO: No place for the distinction between belief and knowledge? Can you please explain yourself?

XANTHIPPE: Willingly. I mean that scandalous stories should be believed only when they are true and proven; otherwise they should not be believed at all. But a belief that is true and proven is knowledge, is it not?

PLATO *(stiffly)*: It's one possible theory.

XANTHIPPE: Hence in this case there ought to be no belief, only knowledge. And since you do not know, it follows that you ought not to believe.

PLATO: There is a measure of sense in what you say. Nevertheless, you can hardly deny that you were an embarrassment to Socrates.

XANTHIPPE: All wives embarrass their husbands, just as husbands embarrass their wives. That is the purpose of marriage. But what in particular do you object to?

PLATO: Well . . . yes, for instance, the way you behaved on the day of his execution, wailing and beating your breast until he had to send you away. I ask you!

XANTHIPPE: But you weren't there!

PLATO: No, but . . . well, Euclides told me.

XANTHIPPE: Euclides! My dear young man! And you say that this slander too counts as knowledge?

PLATO: I admit, it's no more than Euclides' testimony. Still . . .

XANTHIPPE: If you really want to know, O son of Perictione, it was Euclides who had to be sent away, along with Phaedo, Apollodorus, Critobulus, Hermogenes and all the rest, who were making such a histrionic shindy that my poor Socks just stood there with his hands over his ears.

PLATO: Your poor what?

XANTHIPPE: Socks. It's what I call him. In fact I was the only one left at the end.

PLATO: You mean that Euclides wasn't *there*?

XANTHIPPE: Did he tell you he stayed to the end – I would say bitter end, except that it wasn't bitter in the least?

PLATO: He said that he and Phaedo and Apollodorus and several more were there, and that Socrates entertained them with discourses. Phaedo confirms the story. So there.

XANTHIPPE: What, may I ask, was the subject of those discourses, which Phaedo and Euclides heard from Socrates?

PLATO: Well, there is some dispute about it. According to Phaedo, Socrates spoke about his exploits on the expedition to Amphipolis. Euclides claims he was more interested in gardening.

XANTHIPPE: Gardening?

PLATO: Yes. The gaoler, you see, gave them a most learned description of the hemlock plant, and how it was cultivated. One thing led to another until Socrates, as was his manner, began to unfold a whole theory of horticulture, of the best times for planting peas and marrows, and for harvesting artichokes and the like; of the nutrient qualities of cucumbers, beans and radishes; of the uses of fragrant herbs, such as basil, rosemary, dill and thyme, together with the seasons for sowing them, the special humours of the earth on which they depend, and their affinity with the moon and stars. He also argued that we make a great error in not mixing these herbs with our side dishes, or pounding them into relishes. It was all very sublime and inspiring, Euclides said.

XANTHIPPE: But Socrates didn't know a thing about gardening! And when I put basil in his goat one day he coughed it up and cried, 'By the dog, this goat has been wearing Plato's perfume!'

PLATO: Impossible!

XANTHIPPE: I assure you, nothing but the plain and honest truth.

PLATO: I can't believe it! Did he really say that?

XANTHIPPE: Say what?

PLATO: That about the perfume.

XANTHIPPE: Well, you know how he used to joke.

PLATO: I say, would you mind if I sat down a moment? I feel a little – a little weak.

XANTHIPPE: Make yourself at home.

(Gestures to a folding stool which Plato brings from the entrance to the hut.)

PLATO: I suppose it's remembering Socrates again. You know how it is. You think you've got over it. And then suddenly it all comes back, as though it were yesterday.

XANTHIPPE: My dear Plato, had you known Socrates well . . .

PLATO: But I knew him as well as could be. I studied him, revered him, loved him, to the utmost of my capacity. You cannot love what you do not know. So there.

XANTHIPPE: No need to be quite so touchy.

PLATO: Sorry.

XANTHIPPE *(after a pause)*: As a matter of fact, what you say about love is not entirely right. For there are two kinds of love. There is the kind that grows from knowledge, and this, I grant you, is the greatest of goods. But there is the other kind, which, while it may lead to knowledge, may also lead in quite another direction, attaching itself to some quality of the person loved, and prepared to distort what it sees, so that this quality should occupy the foreground. Many who loved Socrates for his wisdom failed to love him as a man. Indeed, to this second love the individual may be such an obstacle that he has to be written out of history and reworked as myth. He must cease to be himself, and become instead the *idea* of himself.

PLATO: But that is why my love for Socrates endures: for ideas are eternal, whereas individuals die.

XANTHIPPE: You don't believe that stuff, do you?

PLATO *(looks at her curiously)*: Well, I . . . I confess that I have my reservations. *(A moment of silence.)* What's that you're working on?

XANTHIPPE: Weaving.

PLATO: Yes, but what?

XANTHIPPE: Oh, it's a story.

PLATO: What story?

XANTHIPPE: You wouldn't know it. I invented it to amuse Socrates when he was drinking the hemlock, because I thought it would cheer him up. Not that he needed cheering that much. By the way, why weren't you there?

PLATO *(clutches his head)*: Don't remind me! How could I have done it! *Oi, oi, otototoi!*

XANTHIPPE: I say, steady on. No need to get so worked up. Just as well you weren't there, otherwise he'd have sent you away too.

PLATO: How can he ever forgive me?

XANTHIPPE: I don't see why not. I'm sure you had a good excuse.

PLATO: The fact is, I forgot.

XANTHIPPE: You forgot?

PLATO: I mean, I forgot it was due to happen that day. I was so distracted, so carried away, so childish, so stupid, so – I don't know why I'm telling you this!

XANTHIPPE: It's clearly time you told *someone*. Carried away by what?

PLATO: You're right, it's time I said it aloud. Mouthing it in silence before the tomb of Socrates is just another way of savouring the bitterness. The fact is Xylophantes and his Screaming Corybants were in Athens all week, and booked to perform in the Odeion that very afternoon. Everyone was going and – well, I had Xylophantes' picture on my wall, knew some of the tunes . . .

XANTHIPPE: Mixolydian, no doubt.

PLATO: Worse. Phrygian.[1] But it was all the rage then, and I just *had* to go. It's almost impossible to explain. But there I was, in the grip of passion, on account of some thick-lipped moron in a leather waistband, with a voice like a constipated donkey. Plato, son of Ariston, jigging up and down with the rest of them, moaning with excitement as Xylophantes came on stage and launched into his signature tune – you know, the one in iambics about the boy with green hair – and then: bang! I remembered. At that very moment they would be giving him the hemlock! And there I was, a mere atom in that seething mass of flesh, gyrating and contorting in time to a fatuous halfwit! I fainted away, and was lucky not to be trampled to death. Someone carried me out, and when I came to I cursed that filthy music and vowed never to listen to another note of it. By then it was too late to get to the prison, and in any case I felt so ashamed, I wanted to hide my face for ever. I left Athens that very evening.

XANTHIPPE: Without saying goodbye to your poor mother.

PLATO: Could I set foot at such a time in the house of Pyrilampes? OK. I was inconsiderate. But you know how young people are: impatient to resolve every crisis in their own favour, and constantly drawing lines through their past. No, I went straight to Megara, to stay with Euclides. And when he told me everything . . .

XANTHIPPE: The whole pack of lies . . .

PLATO: The whole story, which sounded so right and true and noble, I could not contain my grief. I didn't eat or sleep; I just lay there on the couch, weeping and moaning by turns. Euclides thought I was going to die. In fact, I would certainly have died, had it not been for one thing. Why am I telling you this?

XANTHIPPE: Because I am a good listener; and a woman; and the wife of Socrates; and your mother's friend. What is the thing that saved you?

PLATO: Another vow. I vowed to Poseidon that I would travel the world until I found the place where I could raise a monument to Socrates.

---

[1] The phrygian mode was the one normally used in corybantic music, and was associated with the flute. Conflicting accounts are given of its character.

XANTHIPPE: What's wrong with the one in the Prytaneum?[2]

PLATO: I don't mean a monument in bronze. I mean a human community, in which the Socratic ideals could become a reality.

XANTHIPPE: And did you find this community?

PLATO: I thought so; for a few years I was quite excited, in fact. I seemed to have discovered a people whose rulers wished to be philosophers, and who would themselves willingly submit to be governed by a rational plan.

XANTHIPPE: Where were these amazing people?

PLATO: In Syracuse, where Dionysius ruled. My dear friend Dion, his brother-in-law, called on my services.[3]

XANTHIPPE: But of course, it didn't work.

PLATO: How do you know?

XANTHIPPE: This 'dear friend' business. It suggests you had some other motive for being in Syracuse than the desire to improve the local morals.

PLATO: Still, it *might* have worked.

XANTHIPPE: But for one thing.

PLATO: Which was. . . ?

XANTHIPPE: The people weren't ready for it.

PLATO: How perceptive of you! No sooner had we settled on a plan for government, than some faction would arise, claiming that it stood to lose by this new idea, and wanting none of it. And then, of course, the people would split into opposing groups, and strife prevailed. I lost patience, finally, and set sail for Athens.

XANTHIPPE: Having never once written to your poor mother.

PLATO: I wrote letters; but I never got round to sending them. I don't think Mother would have enjoyed them; I could never get the style right, you see, and she cared more about my style than all my other defects put together. Anyway, I hear she died happy.

XANTHIPPE: Who told you that?

---

[2] Athens repented of Socrates' execution, and erected to him a statue of bronze, in the place where distinguished citizens had the right to dine at public expense. However, it seems that his grave would have been neglected, had Xanthippe not tended it.

[3] Plato's services were explicitly called upon only later, in 367 BC, when Dionysius II succeeded to the throne of Sicily. The anachronism mirrors the many anachronisms in the dialogues of Plato himself. And while we are on the subject of anachronisms, is it really plausible that Plato, who was twenty-eight at the time of Socrates' execution, should have still been obsessed by pop-stars? Or was he hiding something?

PLATO: Antiphon. He said that she got regular news of me from her cousin Crates in Syracuse, and that in any case she had rather taken to the amphora in her old age, and wasn't too much bothered by the world.

XANTHIPPE: How little you understand women, my dear Plato.

PLATO: What do you mean?

XANTHIPPE: I mean, how little you understand the constancy of their affections, their ability to care for an individual through every misfortune, and to hide their yearnings and their sorrows when love requires. Your mother was a true Penelope: though I admit, there is a kind of happiness in that. You know that her last words were of you?

PLATO: Nonsense. Antiphon told me how she died. She came into the house, after saying goodbye to some gossip who had been visiting, drank a bowl of wine and keeled over. Her last words – well, if you really want to know, her last words were, 'Yum, yum!'

XANTHIPPE: But her last words to the gossip were, 'Plato will be great, for he will not rest until his soul has been glorified in words.'

PLATO: You're making it up.

XANTHIPPE: I'm not making it up.

PLATO: Then how do you know?

XANTHIPPE: I was the gossip. Almost every other day I came to reminisce about Socrates, and she would speak of you.

PLATO: I see. Well, I suppose I should be pleased. Thanks for telling me.

XANTHIPPE: And don't you grieve for her?

PLATO: I suppose so. But I got used to grieving for her long before she died. Death didn't make much difference to our relations. In fact, it put them on a sensible footing for the first time. I hope that doesn't sound too awful?

XANTHIPPE: It sounds entirely natural.

PLATO: You know, I rather like talking to you.

XANTHIPPE: I'm glad.

PLATO: I feel I can say anything I want to say. *(Pause.)* Tell me something.

XANTHIPPE: Yes?

PLATO: Why are you sitting here?

XANTHIPPE: Isn't it obvious?

PLATO: Not really. I mean, you are not pouring libations, or praying, or chanting – just weaving, as though you were at home, like the woman of whom Semonides writes, you know, the one descended from a bee.

XANTHIPPE: Please don't mention that revolting poem![4] The fact is I *am* at home here. This is where I belong.

PLATO: But how do you live?

XANTHIPPE: The stewards allowed me to set up my loom, and there is the little hut where I sleep. I gave the house by the palaestra of Hipparchus to the boys, and they sometimes visit me. Just down there, the other side of the Dipylon – see? – is the shop of Callisto, wife of Cleinas, who takes the weaving and sells it for me. She keeps a table for strangers too. If you like, we could ask her for wine; it's late enough.

PLATO: Well, I – it's not very regular. Drinking with a woman, I mean. But if you insist. No, no; I'll go. This one's on me.

(Plato gets up and goes off left, with the embarrassed step with which he had entered.)

XANTHIPPE *(musing)*: The same dark eyes; the same cheeks; the same toffee-nosed Attic accent. And the same way of standing, hips to one side, left hand trailing in the air. Some of her spirit too, if only he weren't so prim. Sorry, Socks; I think I rather like him. Poor Perictione!

PLATO *(returning)*: Sweet wine of Samos; I can't tell you how revolting the Sicilian potion is.

XANTHIPPE: So what happened to your vow?

PLATO: I realized I had misinterpreted it: it was not necessary to set up a Socratic state. A smaller community would do – a community of free minds, dedicated to teaching and learning in the Socratic manner; not one of those ghastly word factories, of course,[5] but . . .

XANTHIPPE: A phrontisterion?[6]

PLATO: A school of philosophy. So I vowed to Pallas Athene that I

---

[4] Semonides of Amorgos (*c.* 600 BC) wrote a misogynist satire against women, comparing them to various animals. Only for the domestic bee does he express any sympathy: 'she alone is a woman without reproach/And in her hands life blossoms and bears fruit'. It should be noted that there was a widespread ancient belief, discussed by Aristotle, that the bee is asexual.

[5] i.e. the schools of rhetoric, notably that founded by Plato's rival Isocrates.

[6] Aristophanes' sarcastic name (roughly 'think-tank') for the place where the young Socrates taught the 'crooked logic' (*Clouds*).

would return home, and spend the money that Mother had left me on a shady plot, where I could set myself up as a teacher.

XANTHIPPE: And did you?

PLATO: Yes. I found a nice piece of land, just over the rise there, by the gymnasium in the grove of Hecademus. We've been going a few years now, and I'm thinking of drawing up a constitution, only –

XANTHIPPE: Only what?

PLATO: It sounds funny, I know, but I still can't decide what to teach.

XANTHIPPE: That's easy: you teach what you know.

PLATO: But what *do* I know? Oh, I grant you, my head is stuffed full of arguments and stories: I can give the reasons for and against all the usual doctrines. I can even give a cogent summary of Parmenides.

XANTHIPPE: I don't believe you!

PLATO: As cogent as anyone else. But the problem is, wife of Socrates . . .

XANTHIPPE: Xanthippe.

PLATO: The problem is, Xanthippe, that none of this is knowledge, since all of it can be put in doubt.

XANTHIPPE: It seems to me you are looking for knowledge in the wrong place.

PLATO: What do you mean?

XANTHIPPE: I mean, that you count as knowledge only what you can incontrovertibly prove; hence for you there is no knowledge outside mathematics.

PLATO: Oh, of course I shall teach *mathematics*. It's the rest of the curriculum that worries me. You see, I want to set a standard for the end of time, to have my school painted on all the vases, heaped up in a thousand fragments in the BM.

XANTHIPPE: The BM?

PLATO: The Blessed Mound, where the remains of Athens will one day accumulate.

XANTHIPPE: I see. What a strange ambition.

PLATO: Not really. Through the Academy Socrates will become immortal.

XANTHIPPE: He doesn't actually need the Academy for that.

PLATO: I mean his memory will become immortal. If I can make a go of it. But first I have to know what knowledge is. And there I'm stuck.

XANTHIPPE: Tell me, Plato, do you admit women to this school of yours?

PLATO *(stiffly)*: Not as such.

XANTHIPPE: Not as such. I see. As what then?

PLATO: Well, as men.

XANTHIPPE: How very odd.

PLATO: If you must know, there are two of my pupils concerning whom I have doubts.[7]

XANTHIPPE: Doubts about what?

PLATO: I am no great expert on the female anatomy. Even so, you would have expected a chap's voice to break by the time he's eighteen. This is all off the record, you understand. Anyway, why do you ask?

XANTHIPPE: The reason is that, from time to time, a woman's view of things can be rather useful.

PLATO: There is no such thing as a woman's view; women, like men, are rational beings. That is why, when a new pupil applies for admission, I do not scrutinize his gender, I mean, examine his – you know what I mean.

XANTHIPPE: It seems to me, Plato, that there are two kinds of rational being. For the distinction between male and female runs deeper than you suppose. In this matter of knowledge, for instance.

PLATO: What do you mean?

XANTHIPPE: For you knowledge requires certainty, and therefore proof. Now women are brought up without schooling, and without the faintest idea of theory. Nevertheless they know many things – practical things, like weaving. Thus there arises a store of feminine knowledge, in which proof and theory play no part: knowing what to do and how to do it, knowing what to feel and why.

PLATO: How strange, that you can speak of knowledge, where you cannot speak of truth!

XANTHIPPE: Not strange at all. For truth is revealed to us only after we have acquired the skill of speaking. And language is like weaving: to know it is not to know a set of tasks, but to acquire an art for which we have no theory. If I were to look for a test of knowledge, therefore, I should ignore proof, and rely instead on learning. And I would strongly recommend this test to you too, Plato. You should count as knowledge all those things which can be learned to some

---

[7] According to Diogenes Laertius, III, 46, the two women in question were Lastheneia of Mantinea, and Axiothea of Phlius, 'who is reported by Dicaearchus to have worn men's clothes'.

advantage. You should look on your own experience and ask yourself, how has my mind been improved by it? For certainly, even if this leads to no proof of your opinions, you can be sure that you will do no harm when you teach them to your pupils.

PLATO: You may have a point.

XANTHIPPE: Well then, let's hear what you learned in Sicily.

PLATO: About what?

XANTHIPPE: About the things which made you journey there: the hope for a better government, the scheme to ensure it through philosophy, and the desire to set up a living monument to dear old Socks.

PLATO: I do wish you wouldn't call him that.

XANTHIPPE: He doesn't mind. Tell me what you learned, and I'll teach you about weaving. Does that seem fair?

PLATO: I don't know that I want to learn about weaving.

XANTHIPPE: You will.

PLATO: In a nutshell, then, I learned that Sicily, like other states, should be subject not to the tyranny of men but to the rule of law. And I came to believe that absolute power is bad both for those who exercise it and those who are subject to it.[8]

XANTHIPPE: But how would you define this rule of law, and why is it not itself a form of absolute power?

PLATO: These are questions which have greatly troubled me. If you have a moment, Xanthippe, I should value the opportunity to persuade you to my opinion.

XANTHIPPE: I have all the time in the world, so long as you don't mind my disagreeing with you.

PLATO: It is normal for people to disagree with me at first. When I went to Sicily I believed that the wise and just state is the one in which the wise and just are rulers, and that the bad state is the one in which the rulers too are bad. From such a premise it seems to follow, I think you'll agree, that the good ruler must enjoy as much power as possible, in order to protect his rule from evil people, and to ensure that his edicts are obeyed.

XANTHIPPE: It does indeed seem to follow. So much the worse for the premise. You see this lyre stringed with wool? It is the warp: and this here is the woof which binds it.

---

[8] These very sentences appear also in the Seventh Epistle of Plato, clear proof, I should say, of the authenticity of that particular letter.

PLATO: Eh? Oh, yes, very interesting. Suppose then that our wise and just ruler, surrounded by his wise and just advisers . . .

XANTHIPPE: Why does he need advisers?

PLATO: . . . surrounded by his wise and just advisers, is installed at the helm, enjoying the absolute power that his role requires. One by one his advisers will die, and he too must finally set sail across the Styx. So what will then be left of his reign?

XANTHIPPE: Now I change shuttle, see, introducing a thread of blue.

PLATO: Are you listening to my argument?

XANTHIPPE: Yes. What will be left of his reign? you asked; and the answer is: nothing, save the machinery of power.

PLATO: Exactly. Those who come after him inherit the means of power, but not the end, which was virtue. In fact, our just ruler leaves to his successor the most dangerous gift of all: an infallible instrument for controlling society. Just as power in good hands is a supreme benefit, so power in evil hands is a supreme disaster. And of course, it is more in the nature of evil to covet power, than it is in the nature of good, so that evil will quickly seize its inheritance. I am sure you made a mistake just then.

XANTHIPPE: That was a cross-thread, so that I can change from blue to red. So what is the remedy?

PLATO: The remedy is to enact a law, which will ensure that the successor to our ruler will be as wise and just as he.

XANTHIPPE: And how is that done?

PLATO: Wait a moment. There is another matter which must be considered first. Suppose that the necessary law has been passed, and that our ruler has died. Who now is supreme in the state? Surely, the one who decides upon the successor. But this decision is made by the law. Hence it is the law which is supreme and not the ruler. Furthermore, because our wise legislator will leave nothing to chance, he will decree that his successor, should he cease to act wisely and justly, should thereupon be deprived of office . . .

XANTHIPPE: By whom?

PLATO: . . . should thereupon be deprived of office, and replaced by another more suited to command. And this supreme law – the law of succession, or the Constitution, as one might call it – becomes the very soul of the state, determining the identity of the community from day to day. It will be necessary to forbid its repeal, and to decree that any ruler attempting to change it will be promptly deposed . . .

XANTHIPPE: By whom?

PLATO: . . . promptly deposed and reduced to the status of a subject. In such a state, therefore, the Constitution is supreme, rather than the person who holds office under it. All acts, whether of the ruler or his subjects, owe their legality to this supreme law, and indeed, the distinction between ruler and subject is no longer valid: both are subject to the supreme law, which makes the ruler the servant of those he commands. That, Xanthippe, is what I mean by a rule of law. Moreover, it is not permitted in this life to attain the ideal; we must therefore content ourselves with the second best. I dare say that you will agree with me, therefore, that the second-best state – and the most wise and just that we may achieve – is precisely the one I have described. Now you really have made a mistake: see, there's a fleck of blue in the brown of that tree.

XANTHIPPE: So there is. I was distracted by your most interesting argument. Still, I think I'll leave it – from a distance it makes a nice effect, as though a little fragment of sky had somehow lodged in the bark. The problem, as I see it, Plato, is that you have not renounced your old definition of the good state, as the one whose rulers are good.

PLATO: Indeed not. But experience tells me that we must not leave it to chance that our state acquire a virtuous ruler: the state must be subjected to a higher principle – the law – which ensures that only the virtuous may rule.

XANTHIPPE: But who will enforce this law?

PLATO: The rulers, of course. The rulers enforce the law which appoints the rulers. Oh I admit, it looks paradoxical: but when you study it closely, it is not paradoxical at all. Consider this weaving of yours. Suppose there were no warp, and the woof were taken from the frame: would it keep its pattern?

XANTHIPPE: By no means.

PLATO: And suppose that the strings of the woof were extracted from the warp: would the cloth remain?

XANTHIPPE: Indeed not.

PLATO: Yet, although neither woof nor warp is supported, and both are nothing but strings of wool, they stand firmly together, in a cloth that only the strongest could tear apart.

XANTHIPPE: Naturally.

PLATO: That's how it is in my second-best republic: without the law, the ruler will turn to bad; without the ruler, the law will not be upheld: each supports the other, as warp and woof in weaving.

XANTHIPPE: So what kind of law do you envisage?

PLATO: Whatever law will create virtuous citizens. And as the law succeeds in this aim, so will the citizen the more willingly obey it, until finally the law ceases to be a constraint upon his conduct, and becomes instead the badge of his consent.

XANTHIPPE: Very fine, Plato. But how will law make men virtuous?

PLATO: This, it seems to me, is the whole substance of the legislator's task, and no single law could possibly accomplish it. But no laws will be more important than those which enable men to live together peacefully. Hence the law must abolish all that causes strife. It must aim to produce citizens who in everything return naturally to the ways of peace, as a boat in a tranquil harbour rights itself after each movement of the passengers.

XANTHIPPE: And what, in your view, is the cause of strife?

PLATO: There are three causes: property, family and religion. When I covet your property, you become my enemy and I become yours; when family feelings entrap me, I become the enemy of all except my family; and when my gods differ from your gods, your life to me is sacrilege. What are you doing?

XANTHIPPE: I thought I would start another frame; that story is too sacred. Hold this spindle, will you? So what do you propose to do about these three causes of strife?

PLATO: Easy as pie! Our legislator must pass laws to limit and control these institutions, and to take people – kicking and screaming at first, but soon obedient and finally joyfully consenting – down the path of human happiness.

XANTHIPPE: Now look what you've done!

PLATO: Sorry, I got carried away. Is it broken?

XANTHIPPE: No, but the thread is all unravelled. Here, this way: wind the spindle away from you, so that the thread tightens: that's it. This one is flax, and must be pulled tight.

PLATO: I see. Property, for instance. You will admit that it exists in many forms?

XANTHIPPE: How could I deny it?

PLATO: And that, of all these forms, the most dangerous is money?

XANTHIPPE: How so?

PLATO: For of money, as Theognis says, man cannot have enough, but must always be scheming to increase his store.[9] And I shall tell you why Theognis is right, Xanthippe. Money gives me the power to acquire what I will. It is the universal value against which everything will exchange: food, drink, shelter, arms, labour, even love of a kind. Money, you might say, is crystallized power; and power is a threat to the one who does not possess it.

XANTHIPPE: But do we not benefit from money, which makes a common measure in our commerce? How else could you have bought this delicious wine, or Callisto obtained it from Sarambus at Piraeus,[10] Sarambus bought it from the ship-owner, and the ship-owner from the grower in Samos? Without money, we should have had to travel all the way to Samos this evening, or else content ourselves with the filth that grows on Mount Hymmetus.

PLATO: A small sacrifice, Xanthippe. For remember that the man with money has power over the man without it, and can compel him to sell his labour, reducing him to alienation and slavery.

XANTHIPPE: As I am reduced, weaving these little stories for the tourist trade?

PLATO: Well, I – yes, in a way.

XANTHIPPE: Or you, in charging fees for your tuition?

[9] See Theognis, lines 183–92.

[10] Socrates thought well of this particular wine-merchant: see Plato, *Gorgias*, 518B. The sweet wine of Samos (made from muscat grapes) is still one of the best things to come out of Greece. Oddbins sell it at around £3 or £4 a bottle; yet it is almost a match for the famous French muscat, from Beaumes de Venise in Provence, which retails at £8 or £9. In fact Beaumes de Venise is a rip-off: all over the neighbouring hills the muscat grape is planted, and produces an equivalent wine, sold without appellation, for the same price as the wine of Samos. It should be pointed out that there was a Greek colony in the region of Venise (Avinnae): indeed, the best way to follow the Hellenic migrations is to look for sweet white wine. (See Xenophon, *Anabasis*, 6.4.36.) Until the time of Nasser a burnt brown muscat was even made in the vicinity of Alexandria, probably the same wine as that called 'Mareotês' or 'Alexandreotikos' by Athenaeus (*Deipnosophistae*, 1.33d). I discovered five bottles of this concoction, of uncertain date, when exploring the cellar of *Bait Hind* with one of the 'sisters' (as Hind insisted on calling them). She referred to the cache as a 'great discovery' (*iktishāf kabir*), and insisted that we go upstairs to drink it. Although most of my memories of what followed are confused, I distinctly recall a taste, not unpleasant, of tar, with an afterthought of raspberries. This, my companion informed me, was the *murāhim as-sabābah al-halwa* – sweet balm of love.

PLATO: I don't charge fees.

XANTHIPPE: Then how do you live?

PLATO: Well, people make gifts from time to time, and one way or another the school survives.[11]

XANTHIPPE: I see; the usual story. So what then is your remedy for the scourge of property?

PLATO: The remedy is simple: to assign to each citizen a plot of land, his sole capital, from which he may reap the profit during his lifetime, but which he is forbidden to sell. And to grant to him only so much money as will suffice for his necessities. The right of ownership is then reduced to a right of residence, and the store of property is largely held in common.

XANTHIPPE: And who will fix the price of corn, and other necessary things? For if their price is not fixed, you will not know how much money your citizens will need to spend on them.

PLATO: True, Xanthippe; but for this too the legislator has a remedy. The law will fix prices so as to ensure a just and equal distribution.[12]

XANTHIPPE: And what of foreign money – such as I occasionally receive for my weaving? Will not your citizens begin to use that instead, when it is discovered that the domestic currency is in short supply, and incapable of buying anything save the bare necessities?

PLATO: By Zeus, you are right, Xanthippe, and our legislator must forbid that too. Yes, all foreign money will be the property of the state, and every citizen will be compelled, on pain of death – er, no, flogging maybe – to surrender it to the public coffers. In any case, no citizen will be permitted to travel abroad without a special licence. I think that takes care of your objection. You see, Xanthippe, how fruitful it is to discuss one's ideas? As I always tell my pupils, through dialogue an argument becomes not only more precise, but

[11] Gifts to the Academy from its alumni were often quite substantial. Indeed, by refusing fees, Plato made much more money than those who asked for them. (Kenneth Freeman, *Schools of Hellas*, London, 1897, pp. 202–3.) The same was not true of Socrates; hence Xanthippe's slightly tetchy remark. (See *Xanthippe's Republic.*)

[12] Plato's obsession with material equality (see *Republic*, 416Dff; *Timaeus* 18B) is remarked on by Pamphila, who, in the 25th book of her *Memorabilia* (according to Diogenes Laertius, III, 23), says that the Arcadians and Thebans, when they were founding Megalopolis, invited Plato to be their legislator, but that he, 'when he discovered that they were opposed to equality of possessions (ἴσον ἔχειν), refused to go'.

more comprehensive too, as it broadens to colonize, so to speak, the opposing viewpoint.

XANTHIPPE: I am not sure that I have been, as you put it, colonized: not yet at least.

PLATO: What do you mean? Can you think of a better system than the one I am proposing? Is there a single detail in which you would have it changed? I am impatient to learn, Xanthippe, for truth has always counted more in my thinking than the love which each man naturally bears for his own opinions.

XANTHIPPE: And which women bear for the opinions of others. So please go on, Plato. I am impatient to hear what you have to say of the family. See how quickly it goes with flax?

PLATO: Indeed, but you need to pull the warp a little tighter. Here, let me do it.

XANTHIPPE: Thank you. How did you learn?

PLATO: I've been watching you.

XANTHIPPE: So now you know something which you cannot prove.

PLATO: What do you mean?

XANTHIPPE: You know how to tighten the warp on a weaver's frame.

PLATO: Is this what I should be teaching in the Academy?

XANTHIPPE: It is what I was taught at home, which was my academy. But it seems to me that you wish to destroy the home, or at least the family, which is its meaning.

PLATO: There is no need; it is destroying itself. The whole institution is rotten from top to bottom. Scarcely a child these days has two parents, and most are lucky (if lucky it is) to have even one. I admit, there are people who maintain an obstinate attachment to family life, and who believe that their children are, so to speak, their private property. Such people are, in my opinion, a supreme danger to the state; for they sow suspicion of the public world and nurture those exclusive affections which are the negation of civil friendship, and the cause of so much jealousy and strife. There is a greater evil too.

XANTHIPPE: What evil could be greater than those you have just described?

PLATO: I admit it is hard to imagine one. But it seems to me that it is precisely the family which is the principal enemy of the laws. And this for two reasons: first, that it places in the heart of the community a relation other than law, a bond between people which is also a form of bondage. And the second, that it shields the child from the laws, hides him away from their benevolent supervision, says to them, 'go about your business in the public world, where you belong, but do not cross the threshold into what is mine.' And is this not the greatest of evils?

XANTHIPPE: Hold this shuttle while I think about it.

PLATO: Let me help your thoughts. If the laws are to perform their sacred task of producing virtuous citizens, the child must be surrendered to their care at the earliest age: the age when character is formed, and when reason and passion contend in the soul for government. Children therefore should be the property of the state, which is their true father. They must be rescued from the petty despotism of family life, and brought into the light of the gymnasium, there to be educated in the subjects required by virtue.

XANTHIPPE: Girls too?

PLATO: I have told you, Xanthippe, that I see no differences between male and female, when it comes to the rational soul.

XANTHIPPE: I expect there is still time to learn. So what subjects should these liberated children be taught by their kindly stepparent?

PLATO: As I said before, I'm a bit stuck on this one. Mathematics, of course, since this is addressed purely to the reasoning part. And music and dancing too; maybe weaving, if there is time.

XANTHIPPE: If the matter is as important as you say, Plato, you are being culpably vague.

PLATO: I know. To be quite honest, Xanthippe, my mother made a total Horlicks of my upbringing: it wasn't till I fell in with some Pythagoreans in Sicily that I acquired any real grasp of mathematical argument. Until then, the only knowledge I had of geometry came from her attempts, when she'd had a few too many, to dance it for me.[13] And even dancing, which was her speciality, she taught only in patches. That's why I got hooked on that ghastly music, which all but destroyed my soul.

XANTHIPPE: I think you are being too harsh on her, you know. Also on yourself.

PLATO: Why do you say that?

XANTHIPPE: Fill my bowl, and I shall tell you. It's my view that you

---

[13] Athenaeus, in the *Deipnosophistae*, I, 20D, also records an instance of a dancer, of Perictione's generation, who could dance the theorem of Pythagoras and, without uttering a word, convince the spectators of its validity.

were quite right to go to that concert of Xylophantes, and Socrates, had he known about it, would have completely agreed.

PLATO: Socrates? Never!

XANTHIPPE: Oh yes. For although we hated corybantic music, we had children. In all of us, we saw, there is a part belonging to Dionysus, which prompts us to break out in wild movements and drivelling discourse and to imagine we are free. And if this part is deprived of those orgies in the stadium, it might express itself in the assembly, to far worse effect. I don't say that Dionysus is a liberator, for all that we call him Lusios. Indeed, he is an enslaver, whose promise of liberty is an invitation to decay. But for that very reason, he must be purged from our souls from time to time, lest our strength be exhausted from carrying such a burden. Hence, although he may be the cause of madness, his dances are also used as a cure for it.

PLATO: Your approach, Xanthippe, is more medicinal than ethical; how can you tell me that Socrates would have approved of such a thing?

XANTHIPPE: Shall I let you into a secret?

PLATO: What?

XANTHIPPE: Socrates once took part in the corybantic rites.

PLATO: Impossible!

XANTHIPPE: Oh, he was fairly drunk at the time, and I expect some young man had led him astray. Whatever the reason, however, he came home one evening in a very interesting condition, wailing 'Io! Io!' in the phrygian mode, and dancing round the kitchen, pinching the bottom of Cleio, our one remaining slave.

PLATO: I'll not believe it. It's too scandalous. As I always say to my pupils, in the matter of scandal you should believe only what you know.

XANTHIPPE: Well, have it your own way. But now that we have touched on the subject of religion, why don't you tell me what your legislator proposes to do about this third cause of strife? Surely, even if you are right in thinking that the legislator might refine away, so to speak, the desires for property and family life, he surely cannot hope to eradicate religion, or to dispense with the web of social feeling that it secretly spreads through the community?

PLATO: How exactly you put the problem, O blessed wife of Socrates. For religion is not only natural to man; it is also necessary to the formation of his reason. It is religion that first implants in us the higher goals which are the spur to self-transcendence. Without religion the mass of men would be scarcely distinguishable from beasts. I would go further. The man who has no religion in him, who does not stand in awe of sacred things and knows no place where a god might dwell – such a man is the enemy of order, and a danger to the state.

XANTHIPPE: I'm glad to learn that you believe in the gods, my dear Plato.

PLATO: Well, to be quite honest, I don't. What with one thing and another, I rather lost my trust in them. But that's another story.

XANTHIPPE: It sounds like the same story to me. You are saying that people should worship the gods, but that you yourself do not believe in them?

PLATO: What's wrong with that? The legislator does not consider his own feelings, but only what would be best for those under his care.

XANTHIPPE: I see. So what does your legislator propose?

PLATO: I can think of no solution but this one: that the laws should take charge of religion too, dictating the times and places of the rites and festivals, ordering the liturgies and sacred dances, and establishing the brotherhoods of priests.

XANTHIPPE: And which gods shall be honoured in your second-best republic?

PLATO: It doesn't matter very much, so long as everybody is clear about it. The laws will specify which gods are to be worshipped and in what manner, appointing a particular god as guardian of the city, so that the law may borrow some of his sanctity. All who refuse to worship, or who adopt some alien deity, are to be cast out from the city, so as to live by the laws which are best suited to their spiritual obedience. In this way, all strife of religion is brought to an end, and the instinct for sacred things is both safeguarded and put to the service of the state.

XANTHIPPE: Is that it?

PLATO: Well, there are lots of details, of course. The legislator will have to concern himself with the daily life of the citizens, with the common meals, drinking parties, schools, horse-races, theatres, clubs and that kind of thing.[14] For naturally associations must be vigilantly

---

[14] Here as elsewhere Plato uses the Spartan words for clubs (ἄγελαι) and the secret police (κρυπτεία).

supervised, lest they grow in defiance of the laws and contrary to their improving purpose. The legislator will have need of a regular army and police force, some members of whom work secretly. But the details are fairly straightforward on the whole, and I think you will agree that my plan for a second-best republic is not only appealing in its simplicity, but also impressive in its imaginative breadth.

XANTHIPPE: I am indeed most impressed, Plato. Would you allow me to make a few comments?

PLATO: I always welcome intelligent questions. It is the best way to bring the argument home.

XANTHIPPE: In that case, you take over the weaving, while I ponder the second-best state.

PLATO: Do you think I can manage?

XANTHIPPE: Of course you can: this piece is all in one colour, and the warp is already threaded. Just be careful not to drop anything.

PLATO: How am I doing?

XANTHIPPE: Fine. You'll speed up in time. Now let us imagine a state – call it Magnesia – founded along the lines you propose, and a legislator – call her Aspasia – who is to devise its constitution. Aspasia, like Plato, has a single purpose in mind. Her goal, however, is not virtue or social justice, but health. Nothing matters more to her than the health of the body, and the full meaning and justification of each of her laws is to be found in its contribution to the bodily well-being of those who obey it. Law is a means to health, and this is the reason for enforcing it.

PLATO: Now look what I've done!

XANTHIPPE: Just take the shuttle back to the beginning of the line and send it through again. That's it. Now, you will admit, will you not, that we do not know entirely what is conducive to health?

PLATO: Actually, there's this new chap from Cos – Hippocrates he's called – who is making progress. I've got his books by my bed.

XANTHIPPE: But Hippocrates admits, I'm sure, that people differ, and that what is conducive to the health of one person may be quite harmful to another.

PLATO: Wine, for instance. I always tell my pupils . . .

XANTHIPPE: It is possible, therefore, that the health of one citizen might be injured by obeying a law which improves the health of others. If he were to obey the law, therefore, he would defeat the legislator's purpose.

PLATO: That is indeed possible.

XANTHIPPE: Hence the judge must apply the law only when it improves the sum quantum of Magnesian health. She will reason in the following way, as a doctor reasons: how should this person have behaved, so as to enhance his health and the health of others around him? Would it have been right to obey the law, or to disobey it? The only criterion is Aspasia's ruling purpose: the law itself has no authority in settling the rightness or the wrongness of the act. Hence the act is not judged by the *law* at all; the law is at best a recommendation, but has no special standing in the mind of the judge. It has become a 'rule of thumb' such as a doctor might use, in default of a diagnosis.

PLATO: Is this not a proof that health is a matter for doctors, and not legislators?

XANTHIPPE: Should we not say something similar about virtue? But let me stay with the example. A man's health is affected, is it not, by all his actions and feelings, by his diet, his location and the very air he breathes?

PLATO: Damn, I've done it again.

XANTHIPPE: Are you listening to my argument, Plato?

PLATO: Of course I am. You asked a rhetorical question, to which the answer is yes. And your next step will be to describe the vastness of your legislator's task.

XANTHIPPE: Exactly. Aspasia, legislating for health, must pass laws governing every aspect of her citizens' lives. And these meddlesome laws will not, of course, be laws, since they have no special authority in passing judgment. Their effect will be simply to clutter Magnesian life with interdictions, criminalizing a thousand innocent endeavours, and for all that advising us of nothing, since every law may be just as easily waived as enforced. In other words, Magnesia will be a state crowded with punishments, but with no instructions for avoiding them.

PLATO: Excuse my interrupting, Xanthippe, but you wouldn't have such a thing as a stylus, and a set of tablets?

XANTHIPPE: My dear Plato! What use have I for such things? If I need to record my thoughts I weave them into a tapestry. It is unbecoming, I am told, for a woman to write.

PLATO: What a bore!

XANTHIPPE: Socrates took the view that my arguments are ahead of their time, and that if they were ever written down it would be by someone younger even than you: one of your pupils, perhaps.

PLATO: He could be right. I'll have to memorize everything. But you know, I have such a superb heap of notes from the days of Socrates. You must look them over one day. Carry on with the argument.

XANTHIPPE: Willingly, for there is an important idea now coming, like rosy-fingered dawn, over the horizon of my consciousness, and I am glad of the opportunity to embrace it.

PLATO: What idea?

XANTHIPPE: It seems to me that we should distinguish between activities whose purpose lies outside them, and activities whose purpose lies in themselves. For example, the purpose of medicine is health, is it not?

PLATO: Most certainly.

XANTHIPPE: And since health is something other than medicine, we might describe medicine as a means to health, the good medicine being that which enhances health, the bad that which detracts from it.

PLATO: I say, this sounds frightfully Socratic.

XANTHIPPE: Xanthippic, actually. But he was a ready pupil. Now the purpose of a game – draughts for instance – is the game itself. Draughts is not a means but an end: something we do for its own sake, and not for the sake of some other thing.

PLATO: Are there no benefits that come from playing draughts? After all, it causes us to relax, and to join in friendship with others.

XANTHIPPE: True, but those benefits are not the purpose of the game. If they were, we should soon cease to obey the rules of draughts, and do instead whatever was necessary for relaxation and friendship. In a nutshell, Plato, we must always distinguish the incidental benefits of an activity from its inner purpose. Indeed, sometimes the benefits ensue only because we do not intend them.

PLATO: That needs a commentary.

XANTHIPPE: Well then, consider friendship. Is there not a great benefit attached to it – the benefit of help and sympathy in times of trouble, and joy in times of success?

PLATO: Indeed.

XANTHIPPE: But to whom is this benefit given: to the true friend, who is prepared to sacrifice herself for the one she loves, or the false friend, who looks only to her own advantage?

PLATO: To the true friend, to be sure.

XANTHIPPE: But the true friend is precisely the one who does not calculate the benefit of friendship, who helps the one she loves, not for any reward, but because this and this alone is her desire?

PLATO: You're not telling me that women know anything about that kind of thing?

XANTHIPPE: A little, Plato. In any case, you see what I mean. The advantages of friendship accrue only to the one who does not pursue them, and only because she does not pursue them. If friendship has a purpose, it is friendship itself.

PLATO: Is there no way we could *borrow* some tablets?

XANTHIPPE: I'm afraid not, Plato. Nobody around here can read or write. That is why it's so peaceful. Now, just as there are the two kinds of activity that I described, so are there two kinds of rule. The rules of medicine are discovered: they are tried and trusted procedures which experience and theory have shown to lead us to our goal. Such rules may easily be set aside, should our purpose require it, and our knowledge permit. The rules of draughts are not discovered but invented. They define the game, and the one who breaks them is not amending the game in the interests of some higher purpose, but merely ceasing to play it. To include him again in the common endeavour, we impose a penalty: we ask him to forfeit one of his pieces, or to go back across the dividing line (ἰερα γραμμή).

PLATO: All this is amazingly sensible, Xanthippe.

XANTHIPPE: Now look what you've done. Give it here. What a mess! Three whole rows! There. Which of our two kinds of rule is most like a law, do you think?

PLATO: That's obvious, by Zeus. The second.

XANTHIPPE: So laws are like the rules of a game: they are not techniques, adopted for some purpose, but procedures which define what we are doing. To put it succinctly, laws define the life of the state, and are not the means for achieving it.

PLATO: *Why* did I come without my handbag. I'll never remember all this.[15]

---

[15] Nor did he. The theory of the second-best republic appears unaltered in the *Laws*, which Plato began to write fifteen years later. Plato retained one or two things from his encounter with Xanthippe: first the tapestry, from which he took the story of the

XANTHIPPE: But of course, not every rule of this second kind is a law. To know what law is, we must look at what distinguishes a society from a game of draughts.

PLATO: That's like trying to find what distinguishes a forest from – a handbag. They are so vastly different that one can hardly begin.

XANTHIPPE: The example is much to the point, I think. For if I were to ask myself what *principally* distinguishes a forest from a handbag, I should say that the first is a natural and a living thing, while the second is artificial and dead. If you damage a forest, therefore, it strives to grow again; if you damage a handbag, it lies inert and useless until someone makes a repair.

Now society is natural to man and a part of his life, while draughts are one of man's inventions. We may live a while, distraught and chained by the lawless laws of Magnesia. But always, when the chains begin to weaken, our instinct for society will reassert itself, and the natural law of human community will grow again.

PLATO: What is this natural law?

XANTHIPPE: Let us try to discover it together.

PLATO: Hey, wait a minute. That's *his* technique.

XANTHIPPE: Whom do you mean?

PLATO: Old Socks – I mean, Socrates.

XANTHIPPE: Where do you think he got it from? Now listen. Your legislator wished to make men good, as I recall. And you argued that the first thing he must do is close the doors to Strife.

PLATO: And that is an opinion which I still hold, Xanthippe.

XANTHIPPE: Let me remind you of Hesiod's words:

> Not one Strife only fills the earth
> But two. And he who understands the worth

---

judgment of Socrates. (This story appears in his revised version (the only one extant) of the *Phaedo.*) Secondly, the knowledge of weaving which, being practical, survived the blind hangover with which Plato awoke the next morning, so as to influence the argument of the *Statesman*, probably drafted a few days later. Thirdly, the fumbling attempts in that dialogue to develop a theory of equity as an antidote to written law: surely a reminiscence of Xanthippe's defence of English common law. Plato also remembered (no doubt because Aristotle reminded him) the ideal number of Magnesian households (see below). All this casts interesting light on Plato's view (see *Meno, Second Epistle*, and especially *Phaedrus*, 274C–275B) that one should constantly exercise the memory, and not rely on note-taking.

Of one would praise her, of the other blame:
For in their nature they have nought the same.[16]

The one, he tells us, is cruel and thrives in war and battle. But the other inspires us to honest toil. And what Hesiod means is surely obvious. It is only through competition and the pursuit of gain that men can better their condition, each doing what he can to advance his interests in the free-for-all of life, and each, without intending it, advancing the interests of all.

PLATO: That sounds very strange. Have some more wine.

XANTHIPPE: Don't mind if I do. And you had better put that weaving aside now, Plato: you've drunk too much to keep a straight shuttle. Let us return to the case of Magnesia, whether your Magnesia or Aspasia's. In both cases, the laws have a single purpose, and commerce, as you say, is frowned upon. After all, if you allow men freely to buy and sell, you lose control of the distribution. And who knows whether the new distribution will best serve Aspasia's purpose?

PLATO: I see that you understand not only Aspasia, but Plato too.

XANTHIPPE: But when the law forbids the flow of commerce, it does not succeed in stopping it: for men must follow their nature if they are not to sicken and die. Hence they will buy and sell in secret; they will work in darkness and sell the product underground. In these new circumstances, however, nobody will know the price of anything. For suppose that a law is passed, to establish the price of grain. If the price is set too low, the grain will disappear, to emerge in that secret market, exchanging at ever higher prices; if the price is set too high, the grain will rot away uneaten. But what is the correct price? There is only one answer: the price that men will pay for grain, and the price that they will take for it, when free to buy and sell. In Magnesia nobody will know the *real* price of anything, and if knowledge is a part of virtue, to that extent will the citizens be less virtuous than you desire.

PLATO: I have never supposed knowledge of *prices* to be a part of virtue.

XANTHIPPE: Have you not? Then you make a great mistake, O son of Perictione. For knowing the real price of things is part of knowing

---

[16] *Works and Days*, lines 11–13.

how you stand towards your neighbour: what you owe her for her work and produce, and what she in turn owes you. It is a part of honesty, and if honesty is not a virtue, I should like to know why.

PLATO: To the extent that honesty is a form of justice, to that extent it is indeed a virtue.

XANTHIPPE: So think again of Magnesia, whose economic life takes place under cover of darkness, with furtive looks over the shoulders lest those secret policemen should catch a whiff of what is going on. Is such a city likely to breed honesty in its citizens, I wonder?

PLATO: Well, they might need some extra schooling, it is true; and maybe we should make the punishments a trifle more severe.

XANTHIPPE: If people will not go willingly to Tartarus, it is scarcely more reasonable to whip them there. Besides, consider the scale of the disaster. The economic life of Magnesia will be entirely topsy-turvy. The most easily produced commodities will be in short supply, the price for them having been fixed too low; while those which require the greatest labour may stand in heaps unwanted. People may queue all day for bread, while enjoying an abundance of hair-oil the like of which the Aegean has never known. The knowledge needed to reach equilibrium in these matters is simply not available: outside a free market prices mean nothing, and people cannot know how best to use their savings or their labour.

PLATO: The answer is simple: plan *everything*. Draw up a complete schedule, saying who should produce what, and in what quantities, and at what price; then distribute to every citizen a sum of money calculated to purchase exactly what he needs, while rationing everything, so that nothing will be in short supply. I think that deals with the problem.

XANTHIPPE: But who is to draw up this plan, and from what information? Will he predict the harvest, foresee the patterns of trade among the islands, know by divination of all the minerals that lie beneath the soil for exploitation, and all the fishes that live in the Magnesian sea? And even if he did know these things, the plan would be feasible only for a tiny city, one confined within its walls, with just so many households . . .

PLATO: Exactly, that is my ideal. But how many households do you think would be the maximum?

XANTHIPPE: It is immaterial. Say five thousand and forty.

(Enter Aristotle, slightly out of breath.)

PLATO: Why five thousand and forty?

XANTHIPPE: I don't know: does it matter?

ARISTOTLE: Five thousand and forty is a very interesting number, sir. You will notice that it has no less than fifty-nine factors, including all the numbers from one to ten.

PLATO *(trying to hide the wine)*: What in Hades are you doing here?

ARISTOTLE: I came to fetch you, sir. The students are waiting to sing the evening paean; someone said you might be at the tomb of Socrates.

PLATO: Yes, well, tell them I'll be back in a moment.

ARISTOTLE: Yes, sir.

PLATO: And, er, boy . . .

ARISTOTLE: Yes, sir?

PLATO: If they need to know what detained me, you can say I have had to keep company with this poor bereaved lady here.

ARISTOTLE *(looking at the wine)*: Yes, sir.

PLATO: The wine was necessary for a libation, you understand. When I say that wine is not to be drunk, I of course mean my words to be taken in a broad sense.

ARISTOTLE: Yes, sir, I understand: 'not drinking' is said in many ways. A narrow sense of not drinking wine, and a broad sense.

PLATO: Controlled drinking, by virtuous people, with a view to truthful discourse, might even be recommended, as part of a liberal but disciplined education.

ARISTOTLE: I quite understand, sir. Nothing to excess, so to say.

PLATO: What? Yes, yes, exactly. There's no need to wait around, boy. I'll be along in a minute.

ARISTOTLE: Yes, sir.

(Aristotle goes off, breaking into a run.)

XANTHIPPE: Who was that?

PLATO: One of the new students. Forgotten his name; Arsi something; Aristocles. No, that's my name. I remember: Aristotle.

XANTHIPPE: He seems rather bright.

PLATO: Maybe. Can't stand the sight of him. A little swot, always one step ahead of his teachers, cheeky with it, too. Why, the other day . . .

XANTHIPPE: You sound like dear old Socks.

PLATO: What?

XANTHIPPE: Oh, nothing. I was just remembering. Where were we?

Yes, the size of Magnesia. For this too would have to be strictly controlled: people would be required to produce exactly the number of children which the state needs, and neither to exceed the maximum allowed by your rigid system of surveillance, nor to fall short of replenishing the workforce. An impossible task, if you want my opinion. Indeed, it seems to me that cities are destined henceforth to become ever larger. Any attempt to reverse the process will encounter the stern interdiction of the Fates themselves.

PLATO: A dismal prospect, Xanthippe.

XANTHIPPE: Only if we think it so. But let us suppose that we can control the size of Magnesia. You will admit a free market will still be immensely advantageous. For it will enable our citizens to know what they need to know about the volume of Aegean trade, the availability of olives, the economic prospects of the silver-mines, the cost of labour, and the number of fishes in the Magnesian bay.

PLATO: How on earth is that possible?

XANTHIPPE: All those matters will be signalled in the prices at which goods exchange: in a free market the price of every product is a tiny crystal of information, in which a whole universe of human relations can be read.

PLATO: Your imagery is taking charge of your thought, my dear Xanthippe. For you forget the saying of Anarcharsis, that 'the market is a place set apart, where men may deceive and overreach one another'.[17] It is not merely that the competition of the market is motivated by greed: though this too is true. It is that friendship has no place there: on the contrary, he who offers privileges to his friends will soon go under in the sea of competition. Everybody is equal, the friend and the enemy, the just and the unjust, the wise and the foolish. And this is the reason why people are ashamed of buying and selling, so that we Athenians have enacted a law that an action may be brought for slander, against anyone who makes it a reproach against a citizen that he (or she, for that matter) plies a trade in the market.[18]

XANTHIPPE: But see what follows. Out of the strife of the market-place comes law: not the law that you describe, but the natural law

[17] Anacharsis, a hellenized Scythian sage, *c.* 600 BC.

[18] Theophrastus also mentions this statute.

which I urge in place of it. People buy and sell by agreement, striking bargains, making contracts, exchanging promises and building thereby a network of trust. Nothing in this is shameful, and if we saw matters rightly, our law of slander would not be required.

Suppose then that someone should break his trust, and fail to fulfil his part of a bargain. Surely, he will be at once exposed to blame, not merely from the injured party, but from all those who depend upon the system of mutual trust for their profits. The injured party will seek redress before a judge; and the rest of society will strive to uphold the judgment. An irresistible pressure will exist, for the establishment of impartial courts of law, and for the enforcing of their verdicts against the guilty ones. A kind of spontaneous legality emerges: a legality founded on consent. The law enacted by these impartial courts will therefore strive to uphold agreements, and to ensure that those injured by the breach of them are duly compensated from the goods of the wrongdoer. It will be a law for all, 'extending through the wide air and the immense light of heaven'.[19] Its fundamental principles will be recognized and accepted by all men. And you too, Plato, will recognize them, just as soon as I put them into words.

PLATO: Try me.

XANTHIPPE: For instance: agreements are to be upheld; injury is to be compensated by the wrongdoer; each party has a right to be heard; no man can be judge in his own cause; there is a right of appeal against irregularities.

PLATO: Such principles do indeed seem natural.

XANTHIPPE: Note, then, my dear Plato, that when we adopt those principles, it is not with a view to some purpose to which they tend. We adopt them because this is what judgment requires: a process that did not obey them would not *be* a process of law.

PLATO: In which case, you are giving me no more than a definition.

XANTHIPPE: There is a distinction, nevertheless, between a definition that is purely arbitrary and one which captures the essence of the thing defined.

PLATO: Did Socrates make such a distinction?

XANTHIPPE: He vacillated. But I suspect he was less clear about it in the Agora than he was at home. Let us return, however, to

---

[19] Empedocles, Fr. 135.

Magnesia. Here, you will recall, trade is clandestine. Agreements, therefore, are hidden, and no one dares uphold them publicly, or bring them before a court of law. In the underground economy the bully is king. Of course, a law of sorts exists; but we have already seen that Aspasia's overriding purpose is not always best served by the strict discipline of legality. Her law, therefore, is apt to ride roughshod over those natural principles which I proposed. The legal system of Magnesia must obey Aspasia's decrees, wherever they may lead. And perhaps Aspasia may believe that it best suits her sublime purpose on this or that occasion if a man is made judge in his own cause, or an agreement cancelled and compensation refused, or someone punished without trial. Now do you suppose that, in this new arrangement, there will be more strife or less than in the arrangement that I described?

PLATO: I don't know. Maybe, if the secret police are doing their job, there might be less strife, since people would not dare to quarrel with their neighbours.

XANTHIPPE: You mean they would not dare to quarrel *openly* with their neighbours. Life in Magnesia will be conducted entirely underground: and that goes for quarrels too. But hidden strife is none the less strife, and often of the bitterest kind. In Magnesia conflicts will be deprived of their natural solution in a court of law. They will grow accordingly; hatred and suspicion will everywhere reign in the place of trust. And it is these vast subterranean conflicts that will bring about the downfall of Magnesia. Thinking of this, I cannot but applaud the wisdom of Hesiod. The benign strife of the market is not only different from the bitter strife of war; it is its opposite. And the law that arises from the benign strife is an instrument of conciliation rather than servitude.

PLATO: Now I see a difficulty, Xanthippe. For did you not say that law has no purpose?

XANTHIPPE: I did indeed.

PLATO: And now you say that it has the purpose of resolving and preventing conflict.

XANTHIPPE: I see that I must remind you again of friendship. We acknowledged, did we not, that friendship has no purpose?

PLATO: We did.

XANTHIPPE: But that it has great benefits?

PLATO: Indeed.

XANTHIPPE: More: it has a social function. Friendship binds men together, and secures them against their foes. Without friendship their life is not only more bleak; it is also less secure.

PLATO: Which is why the gods, in their benevolence, conferred the blessing of friendship upon us.

XANTHIPPE: I thought you said you didn't believe in the gods?

PLATO: I was speaking figuratively.

XANTHIPPE: Very well, then. Like friendship, law has a social function, even though it has no purpose but itself. Indeed, that may be *part* of its function.

PLATO: Could you spell that out?

XANTHIPPE: Willingly. The judge in a court of law has only one true concern: which is to establish and enforce the rights and duties of the parties. Suppose, however, that, mindful of his obedience to the ruling Aspasian party, he uses his office to advance that party's goals. He sentences an innocent man who is disturbing the Magnesian order; he awards damages to someone merely because his family is poor and his opponent can afford it. He acts not as a judge but as a statesman – and a very bad statesman too, attempting to reorganize society through the medium of the court. He treats law as an instrument of social engineering, and in doing so destroys it. The court loses its authority, both in his own eyes and in the eyes of those who come for judgment. And, in destroying law, our judge abolishes its real social function – which is to prevent or resolve social conflict. Our Magnesian judge is the creator, not the resolver, of conflict. He sends citizens away smarting with indignation and vengeance; he fills the prisons with the innocent and lets the criminals go free; he cancels rights and allows duties to go neglected, so instilling fear and suspicion in the populace. Such, my dear Plato, is the fate of society, when the law is treated as a means. Law becomes a net, in which everyone is caught, entrapping the citizen more firmly, the more he pulls against its strings. By contrast it is only when it disregards its social function that the law succeeds in fulfilling it.

PLATO: Neat, Xanthippe, I like it. Let's have some more wine.

XANTHIPPE: Good idea. No, I'll go. My turn.

PLATO: I couldn't possibly allow you.

XANTHIPPE: You couldn't possibly forbid me. What other use have I for my honest obols?

(Xanthippe takes the jar and goes off.)

PLATO *(studying her first piece of weaving)*: A remarkable woman. And
here are her thoughts in woven form. Is this not a judge, delivering
his verdict? And who is this standing before him – this snub-nosed
pot-bellied Marsyas with brawny shoulders and filthy feet – by
Zeus, it's old Socks!

(Xanthippe returns.)

Ah, Xanthippe! I was just . . .

XANTHIPPE: I don't mind in the least. In fact, I must get back to work
now; I had hoped to finish it tonight. Maybe I can let you have it
before you go.

PLATO: I couldn't possibly . . .

XANTHIPPE: Oh, not as a *gift*: you can pay the going rate, which is two
drachmas.

PLATO: Two drachmas! But that's sheer robbery![20]

XANTHIPPE: It's what I get from Cretan tourists.

PLATO: One drachma at the most.

XANTHIPPE: Tell you what: one drachma, three obols, and not an obol
less.

PLATO: Well, I'm not sure. Let me think about it.

XANTHIPPE: Suit yourself. I'll finish it anyway: the last rows are easy; I
can do them while we talk. Where were we?

PLATO: I was about to ask you what you propose by way of legislation.

XANTHIPPE: For whom?

PLATO: For anyone. I mean, anyone who had the task of founding a
new city, and who hoped that it would be just.

XANTHIPPE: I would propose nothing. Are you sure you haven't been
tampering with these threads?

PLATO: I promise I didn't touch a thing. Tell me, that wouldn't be
Socrates there, would it, standing in front of the tree?

XANTHIPPE: You recognized him? I was beginning to think you had
never met.

---

[20] Quite cheap actually, one drachma being the price of a day's skilled labour at the
end of the fifth century BC – a price which must surely have risen by the time of
Xanthippe's meeting with Plato, since in all probability the loss of Athens's traditional
trade-links at the end of the fifth century led to a period of sustained inflation. By the
middle of the fourth century, however, economic life (as testified by the speeches of
Demosthenes) had fully revived. See Claude Mossé, tr. J. Stewart, *Athens in Decline
404–386 BC*, London, 1973, Chapter 2. Unfortunately Mossé makes no mention of
Xanthippe's role in this transformation.

PLATO: What makes you say that?

XANTHIPPE: The fact that you do not respect him.

PLATO: What? Plato not respect Socrates? Plato who has dedicated his life to the Socratic idea? You must be joking!

XANTHIPPE: To respect Socrates is to respect his widow; and what better way of doing so, than to pay an honest price for her labour?

XANTHIPPE: By Zeus you are right, Xanthippe! One drachma, two obols.

XANTHIPPE: Two and a half.

PLATO: Done. Here, take the money.

XANTHIPPE: Thanks. You're a gentleman, Plato.

PLATO: But why do you propose nothing for our new Republic?

XANTHIPPE: To the founder of a republic I would propose no laws, but only law, by which I mean judges duty-bound to hear each case and to decide impartially between the parties. And I propose that when the time comes for legislation the laws should be so devised that no one – not even the legislator himself – should be able to escape them. And since no legislator can foresee the changes to which society is liable, I shall grant to the judges full power to decide as they see fit, case by case, provided that they formulate impartial rules, and that the parties may appeal against their decisions, to some higher court in which the oldest and wisest preside.

PLATO: Great Zeus, this is madness! Not only are there no laws in your state, but there is no legislator either! Everything is left to the arbitrary decision of the Areopagites!

XANTHIPPE: You mistake me entirely, Plato. My judges are very far indeed from those who sat on the Areopagus. Their judgments are made only after all the existing authorities have been consulted, and where there is a decision that bears on the case, they will be duty-bound to follow it. Only the higher court can overrule decisions already made and accepted. It follows that laws will emerge automatically from judgments, and will have all the more authority in that nothing motivates them besides the facts of the particular case, and the intention to do justice in the light of them.

PLATO: And what ensures that your judges will be impartial, or that they will remain so under the temptations of office? For if, as you propose, there is no settled legislation, who is to foresee what may come to pass? New men may arise to power:

those who before knew nothing of lawsuits, nothing of laws,
who went about with goatskins flapping over their shoulders,
who lived on the ranges, far out from the town, like wild
deer . . .[21]

And who will have the power to eject the judges from office, should
they prove corrupt?

XANTHIPPE: Those are very good questions, Plato.

PLATO: Indeed, they are the questions that you asked of my imaginary
ruler. And I wish to know whether you are better placed to answer
them.

XANTHIPPE: To do so, we shall have to go deeper by far, into the
origins of social life.

PLATO: Then let us undertake this journey together, Xanthippe.

XANTHIPPE: There are two other matters that I must first consider.
For do you not see a difficulty, in my desire for a law without
legislators?

PLATO: A thousand difficulties, and not the least of them is this: that the
problems of social life cannot always be resolved in the court room,
but need discussion, expertise, and consultation with the citizens.

XANTHIPPE: I see that you understand my meaning. And often it may
appear to those who are overcome by this fact, as though the judges
were nothing but the tools of legislators, duty-bound to apply a law
which they have no part in creating. And then it may seem anew as
though the law were but an instrument to the legislator's higher
purpose, and the whole Xanthippic theory little more than a wishful
delusion.

PLATO: How wonderfully self-critical you are.

XANTHIPPE: It is you who inspire these thoughts in me, and I assure
you they are far from welcome. So let me for the last time return to
the case of friendship. Although the true friend is the one who
disregards her own advantage, she will not, I think, be wholly
insensible to the asset that she has acquired, in gaining a friend.

PLATO: Indeed not.

XANTHIPPE: Having a friend, therefore, she may plan things which she
could not achieve alone. For example, she may build a house, open a
hostel or set up a factory for the production of tapestries, of the kind
that two people are needed to weave. Once friendship exists, it can

---

[21] Theognis, 54–7.

certainly be put to use, even if the use is not the motive of the friendship.

PLATO: I agree entirely. And I see now the answer to your problem. You will argue that the same is true of law: that, once in existence, it can be put to use, but that the use is not the motive.

XANTHIPPE: Exactly: the law is its own end, and exists just so long as the courts pass judgment, according to the principles of natural justice. Once in place, however, the law may be put to use: and it is here that the legislator's task begins. She may discover that some problem can be solved only by formulating a rule, which will be imposed through the courts exactly as though it were a natural law, and upheld with the same studious impartiality as the principles of justice. But the legislator must be careful not to usurp the functions of the judge; she must avoid passing laws which undermine the inner purpose of legality, just as the friend must avoid putting her friendship to a use which undermines her love. The legislator, therefore, must always take second place to the judge, and when the legislator's decrees conflict with natural law, it is natural law that must prevail.

PLATO: How exactly you put the point, O Xanthippe. But tell me; how would you define the just state? Or do you think that there is no such thing?

XANTHIPPE: Indeed, there is such a thing. But I make a great distinction between those who believe that justice resides in some distribution of privilege and property, and who see the law as a means for achieving it, and those of a more Xanthippic persuasion, for whom the justice of a state lies in its procedures alone. In my view, a state is just to the extent that justice is done in it; and justice is done when impartial judges give judgment according to natural law. In such a state the innocent go free and the guilty are punished; contracts are upheld and obligations enforced. And what distribution of goods may result from this process there is no foreseeing.

PLATO: Your theory at least has this in its favour: that we know how to achieve the state that you describe. But you were going to speak of another matter, before we embark together on our journey.

XANTHIPPE: Indeed I was. For it seemed to me that I must return to those other sources of strife to which you referred: the family and religion. As I understand you, your legislator would abolish the first, and impose an iron conformity on the second.

PLATO: Do you see any other solution?

XANTHIPPE: Better to ask whether I see any problem. For I entirely disagree with your view that the family is a source of strife. On the contrary, strife is introduced when the legislator, busily forbidding the natural commerce of our species, expropriates the children and makes them slaves of the state. For then the state becomes the enemy of every parent, and every parent its enemy. And when the state, in the name of virtue, herds the children into schools, there to tell them lies about equality and to impose a dreadful conformity of opinion that has nothing to do with truth, it oversteps the mark of reason, becoming – however rational its plans – the friend of irrationality and, if it is not too severe a thing to say, the enemy of man. And what I say applies, not only to the family, but to all associations.

PLATO: Surely not to the communal dinners?

XANTHIPPE: The nice thing about you, Plato, is that, for every institution you wish to destroy, you earnestly look for another that might replace it. So let me explain what I mean. You will admit that reason is of two kinds – the theoretical and the practical?

PLATO: Watching you weave has almost persuaded me.

XANTHIPPE: And the person with practical reason must, if he is to reason properly, choose the appropriate means to his ends?

PLATO: Indeed, he can do no other.

XANTHIPPE: But suppose his ends are unreasonable?

PLATO: Then so are the acts which lead to them.

XANTHIPPE: So if he is to act reasonably, his goal too must be reasonable?

PLATO: Certainly. From which it follows that the man with practical reason must possess goals that are reasonable not as means only, but as ends.

XANTHIPPE: Exactly. There must be goals that are valued, and rightly valued, for their own sake, and not merely for the sake of something else.

PLATO: I think I see where this is heading.

XANTHIPPE: Do you, Plato? Then you have better eyes than I; for I merely follow where the argument suggests, and as yet I see no conclusion to it.

PLATO: Is the argument not leading us back to friendship?

XANTHIPPE: Possibly. But I fear that things will not be so simple. For I now have another question before my mind, that seems brighter and more urgent than the last.

PLATO: Which is?

XANTHIPPE: How, I ask myself, does a rational being acquire the idea that some things are intrinsically valuable? And I see a little clue: the thing that he values intrinsically is the thing which, in his eyes, casts credit on the one who possesses it, and perhaps shame on the one who does not. It is an object of pride, whose possessor secretly demands the applause of others.

PLATO: Virtue?

XANTHIPPE: Virtue, among other things. But whence does this idea of honour (τιμή) arise?

PLATO: Why call it honour?

XANTHIPPE: The word chose itself. And no sooner had it done so, than an answer came to the bright question that troubled me. Look again at the game of draughts: he who plays it has no purpose save the game: playing it, and if possible winning it. The winner gains honour in his own eyes, and endeavours to translate his feeling into some public monument. If we were to be honest with ourselves we should say that the sweetest of all our experiences on earth is praise; and of all the varieties of praise, none is sweeter than that which we offer secretly to ourselves, when we recognize that what we are and what we have are things worth while. That is why we are moved by the Odes of Pindar – those tributes to dead athletes, whose triumphs can hardly concern us, but in which the experience of praise is captured and immortalized.

PLATO: Yet there is a great mystery in Pindar. For how is it that we take these invocations of the divine order so seriously, when the only matter of the poem is the brief success of some vanished athlete?

XANTHIPPE: I see an answer to this mystery, Plato. The sweetness of self-praise, our poet saw, has something divine in it. But to put this experience into words is by no means easy. Even the instruction of Corinna could not produce the perfection of style that would be needed, if the experience of life as a thing intrinsically worth while were to find its equivalent in words. The poet needed an earthly occasion – a time and place and person to which his praise could be attached. And what better occasion that a Pythian triumph? Of all our activities, a game is the readiest instance of something done for its own sake. Its meaning lies within it; and for that reason games are chief among the goals of life, offering places of rest, moments of bliss, and gifts of honour to the gods. That too is why the poet, when he envisages Elysium, can offer us no better image than this one, saying 'some take their joy in horses, some in gymnasia, some in draughts'[22] – and had he mentioned music and painting and poetry, he would have all but completed the list of heavenly pleasures.

PLATO: You have forgotten weaving.

XANTHIPPE: Weaving, yes; and also love. Which brings me to the point. These brief experiences, from which we form our vision of intrinsic value, are not available in solitude.

PLATO: You are certainly right, Xanthippe. For the solitary man compares himself with no one, and – like Diogenes, whom they call 'the dog' – is blind in his heart to honour as he is blind to shame.[23]

XANTHIPPE: But the person who is compelled into the company of others, by a tyrant, say, who is forced to march to another's tune or brave another's danger: such a person, I imagine, does not regard success as honourable, or failure as a thing of blame. For his goals are not his own. He acts for a purpose, certainly, and reasonably: he marches beneath the alien banner for fear of the whip at his back. But his action is a means and not an end, and its fulfilment is no fulfilment of his.

PLATO: I begin to see what you are getting at.

XANTHIPPE: I too begin to see it. For it follows, does it not, that free associations are the true source of whatever is ultimately worth while, and of the motives – honour and shame – which make it so. It is from our little institutions – and I count the family as the most important among them, along with the brotherhoods and sister-hoods, the groups of kinsmen, the religious guilds and dining

---

[22] Pindar, Fr. 129, 6f.

[23] Diogenes, 'the dog', so-called because of his cur-like habits, lived in an earthenware tub and snarled and cursed at the passing folly of Athens. Plato's knowledge of Diogenes' existence is testified to by several ancient writers (e.g. Aelian, *Var. Hist.*, XIV, 33). It is anachronistic to suppose, however, that Diogenes was resident in Athens at the time of this dialogue, just as it is anachronistic – incidentally – to suppose that Aristotle would have already been studying at the Academy, despite the strong internal evidence that Aristotle became Xanthippe's pupil.

clubs[24] – that the meaning of life, or rather the many meanings of life, derive. Without them, deprived of our goals, we can do nothing of value: all our actions then become means, and since nothing has intrinsic purpose, nothing has purpose at all. Our lives become lost in calculation, but the only object of this calculation is to survive the present moment and calculate again. Would you consider that to be a good life for a rational being?

PLATO: By no means.

XANTHIPPE: Indeed, it is not the life of a *rational* being at all, since no part of it is reasonable: nothing is done for a reasonable end, and therefore everything is done without reason.

PLATO: I really must take up draughts, Xanthippe; or should I put myself in for the Pythian games, do you think?

XANTHIPPE: You have what you require in your Academy, so long as you recognize that it is not Socrates you are honouring there, but Plato. Now if, as I say, a rational being finds purpose and fulfilment in these associations, it becomes the duty of the legislator neither to forbid them nor to pillage them, but on the contrary to protect them, to endow them with legal guarantees, and to uphold their independence. You might say that, in any republic suited to the life of reason, there must be two spheres of social existence: the state (πόλις), which is the sphere of law, and civil society (κοινωνία), which is the sphere of free association. And it is from this second sphere that our conceptions of the good derive. Hence, without civil society, we are so much the less disposed to recognize the authority of law and to obey its precepts. Just as civil society depends on the state for its protection, so does the state depend upon civil society for the habit of obedience.

PLATO: My mother used to prophesy the birth of a new Parmenides, who would understand the whole world in terms of three stages of development, from unity through separation to final completion in the whole. I imagine that this new Parmenides would be quite interested in your theory, Xanthippe. For he would say, would he

---

[24] Athens was rich in 'little platoons', as Burke was to call them. Some, such as religious brotherhoods (φράτρια), groups of kinsmen (ἀγχηστεία), and religious guilds or clans (γένη), formed part of the political order; others – e.g. the ἔρανοι (dining clubs), θίασοι (religious associations), and colleges of ὀργεῶνες (votaries) – were more or less autonomous.

not, that the individual enters society in three stages: first, as a member of the family, immersed in the bond of unthinking love; second through the market of strife, separated from his fellows and creating by agreement the sphere of free institutions; and thirdly joined once more to the totality and unity which is the law-giving and law-abiding state.

XANTHIPPE: Maybe if I had attended a few of the lectures at your Academy, I could express the point in just such words. You make me quite ashamed, my dear.

PLATO: Oh, you put the point rather better, I feel. But not so well that I do not have a host of questions crowding in upon me. For example, will there not be a chaos of conflicting institutions in your republic? And how are the associations and the families to be reconciled? And how will the future of society be planned?

XANTHIPPE: Your questions are so diverse, Plato, that I am over-whelmed by them. But let me make two observations in response. It seems to me that you share with my Aspasia the desire for a supremely rational ordering of society. Or rather, you see political existence as a problem, and the laws as a *solution* to it. And this solution requires you to impose on the whole of society a common goal which, whatever it may be – health, or virtue or 'social justice' – has the immediate effect of destroying the law and putting in the place of it the web of unpredictable punishments which I described. Society then becomes a vast machine, running out of control, towards a condition that none can envisage. However desirable our original goal, it recedes from view to the extent that we devote ourselves to pursuing it. For we lack the knowledge that would permit us to pursue it through a plan. The happiness of society does not come through pursuing it, but through doing what is natural to us in association with our kind. Just like the happiness of the individual, it is a side-effect, the result of pursuing other and more immediate objectives.

This means that there is no such thing as the *solution* to the social problem as you envisage it. Hence there is no such thing as the problem. Our goals emerge spontaneously, as we join with others in friendship, competition and love. And until they have emerged, nothing that we do is fully reasonable, and virtue itself only a sketchy premonition of what we must later make into a reality.

So now, suppose that our goals conflict: is there harm in that? Is not this the beginning of dialogue, in which each party agrees to renounce some part of his purpose, in return for a like concession from the other party? And is it not true of institutions, as it is of individuals, that they live together through this habit of mutual renunciation? The true enemy of society, it seems to me, is the one with a non-negotiable purpose, the one who wishes to reform the world in his own favoured direction, and who allows the world no right of reply.

PLATO: I think you mean me.

XANTHIPPE: No, no.

PLATO: But you see, Xanthippe, you fail to understand what motivates my thinking. It is precisely because not every problem can be solved in the way you describe that we stand in need of a more comprehensive picture, an over-arching plan.

XANTHIPPE: But I rest my faith, all the same, in law, as the ultimate solution to human contest. For it is the function of law – the function, mind, not the purpose – to guide us out of confrontation, back to the market-place, where concession and compromise are the rule.

PLATO: But you still haven't told me about those judges of yours. Who trains them and how, and who ensures their impartiality? Or are we to rely on our Athenian system, with the people sitting in judgment, swayed by inflammatory orators, and voting irresponsibly for verdicts whose meaning they cannot fathom? If so, then I fear the trial of Socrates will be many times repeated in your new republic.

XANTHIPPE: If I postpone this most difficult question, it is because we must consider religion first; only then, my dear Plato, can we embark together on the journey that you promised.

PLATO: And about religion too I sense a disagreement.

XANTHIPPE: But an interesting one, I think. For you would impose a single faith on the citizens of Magnesia, despite the fact – maybe even because of the fact – that you personally have none. Whereas I, who know that God exists and demands my obedience, would leave the citizens of my republic free to worship as they should choose.

PLATO: How can you grant them such a freedom when, by your own admission, it may lead them into the gravest error?

XANTHIPPE: Because faith cannot be compelled, and faith which is founded on a lie, however noble, is not faith at all, but a kind of corrosive irreligion. The gods will nowhere be more dishonoured,

Plato, than in your second-best republic, where they are honoured by force.

PLATO: But now I perceive a serious problem, and I should be most favoured by an answer to it. Suppose that two rival gods are worshipped in your city, the one jealous of the other, and eager to overcome him. Is this not strife of the evil kind – the kind which leads to civil war? For the gods are implacable against their enemies, and against none more than the mortals who worship their rivals.

XANTHIPPE: I cannot deny it, O son of Perictione. And certainly the happiest society is one in which a single faith, growing spontaneously and enshrined in worship and priesthood, unites the people in prayer. From such a gift all other institutions take added life, and civil society flourishes at its utmost strength, the gods standing vigilant wherever doubt might enter the affairs of the citizens.

However, such a happy state can never be planned, nor can it be imposed by law. The gods give life to the law; but the law can only destroy the gods' authority when it compels us to worship them. And when two religions grow side by side, then is the life of the state most difficult. It would be better for our republic to break asunder, to become a loose federation, than to continue the pretence that society is one, and the citizens united in their obedience.

PLATO: And when spiritual life decays, so that instead of possessing more than one, the state possesses less than one religion?

XANTHIPPE: I suspect that we are not far from such a condition, Plato.

PLATO: So what remedy do you propose?

XANTHIPPE: Not every condition has a remedy. Societies are natural things: as they live, so must they die, and I warrant that even your Academy will not live for ever, and will disappear as you foretold, along with the rest of our beloved city, to be cast up in fragments on the Blessed Mound.

PLATO: You are right, alas.

XANTHIPPE: But why is this a cause of lamentation? Is it not our opportunity to understand what God has given us, and to go with our knowledge to the grave? The owl of wisdom flies only with the gathering of the dusk. All that we have worshipped will one day be forgotten, and we the worshippers too. In the end, even our beliefs are mortal.

PLATO: How can they be mortal and also true? For isn't truth eternal?

XANTHIPPE: Look, I have finished your tapestry. And by way of answer to your question I will tell you the story of it. For it is the gateway to our journey.

PLATO: I am all ears, Xanthippe.

XANTHIPPE: When the gaoler came with the hemlock, Socks and I were alone together. I have to say a certain melancholy came over his dear old face. 'Would you believe it, Xanthippe,' he said, 'but I'm actually in a bit of a panic. I mean, where am I going, and what awaits me?' I told the gaoler to come back in half an hour. 'Listen, Socks,' I said; 'there are worse ways to go than hemlock. For your reputation's sake, you've got to keep a stiff upper lip.' 'You are absolutely right,' he replied. 'I suppose it was those weepy young men who rattled me. Still, it is hard, you know.' 'I know,' I said. 'But I'm confident that it'll be better on the other side. Looking back on it, you will regret you didn't make the journey earlier.' 'You think so?' he asked. 'I know,' was my reply. 'Then I beg you,' he said, 'as your last favour to me, your faithful disciple, to persuade me that you are right.' 'Willingly,' I said, and told him the following story.[25]

The other world to which you are about to travel has been described by the poets, who have divided Tartarus from Elysium, and spoken beautifully of the rivers of the dead. I shall not remind you, Socrates, of those tales which are so well known to you, but only add to them what I have discovered. For last night in a dream I was visited by a daimon, who said 'Be of good cheer, O wife of Socrates; for even as I have guided your husband through life, I shall speak to you now of his death so that you may comfort him.' And this, Socrates, is what he told me.

When you have crossed the Styx, and stepped from Charon's boat onto the shore of the other world, the voice of your daimon will sound again in your ears, just as it sounded on earth. And it will be as though he appears before you, though in what form it is forbidden to you yet to know. Taking you by the hand he will lead you then before your judge, who is the judge of all and the truest lover of your soul. And sentence will be passed upon you, as it is passed upon all the dead, according as they have lived well and piously or not. Now those who have lived neither well nor ill, who are the mass of

---

[25] It is interesting that, in the version of this story used by Plato in the revised *Phaedo*, no reference is made to Xanthippe's renewed criticism of the Cave. (See also *Xanthippe's Republic.*)

mankind, go to the river Acheron, and embarking in any vessels which they may find, are carried in them to the Acherusian lake, far below the earth. And there they dwell and are purified of their evil deeds, and having suffered the just penalty for the wrongs which they have done to others, they are absolved, and receive the rewards for their good deeds, each according to his deserts. But those who appear to be incurable by reason of the greatness of their crimes are hurled into Tartarus, which is their proper home and from whence they never emerge. Those again who have committed crimes which, though great, were in some measure involuntary – who in a moment of anger, say, have done violence to a parent and thereafter repented for the remainder of their lives – these too are plunged into Tartarus. But at the end of a year the wave casts them forth onto the rivers of the dead, whence they are borne to the Acherusian lake. And there they lift up their voices and call upon their victims to have pity and forgive them, so that they may come forth from the lake. And if they prevail, they come forth and are released from their troubles: if not, they are carried back into Tartarus and from thence into the rivers unceasingly, until they obtain mercy from those whom they have wronged.

But it is not of such people that I wish to speak, my dear Socrates, but of those who obeyed the voice of conscience, and lived their lives in piety towards the heavens, and justice towards men. For your judge will most certainly count you, for all your vanity and humbug, as among the pious and the just. Already the souls of the dead, eagerly awaiting your arrival, have spoken their forgiveness for the insignificant wrongs that you have done to them. And your wife's prayer that the crime of philosophy be discounted has been heard. Most certainly, therefore, when released from the prison of this life, you will ascend, like the philosopher from that cave of which you spoke, away from the world of shadows and deception, into the purer earth where the souls of the blessed dwell for ever. And although it is forbidden to us below to know the life of that higher sphere, or to grasp its brightness and splendour, yet are we assured that its mansions are of the fairest and freest, and that those who dwell there dwell in bliss. And if you wish me to say further what your new life in that fair abode will be, I can only speak in figures and images, referring like Pindar to our games below, and asking you to see therein some premonition of your final end. Yet never were truer words sung or spoken than Pindar's, that 'the sins committed in this realm of Zeus are judged by One who passeth sentence stern and eternal; while the good have the sun shining for ever more.'[26]

Enough, however. The fate which awaits you is the one for which always you have longed: a release from the imperfect world of shadows, into a realm where all will be radiant with worth. And not only will you enjoy, then, your heavenly reward, but those of us who remain below will be saved from your philosophy, nor need we fear that you will ever return from that blessed region whither you go. For you may recall, Socrates, that you wished your philosophers to ascend into the light and descend again to our shadowy regions, there to disrupt the comfortable scheme of things. But as I said at the time, you mistook the voice of your daimon. What he had wished to say, and what he said to me in my dream last night, is that the image of the cave is indeed a most useful summary of the deepest truth of our condition. But departure from the cave is death, and the light to which we ascend is not the light of understanding, but something far greater and more wonderful, which is promised you, dear Socrates, as it is promised to all who live justly and well.

PLATO: What an extraordinary story. And did he believe it?

XANTHIPPE: A man who is about to die sees things in a new light, my dear Plato. And he understood, as he had never understood before, that there are ideas which only stories can convey. 'A man of sense,' I said to him, 'ought not to say that the description which I have given of the final judgment and the soul's reward, is exactly true. But, inasmuch as the soul is immortal, something of this kind is likely, and we can approach it in our thinking as best we can, and take heart that the justice which rules in our souls, rules also in the universe.' And, hearing this, Socrates embraced me, summoned the gaoler, and polished off the hemlock in a single gulp. He died a few minutes later, with the serenest smile on his lips. And I too, seeing him, was happy.

PLATO: Zeus!

(A moment's silence.)

PLATO: There is one matter, Xanthippe, concerning which I beg to question you.

---

[26] Pindar, *Olympian*, II, 58ff.

XANTHIPPE: By all means, my dear.

PLATO: When you say there are truths which only stories can convey, what do you mean?

XANTHIPPE: I wish I knew. But I see that this is indeed the first crossroad on our journey. So let us proceed. Astronomy, you will agree, contains many truths?

PLATO: Undoubtedly.

XANTHIPPE: And when we say that a proposition of astronomy – for example, that the sun goes round the earth – is true, we mean something quite specific, do we not?

PLATO: Yes, but what?

XANTHIPPE: How shall I say: that our proposition corresponds with the facts? But we must recognize that the facts of astronomy exist independently of us. The world is composed of such facts, which are as they are, regardless of our thinking.

PLATO: That does indeed seem to capture what we mean by truth.

XANTHIPPE: But there are other thoughts, equally true, which seem not to describe the world of facts; or rather, the world they describe is not separable from the interpretation that we place upon it.

PLATO: And I suppose you will say that, being so, these strange new truths cannot be explained, but only illustrated?

XANTHIPPE: I fear that I may be driven to such a course, Plato. At least, it is by way of an image that I can best make clear what I mean. So consider this tapestry. Here, you see, is old Socks.

PLATO: By Zeus, so he is!

XANTHIPPE: And here, on the other side of the tree – which I call the tree of life – is his judge, whom I have tried to endow with perfect wisdom.

PLATO: Indeed you have succeeded, Xanthippe. And I see that the fleck of blue in the tree-trunk was not a mistake at all, but expresses the heavenly nature of this scene, and of the creatures shown in it.

XANTHIPPE: Not all of them are creatures, Plato; one of them, I think, is their creator. Be that as it may. How many things we see in this simple piece of weaving: not only Socrates, but his judge, the tree, a landscape, the souls that are waiting, and the promise of light on the far horizon!

PLATO: Indeed.

XANTHIPPE: Yet how is this possible? For all that lies before us is a piece of coloured wool.

PLATO: True; but it resembles the scenes you described. And in noticing those scenes, you are simply seeing the resemblance. Is that not what we mean by imitation?

XANTHIPPE: I think not, Plato. For look: this part of the tapestry resembles Diogenes just as much as it resembles Socks; this part is as like a staff as it is like a tree-trunk, and this resembles a woollen ball as much as it resembles an apple. Yet, although we notice those resemblances, we do not see Diogenes standing by a staff upon which woollen balls are hanging. No, we see Socrates by the tree of life, face to face with his judge.

PLATO: You have made the matter sound most mysterious, O Xanthippe.

XANTHIPPE: Indeed? Well, the mystery is even greater than I have said. For all these things that we see in the tapestry stand in relation to each other. Socrates is in front of the tree, his judge a little way further off, and the souls awaiting judgment further still. And the horizon – how far would you say it was from the shore in the foreground?

PLATO: I should say two leagues; maybe three.

XANTHIPPE: You see? You can even calculate the distance. Two leagues, you say, between this bit of wool and this, scarcely a foot away. What is the meaning of such a measurement?

PLATO: You tell me, Xanthippe.

XANTHIPPE: It seems that there is a true description of this picture, and also many false descriptions. Do you not agree?

PLATO: Most definitely. For the picture shows Socrates awaiting judgment, and not Diogenes lecturing a rabble of naked ladies before the king of Persia, which it resembles just as much.

XANTHIPPE: Thanks, Plato.

PLATO: Almost as much.

XANTHIPPE: The true description is not, then, merely a description of what it resembles?

PLATO: No.

XANTHIPPE: What then does it describe? The facts, like our proposition of astronomy?

PLATO: I think not; for it is true that this part of the picture is two leagues away from that part, and yet the piece of wool which shows the horizon is but a foot away from the piece which marks the shore.

XANTHIPPE: Excellently said, O son of Perictione. The facts about the tapestry do not include the story that we have told. And yet, the story is a true account of what we see. How is this so?

PLATO: I confess that I am entirely at a loss, Xanthippe.

XANTHIPPE: Let us now take another example, Plato, for it will guide us further down the road we are travelling. If I look at your face, what do I see?

PLATO: Why, you see my face.

XANTHIPPE: And this face: what is it exactly? Cheeks, eyes, nostrils, lips, chin, and so on, I suppose.

PLATO: Certainly, those are parts of the face.

XANTHIPPE: But not every arrangement of those parts is a face, I take it.

PLATO: Indeed not.

XANTHIPPE: But suppose those parts are arranged just as they are in your face, my dear Plato, but rigidly, and that the whole is attached, not to the head of Plato, but to the posterior of a dog. Would that be a face?

PLATO: Only, I think, in a somewhat broad sense of the word.

XANTHIPPE: So the face is not composed of its parts in the way that a wall is composed of stones. For the parts of a face may be correctly composed, even when there is no face.

PLATO: That seems to be the conclusion.

XANTHIPPE: Something else occurs to me too, Plato. You remember that our tapestry seems, so to say, to have two natures. On the one hand it is nothing more than a piece of threaded wool, coloured in parts, and two foot square. On the other hand, looking at it, we see the judgment of Socrates, occupying several leagues, with many characters and episodes. And if we ask for the facts about our tapestry, only the first nature would be counted among them. The second belongs to our interpretation.

PLATO: That is indeed how it seemed.

XANTHIPPE: Is it not the same with a face? For here also there are two natures: the one studied by the anatomist, and the one familiar to you and me. The first is a matter of flesh and bone, of nerve and muscle and bodily humours. The second is not like that at all: it is a matter of smiles and frowns, statements and interrogations – in a word, expression. And an expression, like a picture, is something that we interpret.

PLATO: I begin to see what you are getting at.

XANTHIPPE: Once again, Plato, you go more quickly than I do. But the path we travel is interesting, and it is right to dawdle by the way. For I am reminded of the fact that other animals, who lack the gift of reason, nevertheless have eyes and lips and nostrils. Horses, for instance, dogs and lions. And some resemble us quite closely, as do the apes. Yet never have I observed an animal to frown or smile. Or if they do so, it is only in the way that a mask may smile, by imitating a condition which it does not possess.

PLATO: Do you mean that the second nature of the face – the one which we interpret – is its rational nature?

XANTHIPPE: I mean that the expressions in a face reveal the workings of a rational soul; and they are revealed only to us, who have the reason necessary to interpret them. For the anatomist a smile is not a smile, but a distortion of the flesh. And such a distortion can be witnessed in animals, who cannot smile. The smile on a face seems like the scene in a tapestry. It is something we see, but which is not among the facts before us.

PLATO: There is something in what you say, Xanthippe. But how important is it?

XANTHIPPE: Important because it leads us one step further along our journey, my dear Plato. For when I think of the rational soul, and the face which is its first expression, I cannot prevent myself from experiencing an enormous wonderment. For it seems as though every aspect of our lives has this dual nature which we discovered in the tapestry and the face. All my actions are also movements of the body, to be explained by the anatomist, just as he would explain the movements of a horse. But they are also interpreted. The one who interprets my action, regards it as free, and Xanthippe as responsible for its outcome. No horse is free, and no horse has proceeded through life accumulating liabilities. I grant you that the horses of Achilles weep for Patroclus: but this is Homer's poetic licence; the tears which we see in a horse's eyes are not real tears, just as their grimaces are not smiles nor their neighs interjections.

It is not only my actions that are understood in this double way. My passions too have a dual nature: on the one hand, they are bodily effects, in which the humours exert their influence over me; on the other hand, they are reasoning responses to a perception of the world. Consider anger. For the student of physiology, this is like the rage of a bull: a rush of blood to the heart, a rousing of the limbs, a concentration of the faculties in a bid to destroy. But for the interpreter of human conduct it is not that at all. He will ask, not what caused this flow of blood, but rather, what is Xanthippe's *reason* for her aggressive humour, and is she justified? And if he discovers that Xanthippe has been victim of some gross injustice, and is determined to assert her rights, then he will conclude that Xanthippe is rightly angry, and that only a less than reasonable person would have reacted in another way. In short, in every area of his life – action, emotion, expression and will – the rational being behaves as though he had two natures, the animal and the rational, and is understood accordingly. When understanding him as rational we do not explain him, as a physiologist would explain a dog. We interpret, criticize, evaluate; and he has what the dog could never aspire to: a natural right of reply.

PLATO: What you say finds an echo in me, Xanthippe. Though I cannot help wondering whether this dual nature to which you refer is not an illusion – I grant, an illusion deeply rooted in us, but an illusion for all that, like the belief in gods and the sightings of heroes among the stars.

XANTHIPPE: I will come to that in a moment, Plato. For we must journey a little further down our road before I can answer you. Until now I have followed old Socks, and identified the rational being in those words: as though reason were his defining feature. But you know there are many other characteristics which are the equivalent of this one, and involved in its definition, just as reason is involved in theirs. For instance, I might have described him as a laughing being, or a smiling being; as a free being; as one who studies the future and lives by the law; as a religious being, or as one who guides his conduct by good and evil, right and wrong. All those take us in the same direction; and while none is clear when considered in isolation, together they present us with an irrebuttable sense that this rational being is of a wholly special kind, and that his every gesture is to be understood in ways that are peculiar to him. And maybe it would do no harm if, in order to focus our argument on the matter that concerns us, I were to choose yet another description, and define this most mysterious of nature's creations as a 'responsible being': one who may answer for his acts, and who in consequence may be praised for them, and also blamed. For it is from this that came the two great gifts of Zeus: justice and shame.[27]

PLATO: That would certainly take us a step further along our road. For now we are beginning to see why, of all the creatures in this world of ours, it is men alone who live by law.

XANTHIPPE: You understand my meaning well, Plato. For now we know why it is that our orators, when they wish to put their case before a court, summon the laws to witness, as though the laws too had a soul, and could reason with us on terms of equality. In the reasonable republic, the laws must answer for themselves. Are you right to forbid this action, we ask them; and have you rightly weighed the consequences of doing so? And if they fail to satisfy us, we carry our argument further, to the assembly, and urge the laws to change. And if we win the argument, change they must, just as every rational being must renounce the opinions and the decisions that have been refuted by argument. The laws, therefore, are responsible for what they do, just as we are, and may be praised or blamed accordingly.

PLATO: But when we address the laws as people we are speaking rhetorically, using a figure of speech. *Prosopeia*, those wretches[28] call it.

XANTHIPPE: In some measure, certainly. But let us consider this term '*prosopon*' – the actor's mask, the *persona*, that which 'comes before our eyes'. The creature with a *prosopon* – the person as we may call him – is the one whose appearance is *to be interpreted*, with a view to praise and blame, love and hate, friendship and anger. This term too refers to the rational being, bound to us by relations of right and

---

[27] Xanthippe is presumably quoting Protagoras: see W. K. C. Guthrie, *The Sophists*, Cambridge, CUP, 1969, p. 66. Indeed, if Aristotle is to be believed, many of Xanthippe's ideas had already been put forward by the sophists. For example, the minimalist view of law as 'a guarantor of men's rights against one another' is attributed by Aristotle (*Politics*, 1280b, 10) to the sophist Lycophron, while the advocacy of a law without legislation, subject to a supreme court of appeal, he attributes to Hippodamus (*Politics*, 1267b, 37H). It is disappointing that Aristotle, who learned his political philosophy (we may reasonably assume) from Xanthippe, should have refrained from mentioning her, preferring to credit her insignificant precursors. Perhaps, however, he made good the omission in his *Life of Xanthippe* (referred to by Sosipatra, *On Notorious Women*, 420D, and Hypatia, *Dipsosophistae*, 19, i). Like all of Aristotle's finished works, the *Life of Xanthippe* is lost.

[28] Presumably the teachers of rhetoric.

responsibility, whose every gesture bears another meaning than the physical fact of it. And we see that our world contains many persons who are not, like us, creatures of flesh and blood, who are not mortal animals, raised by their language and their reasoning powers into the precarious condition of responsibility. Your clubs and societies too are persons, with rights and duties, not only in the court of law, but also in the ethical sphere, where we encounter them. Your Academy is a person, animated, as you think, by the spirit of Socrates, and in any case as much sustained by rights and burdened by duties as you and I. And our laws recognize this personality.[29] The Academy owns property; it may appear, through its representative, in the courts, suing for its rights, or sued for its liabilities.

PLATO: This is indeed remarkable, Xanthippe. But what bearing does it have on our discussion?

XANTHIPPE: A great bearing, I think. For now I see the answer to your question about the judges: the question how we guarantee their impartiality.

PLATO: I would gladly hear what you have discovered. For I cannot see that we have advanced by a single step.

XANTHIPPE: Well then, let me begin, in the manner of Socrates, with a distinction. There are, I believe, two kinds of state, the personal and the impersonal. In the personal state rights and duties are honoured and upheld. The law holds us to our responsibilities, and every person is acknowledged and respected as such: whether he be human, like you and me, or discarnate, so to speak, like your

---

[29] It has been argued (e.g. by Sir Moses Finley, *Studies in Land and Credit in Ancient Athens*, New York, 1973, p. 89), that the concept of corporate personality was unknown in Athenian law. Even if this were true, the *moral* personality of corporations was recognized by the law, just as it is recognized by the English Law of Trusts, without recourse to the legal concept. It used to be thought (under the influence of Wilamowitz) that the Academy was constituted as a cult-community, or *thiasos*, and as such could enjoy rights and incur obligations in law. (The foundation of such a community was a legal formality, like establishing a company under English Law; it was enough to choose a deity or deities, to whose service the property of the community would be dedicated – Plato chose to dedicate the Academy to the Muses.) In fact it is now doubted that the Academy was a *thiasos* (see J. N. Lynch, *Aristotle's School*, Berkeley, California, 1972, pp. 106–134, and John Dillon, 'What Happened to Plato's Garden', in *Hermathena*, 1983). Still, Xanthippe's point does not hinge on this. In any case legal personality was effectively attributed to many of the Athenian associations mentioned above (footnote 24): see Ludovic Beauchet, *Histoire du droit privé de la république athénienne*, Amsterdam, 1969, vol. IV, pp. 354–71).

Academy. And this is the kind of state which emerges from natural law.

PLATO: And does your personal state make room for slaves?

XANTHIPPE: I think not, my dear Plato. For the law of our state will uphold agreements, but never endorse coercion.

PLATO: In that case, in existing economic conditions, it will not last long.

XANTHIPPE: But existing economic conditions will be the first thing to change, when everyone is free to sell his labour.

PLATO: An interesting suggestion, Xanthippe. However, I am still at a loss to know why you call this state of yours personal.

XANTHIPPE: Because the state too is a person, and its laws rightly personified by the orators who address them. The personal state takes responsibility for its actions, can be praised, blamed and criticized. It may also be persuaded – through the law courts or the assembly – to change its ways. More, the actions of this state are rational: for it respects those free associations whence our goals derive; it withdraws discreetly from every sphere where worth and value grow according to their nature. It too, therefore, can pursue the good, not by taking charge of the good, but by following civil society in the search for it.

PLATO: And the impersonal state?

XANTHIPPE: Of course, this will be in every way the opposite. Not a person but a machine, which takes no responsibility for its actions, but grinds on relentlessly in pursuit of its unattainable objectives. In the impersonal state rights are despised and duties neglected. Men are forced to bend to the plan which governs them. And even if the plan is to make them virtuous, my dear Plato, this very fact will only serve to enhance the state's unaccountability. For no reason can have authority with this state, nothing can dissuade it from its purpose. The laws and the assembly are merely instruments, and can provide no obstacle or argument against its plans.

PLATO: Suppose that I grant you this distinction. How then do you answer my question?

XANTHIPPE: Men, you will agree, are creatures of habit. And it is through the courtyard of habit, so to speak, that they enter the palace of reason. In my personal state it is the habit to take responsibility. Men know that they are answerable for their acts and omissions, and take care, therefore, to discharge their duties towards their neighbours. In such an atmosphere the feeling for law, and the respect for impartial judgment, grow naturally in the citizen, as part of his political culture. Nobody forces the judges to be impartial; but they are so by nature, since they incline in no other way. And if, from time to time, one of them should lapse into fraud and corruption, public opinion will suffice to eject him. Therefore, Plato, I think it is only you – the defender, if I may say, of an impersonal republic – who have the problem that you envisage. It is only you who must give guarantees that those who hold office will not abuse it. And the very fact that guarantees are so urgently necessary, suffices to show that they will never be found.

PLATO: Is this the end of our journey?

XANTHIPPE: Not exactly, Plato. For I confess that there is something missing from the personal state as I have described it, and this thing greatly troubles me.

PLATO: You mean slaves, of course.

XANTHIPPE: I mean religion: which has been the secret theme of our discussion. At least, that is the way I understand it.

PLATO: *I* didn't understand it so.

XANTHIPPE: No, but religion is in the eye of the beholder, just as pictures are.

PLATO: I see; we are back to that.

XANTHIPPE: We are back to the thing on which a political culture depends, which is, if I may so express it, the web of piety. Socrates questioned many things; but he never poured scorn on piety, and for that, I believe, he will be rewarded in the place where he now resides.

PLATO: You rebuke me, Xanthippe, and rightly.

XANTHIPPE: Not at all, Plato. I wish only to return you to the path on which you proposed to guide me. For now I see the end of our journey before us. This thing that I have called personality: is it not revealed in the universe itself? 'Everything is full of gods,' said Thales. Every place invites our worship, and every created thing looks upon us as a face may look, with an invitation to dialogue. Our world is enchanted, and that is why we take pride in our condition. Reason, freedom, personality – this thing that distinguishes us from the rest of creation – puts us in communion with the gods. There lies the truth of the story that I told to Socrates: in everything there is judgment, and personality abounds in the world. Certainly, therefore, our destiny is distinct from the destiny of animals, and far happier than theirs.

PLATO: What you say is most intriguing; and I should like to counter it, not with an argument, but with a vision. Do please tell me why this rival vision should not be accepted.

XANTHIPPE: I shall do my best.

PLATO: Know, then, that the disciples of Anaximander of Miletus[30] have completely departed from the thinking to which you subscribe. Man, they say, is not the special work of the gods, nor have the gods shown the slightest interest in him. Indeed, it is only recently, and as a result of a natural development, that man has existed on this earth at all. Prior to him the highest of animals was the ape, from whom man is descended. And we can guess at the process of descent, when we observe how the stronger races, competing with the weaker, will always prevail.

Now the ape, say the disciples of Anaximander, is descended from a more primitive animal which ran on all fours, like a dog or a horse; and this more primitive animal from something still rougher and less polished, until, proceeding down the ranks of our far from distinguished ancestors we come at last to those who lived in the womb of the original mother, in the Ocean herself, and who took the form of fishes. And the fishes were descended in turn from the primeval slime that gathers in the ocean depths, and is warmed into life by the rays of the sun. And this theory – which, as an aristocrat, I am most reluctant to believe – tells me that the vast majority of my ancestors were not only devoid of reason but also fairly defective in their social and moral standing. Nevertheless, it strikes me as quite plausible, and I would gladly know how to set it aside.

XANTHIPPE: In what way is it plausible?

PLATO: In the way that all theories are plausible: by explaining what is otherwise unexplained. And on two things in particular the theory of Anaximander sheds light. First, there is the remarkable similarity, which you have already referred to, between the forms of animal life, including the fish from which we are descended. All have two eyes and a mouth, a stomach, liver and heart. And all, once they have

---

[30] Anaximander of Miletus, born 610 BC, who argued for a unified science, governed by a single law. It is sometimes doubted whether the theory of evolution, put forward here by Plato, should be attributed to Anaximander, his pupil Anaximenes, or some other member of their school.

emerged from mother Ocean, have limbs, with mobile joints and cunningly wrought extremities; ears too they have, muscles, blood and lymph. In short, they seem like so many variations on a single theme, just as the several sons of a single father.

Secondly, there is the miracle of life itself: why it exists in so many forms, each form perfectly adapted to survival, with nothing redundant – but every part working, so to speak, for the common good. How is this to be explained?

XANTHIPPE: Clearly, by God's benevolence.

PLATO: But suppose we had no need of that hypothesis? Suppose we could explain this miraculous harmony purely by reference to the things of this world, and assuming no divinity. Would that not be a better theory?

XANTHIPPE: Why better?

PLATO: Because simpler, neater, with fewer and clearer assumptions.

XANTHIPPE: Bad manners too are simpler and clearer than good, and make fewer assumptions. Still, have it your way.

PLATO: Well then, here is Anaximander's explanation: the forms of life, he argues, emerge from a prolonged competition for survival, each new species branching away from its origins, and struggling in the free-for-all of nature. Resources are scarce, and conditions harsh. It follows that the species that is best fitted to survive will survive, whereas that which is less well adapted, however slightly so, must inevitably claim less than its needed share of the earth's resources, and bit by bit lose ground to its competitor. And the successful species will pass its attributes from father to son, much as we do, until at last displaced by some new form of life.

XANTHIPPE: And whence comes this new form of life?

PLATO: Anaximander does not say. But I have heard it suggested that the new forms of life emerge spontaneously from the old, by some chance operation of the sun's rays on the lymph. For often you see, do you not, these prodigies: a child with three legs, two heads, or a single eye. Do you not suppose that, were one of these prodigies to be better equipped for life's battles than we are (being born, so to speak, fully armed like Pallas Athene) he would people the world with his offspring, and gradually drive us to extinction?

XANTHIPPE: I very much fear that he would.

PLATO: Well, then. Let us see what Anaximander would make of your theories, Xanthippe. At a certain stage, he might argue, the ape gives way to the rational being: not in one generation only, but gradually, much as the strands are added to a tapestry until suddenly the image is there. How come, therefore, that the rational being has an immortal soul, of which his simian and ichthian ancestors knew nothing? The suggestion is quite incongruous. The change from them to him was long and intricate, and reason no more than the last refinement, the last thread in the tapestry which causes the face to emerge. Reason, like sight, is a product of evolution. And if it exists, it is because it improves our chances of survival. Moreover, just as the eye colours the world, so to speak, in the act of seeing it, so does reason in the act of understanding it.

XANTHIPPE: But is not the world already coloured?

PLATO: By no means, Xanthippe. And this I can easily prove to you. For suppose the sea were really blue. Would it not be an error, then, to see it as grey or green or wine-dark? And yet those perceptions involve no error at all; on the contrary, a man who saw the sea as blue, on a day of cloud and storm, with the grey breakers beating on the rocks and sending the flecks of foam upwards to do battle with the rain – such a man would be in error. On such a day the sea looks grey, as at other times it looks green, or yellow with sunlight or red with the glow of evening. In truth the sea has no colour. Colour is an appearance, contributed by the eye. And suppose our disciple of Anaximander were to go further, and say that something similar is true of the soul. For could he not turn your own argument about the tapestry on its head, and refute you with the very instances that you chose to prove your point?

XANTHIPPE: What do you mean?

PLATO: Could he not say that, when we see Socrates in the tapestry, it is not Socrates that we see, but an image, and that this image exists only in the eye of the beholder? For there is surely no Socrates before us: nothing, in fact, but a piece of wool. Nor, indeed, do we think otherwise. For what person, confronting your tapestry, would believe himself to be in the presence of Socrates?

XANTHIPPE: Certainly, only a fool or a madman.

PLATO: What then of the *prosopon*: the face or mask or person? Granted, our disciple of Anaximander will say, the rational being presents a remarkable appearance to the world. We can describe him in all kinds of interesting ways: we see his actions as free, his emotions as reasonable, his relations as duties and rights. This may be the way rational beings *see* one another; but is it the way they *are*? Could not freedom be an illusion – after all, it is hard enough to explain what we mean by it? Could not rights and duties be illusions too, and all the other things that seem so important to us? Perhaps the soul is a mirage. Personality is the mask of the human animal, but not the animal itself. And if you wish to see the reality, strip the mask away.

XANTHIPPE: Do you really believe that, Plato?

PLATO: I don't say I believe it. I want not to believe it; for like you, I am a lover of enchantment.

XANTHIPPE: Then here is what I say to you. Anaximander tells me that Xanthippe is descended from a fish: all well and good. He tells me that Xanthippe's rational part is a product of the struggle for survival. Fine. He tells me that, just as the colours Xanthippe sees lie in her eyes, so do the meanings of her world lie in her intellect. Neither colour nor meaning is listed among the 'really real'. That too is fine. For the catalogue of the really real is no better a guide to our world than a book of anatomy is a guide to human beauty. I do not say that its list is false; merely that all the most important things are excluded from it. Even God is excluded.

PLATO: Which is hardly surprising if he doesn't exist.

XANTHIPPE: True enough, Plato. But you too are excluded, and so am I and Socrates. And should we therefore conclude that we do not exist?

PLATO: By no means, Xanthippe. But I marvel at your saying that I am excluded from Anaximander's catalogue. For am I not a creature of flesh and blood?

XANTHIPPE: Indeed; but you are also more than that, and less. When you look upon yourself it is not flesh and blood that you contemplate, but this thing called 'I', whose every state is revealed to you. Do you imagine that such a thing was true of your ancestor the fish?

PLATO: Certainly not.

XANTHIPPE: And when you look on me it is not flesh and blood, I think, which capture your attention, but the words I utter and the things I do, in which 'I', Xanthippe, am revealed.

PLATO: True; but this 'I' means nothing. Like 'here' or 'now' it marks a place that some other name must fill.

XANTHIPPE: Perhaps. But we have discovered another aspect of the rational being: he can speak in the first person of his acts and attitudes, and lay claim to them as his. And do you not find it most wonderful, my dear Plato, that the very thing we describe as rational, personal, and free, should also know itself as 'I', and that of nothing else in the world can this be said?

PLATO: I admit, there is something strange about it.

XANTHIPPE: So should we not say that personality and the self are one, and that the mystery of the individual is contained in their conjunction?

PLATO: It would be a bold conjecture.

XANTHIPPE: Having come so far we have no choice but to be bold. That is why Heraclitus said 'Of soul you shall never find boundaries, not if you track it on every path, so deep is its *logos*.' For the soul is the self; it knows no limits, for all limits are comprehended within it, from its own perspective. To circumscribe the self, to hunt it to earth in the world of its own awareness – this is as impossible as to catch sight of your own point of view, so as to confirm that it is indeed you, and not another, who peers from it.

PLATO: You are making me dizzy. And even if I should accept what you say, you must tell me why this elusive thing called self or soul is also the seat of personality.

XANTHIPPE: I wish I could, Plato. But let me make a beginning. You will admit that I am free?

PLATO: You are not a slave, certainly.

XANTHIPPE: I was not referring to political freedom, but to another freedom, which the slave too possesses: the quality of mind which some call practical reason (*phronesis*) and some call choice (*prohairesis*).

PLATO: More names, I imagine, for reason itself.

XANTHIPPE: Indeed, Plato; but the many names of reason are like the many names of a god: each adds to the god's splendour, and reveals some further secret of his power. So let me tell you what it means to say that I am free, and you will see if you agree with me.

PLATO: Go ahead.

XANTHIPPE: It means that whatever Xanthippe does stems from me. I am not the channel through which external forces pass, but the originator of my actions. And the very thing that is revealed to me, when I look into myself and speak in the first person, is the thing that acts. Xanthippe's words and deeds are to be explained, therefore, in a manner that has no mention in Anaximander's catalogue.

PLATO: I wish you would give me an example, Xanthippe.

XANTHIPPE: Suppose, then, that you jump up suddenly, clap your hand to your forehead, crying 'Oh!', and I ask you 'Why?' You could answer in two ways. First you might speak the language of Anaximander, saying: 'a sudden rush of animal spirits to Plato's heart caused the limbs to heat and the muscles to contract, so that the Platonic body jerked to its feet and a rush of air from the Platonic lips made a sound of "Oh!" '

PLATO: Not much of an answer, Xanthippe.

XANTHIPPE: True, nevertheless. But, as you rightly imply, there is another and better answer, which is Plato's: 'I remembered my dear mother,' he declares, 'and in a fit of remorse rose to my feet, resolving there and then to say a prayer at her grave.' In what way does this second answer differ from the first? I will venture to tell you. The first, it seems to me, is a hypothesis, which must be confirmed by experiment and investigation. The second is not a hypothesis at all, since you, Plato, are absolute authority in pronouncing it. In such a case the sincerity of your words is a guarantee of their truth, and no one could ever refute them. More; your words do not only explain your action – they also justify it. They show its place in the stream of questions and answers which is Plato's conscience. I may argue with your words, seeking to dissuade you from your new resolve; you in turn may convince me that I am wrong and you are right. And in this argument I engage directly with you: we meet each other 'I' to 'I'.

PLATO: You are describing something ordinary and day-to-day. And yet you make it sound so mysterious.

XANTHIPPE: It seems to me that many things we take for granted are really mysteries. But let me return to my conjecture. Is it not because you speak in this way, proposing your own future, and undertaking to change the world, that I can enter into dialogue with you? And is not this capacity for dialogue the root of all the relations between us? Without it I should have to treat you as an animal. With it, I can think of you as a person, with rights and duties. In everything, it is the 'I' of Plato, expressed in Plato's voice, which is the gateway to my dealings with the real Platonic you.

PLATO: I think you may be right, Xanthippe.

XANTHIPPE: And there is a further consequence. Because I can argue

with you and dissuade you from your purposes, there is established
between us the kind of reciprocity that engenders praise and blame,
friendship and enmity, and the instinct for justice. And from this in
turn springs the possibility, and also the necessity, of love.

PLATO: Why necessity?

XANTHIPPE: That, my dear Plato, is another story, and it is getting late.
There is something else that I must remark on. Love, whose object
is an individual, can be felt only towards a free being, and only on the
assumption of his freedom. Is that not strange? For Socrates used to
say that the target of reason is always an idea, and that ideas are
inherently general. The real target of reason, it seems, is the free
individual; the rational being, who is both subject and object of our
real emotions.

PLATO: But do not the beasts love their kind? And do they not perceive
each other as individuals?

XANTHIPPE: I think not, Plato. For consider a horse. He does indeed
become attached to his neighbour in the stable. But substitute
another horse that is exactly similar in appearance and he will be
content. Even a dog's love for his master would be satisfied, if we
could find another man with the same smell and the same tone of
voice. Whereas we, who focus upon the freedom of another, focus
on the nameless essence – the 'I' itself – for which there is no
conceivable substitute.

PLATO: There is truth in what you say.

XANTHIPPE: Now this thing that we have described from so many
points of view – freedom, responsibility, personality, the self – you
will grant that it has no place in Anaximander's catalogue?

PLATO: I can see no other possibility.

XANTHIPPE: But that is precisely what is wrong with the search for the
really real: it peels away the personality of the world, and then
complains that what it finds is meaningless. In things that matter it is
only a superficial person who does not judge by appearances. And
the old stories, such as the one I told to Socrates, owe their truth
to this: that they show the world as it seems. There is no fact of
judgment, to appear in Anaximander's catalogue. But it is true, none
the less, that we are judged, and that this judgment sounds through
all eternity. And only when we recognize this truth do our lives
acquire their meaning.

I know I speak in riddles: for it is easier to weave my thoughts than to find the words for them. But let me try to say what I have learned in this sacred grove. Everything I do belongs to nature, and flows from causes that I cannot control. But as it flows it forms a pattern, and this pattern is Xanthippe. You too see the pattern, and respond to its uniqueness, just as you see the figure in the tapestry. Yet *I* know the pattern in another way, with the immediacy that comes from being what I know. Some would say that Xanthippe is two things – the body that lives and dies, and the immortal soul. But that too is a metaphor. Xanthippe is not two things, but one: a soul incarnate. Yet this thing is known in two separate ways.

When I encounter another person, I am granted a strange experience – though so familiar that its strangeness is lost to all but the philosopher. This encounter with the other is like a revelation. And the meaning of the revelation is expressed in action, not in thought. The other is sacred for me. He is not to be treated as things are treated: he is not a means to my purposes, but an end in himself. The calculation of my own advantage, which runs riot through the world of objects, ceases abruptly at the threshold of the other, awaiting his consent. In this way the world of nature is filled with meaning. Everywhere I encounter value, not as an abstract idea, but as a host of incarnate individuals, each of whom is unique and irreplaceable.

PLATO: But this grove too, you said, is sacred. Does a grove have a self, a point of view, an 'I'? And if we say this of places, why not of times?

XANTHIPPE: This, my dear Plato, is the strangest thing of all. Sometimes it seems as though personality shines in what is most contingent: in a stone, a tree, a patch of stagnant water. Those attitudes that I direct towards the human person – and which cause me to see a face as part of nature and at the same time outside nature – those very attitudes I may direct to any part of the created world.

PLATO: Yes, with a stretch of the imagination.

XANTHIPPE: Imagination, like reason, is a seeker after truth: it is part of the alertness with which we encounter one another, and those who lack imagination see less than the whole. Our experience of the sacred is the sudden encounter, in the midst of contingent things, with the creator's freedom. It is the recognition of purpose and personality in that which contains no human soul. That is surely what Thales meant, when he said that 'all things are full of gods'; and it is why

The gods, like strangers from far distant zones,
In every shape and manner haunt the towns.[31]

And just as there are sacred places, so are there sacred times –
those holy festivals, when the very air we breathe on waking
seems sweeter than the air of normal days. How we explain these
experiences, I do not know. Perhaps Anaximander would say that, in
some dread time, long before Homer, two races of men walked the
earth, the one alert to sacred things, the other dead to them. And the
experience of the sacred, he might argue, was a source of strength in
times of danger. Hence the religious race survived, while its rival
perished. Do not our poets teach that impiety is also visited with
destruction? I am content for Anaximander to have the last word in
the matter. After all, to explain an experience is not to discount it.

PLATO: But if Anaximander is right, our religious experiences could
exist, even though there are no gods who cause them.

XANTHIPPE: The meaning of an experience is not its cause. Those
who communicate with the Creator through prayer are no more cut
off from him by the knowledge that nature does not contain him,
than they are cut off from those they love by the knowledge that
words, smiles and gestures are nothing but movements of the flesh.

PLATO: In what way does this faith of yours provide a weapon against
death, I wonder?

XANTHIPPE: What a pity that you were never initiated into the
mysteries, my dear Plato. Your mother and I discussed it, and I was
all prepared to broach the question with the High Priest, but at the
last minute Perictione decided otherwise. 'Too embarrassing,' she
said.

PLATO: Typical! But don't worry on my behalf. I got enough in that
line with the Pythagoreans in Sicily.

XANTHIPPE: Yes, I was rather afraid of that.

PLATO: In fact it was Mother who put me on to them. Not that I have
much time for metempsychosis: for what is the difference between
extinction and rebirth, when you are born without memories of your
former life?

XANTHIPPE: Little enough, to be sure. But all such doctrines exist, you

---

[31] Od. xvii, 485–6.

know, in vulgar and elevated versions. In the language of the vulgar, we speak of salvation as survival: an endless sequence of good things. The poet, however, scorns such a vision, and speaks not of endless time but of eternity.

PLATO: And how do you distinguish the two?

XANTHIPPE: Not as you and Socrates distinguish them, by referring to the eternal truths and the forms. To join such fragments of eternity, I should have to lose my individuality, and that too would be no better than extinction. I mean, rather, to the eternal in time, as we perceive it in our hours of peace.

PLATO: What hours?

XANTHIPPE: The hours you have no time for. Listen, suppose I borrow a drachma from you, promising to repay it on the morrow. And suppose that, when the morrow comes, I fail to pay. Do I escape the obligation to return the money?

PLATO: By no means.

XANTHIPPE: Indeed, however much time elapses, my obligation remains?

PLATO: Of course.

XANTHIPPE: Time, then, is of no account, so far as this particular relationship is concerned.

PLATO: Certainly. Though generally I charge interest at a modest rate.

XANTHIPPE: And is not something similar true for the other relationships that are founded in freedom? If my obligations to you have not been discharged by the time of your death, in no way does your death extinguish them. Remorse and shame, pride and glory, remain unchanged and uneroded as the years wear on. Nor does death really affect them, except by changing their expression. The same is true of love and friendship, which owe no tribute to time. Whatever freedom undertakes, is done for eternity's sake. If freedom finds its reward in the here and now, it is only in those things that are also outside time and change: the communion of the mysteries, the glance of a loved one, or the visionary statue of a god. To know such things is to store up the matter of eternity, and to win release from death. What form that release can take it is not possible to say, since to speak of it is to speak of it in time. Such stories as the one I told are therefore allegories: the truths they convey are shown but not described. To understand them we must receive them as the work of poets or gods.

PLATO: That is to give much honour to poetry, Xanthippe.

XANTHIPPE: Indeed. And although the divine Corinna did well, when she advised Pindar that verse without myth is less than living, it is true too that myth will die when not refreshed in verse. And it is this, above all, that causes me to think that this Athens of ours will not long survive.

PLATO: What do you mean?

XANTHIPPE: That our priests – even those of the mysteries – have rebuked the muses and shooed them from their shrines. Their rites are prose, their sermons political speeches. The stories themselves, recounted in the journalese of heralds, can no longer convince the mass of people, who believe them only when they are sung and when belief and feeling come together in an act of assent.

PLATO: Like my mother, you believe that faith and sincerity are matters of style.

XANTHIPPE: Not style, exactly; but certainly they involve an attempt to 'keep up appearances'. And, as I said to you, no appearance is more important to us, than that of judgment. For it is through this idea that we can confront our death and take comfort in it, knowing that rewards and punishments are distributed thereafter.

PLATO: Thereafter?

XANTHIPPE: Say then, eternally. It is only in time that 'thereafter' makes sense, and I see that you are quick to spot the contradiction. The man who abuses his freedom kills the eternal in himself. Is it not reasonable to suppose, therefore, that death for him is a punishment that it would never be for one who is truly good, and who has lived his life for the sake of its end?

(Enter Aristotle, still running.)

PLATO: Such an ambiguous remark, Xanthippe. 'For the sake of': how many meanings does that have? 'End': how many more?

ARISTOTLE: I would recognize, sir, a broad sense of 'end' and a narrow sense.

PLATO: What? You again, you devil? I'll 'broad sense' your end for you all right.

ARISTOTLE: Yes, sir. I came to fetch you, sir.

PLATO: Is something the matter?

ARISTOTLE: A little controlled drinking, sir. I thought, maybe it would be better if you were there, sir.

PLATO: Controlled drinking? What in Hades do you mean?

ARISTOTLE: They were impatient for the paean, sir. So to while away the time I gave them a lecture, along the lines you had indicated, sir, on how abstinence must not be taken to excess, and controlled drinking of good wine by virtuous people with a view to truthful utterance was part of the care of the soul.

PLATO: I don't recall saying anything about 'good' wine.

ARISTOTLE: It was an oversight, sir. I'm sure you would have added that bit, had you expounded the thesis at greater length, sir. In order to take care of the headache factor, sir.

PLATO: I don't like the sound of this.

ARISTOTLE: And it so happened, sir, that Hipparchus had discovered an amphora of excellent Chios, in a shed behind your study, sir.

PLATO: What?

ARISTOTLE: Yes, sir. And he proposed that, being the most virtuous among us, he should act as symposiarch, and that together we should try this new form of education. For the sake of scholarship, sir. I think you'd better come, sir. It's not a pretty sight.

PLATO: I'll be straight there.

(Aristotle exits at a run.)

My very last amphora! The dogs! This is a whipping matter. They'll feel this one, the savages!

XANTHIPPE: But should you not follow the advice of Socrates?

PLATO: What's that?

XANTHIPPE: Wait until you are less angry before you strike. Besides, you are rather drunk, you know, Plato. Better to take it easy.

PLATO: Perhaps you're right. My head is certainly reeling somewhat. Thanks for the discussion: most interesting. Must try to write it down. Drop by some time at the Academy: I'll show you my notes. Well. Home to bed, I suppose. The little blighters!

(Plato goes off with embarrassed step.)

XANTHIPPE: Goodnight, my dear Plato.

PLATO: Goodnight. Goodnight.

(Exit; a pause.)

XANTHIPPE: Oh! He's forgotten the tapestry. Maybe he'll come back for it. I hope so. I'd better turn in; just say goodnight to the old boy.

(Turns to the tomb.)

XANTHIPPE: How did I do?

(The ghost of Socrates enters from behind the tomb.)

SOCRATES: Better every day.

XANTHIPPE: Dear Socks!

SOCRATES: Shh! Don't call me that! You've no idea how they laugh at me over there.

XANTHIPPE: They can't hear us, surely?

SOCRATES: Can't hear us? They hear everything! The faintest whisper that affects the reputation of the dead is carried to their ears. The air of Elysium hums with rumours like a meadow in summer, and each little blade of grass will speak your name.

XANTHIPPE: Sorry. I would never have guessed.

SOCRATES: Actually, if your reputation stands high it's all rather agreeable.

XANTHIPPE: But not, I hope, the greatest of your joys?

SOCRATES: Of course not; just a small thing in which one rather depends on those left behind. By the way, you were terrific with young Plato: I must say, he has certainly improved.

XANTHIPPE: You didn't mind my mentioning the escapade in the kitchen?

SOCRATES: Not at all. They know all about it over there. Actually it is counted rather to my credit.

XANTHIPPE: Really?

SOCRATES: Yes, everything except the bum-pinching, which I admit was overdoing it. You see, their view is that human dignity should never aspire to be god-like, and that one should run amok from time to time. The alternative is hubris.

XANTHIPPE: Sensible enough. By the way, I hope you're getting enough to eat?

SOCRATES: Actually, the catering's quite good. You might have poured me a libation, though.

XANTHIPPE: I clean forgot! Sorry, dear. You wouldn't have liked it, however: too sweet.

SOCRATES: Still, it's the thought that counts. That was a nice story you told, by the way. Good to hear it again. Let's hope that Plato writes it down. Of course, as you say, all very allegorical.

XANTHIPPE: I know it's not *like* that, Socrates.

SOCRATES: Actually, it's not like *anything*. When are you coming?

XANTHIPPE: Soon. But you know, dear, I ought to stay around for Sophroniscus' sake.

SOCRATES: Sophroniscus, yes. I wonder what we did wrong? You know, he was chewing some of that stuff this afternoon, crying 'Io, io

Bacchus!' and believing himself to be riding in the chariot of the god himself.

XANTHIPPE: He's hooked on it, I fear. Like so many young people today. Of course, it doesn't help that he was brought up without a father.

SOCRATES: I don't suppose he appreciates your staying around. Why not throw in the towel and come over?

XANTHIPPE: I am surprised at you, Socrates. Should I not put duty before pleasure?

SOCRATES: Of course, old girl. As long as duty is a pleasure too.

XANTHIPPE: How lenient you have become!

SOCRATES: No, not really. Just a trifle more serene. Also, I used to talk a lot of tosh about morals, you know.

XANTHIPPE: Really?

SOCRATES: Yes: this young man will explain.

(Aristotle enters at a run; Socrates vanishes.)

ARISTOTLE: Please, ma'am; the tapestry. The master forgot it.

XANTHIPPE: Here it is.

ARISTOTLE: Thank you, ma'am.

(Makes as if to go.)

XANTHIPPE: Do they give you any free time, Aristotle?

ARISTOTLE: How did you know my name, ma'am?

XANTHIPPE: Your master told me. Would you have an hour to spare tomorrow?

ARISTOTLE: It's not out of the question, ma'am.

XANTHIPPE: Then can I expect you?

ARISTOTLE: Yes, ma'am. Before the paean.

(Exit.)

XANTHIPPE *(looks after him wistfully)*: If only!

FINIS

PHRYNE'S SYMPOSIUM

Thaïs (a courtesan), writing to Euthydemus:

We are no worse educators. Compare if you like Aspasia the courtesan and Socrates the sophist, and ask yourself which was the better educator. You will notice that Pericles sat at Aspasia's feet, Critias at Socrates'.

Alciphro (2nd century AD), 1, 34, 7.

(Note, however, that according to ancient tradition, Socrates also sat at the feet of Aspasia, so as to learn the art of love.)

For beauty is engendered of a proper shame.

Lycophronides, Fragment 1, quoted, according
to Athenaeus, *Deipnosophistae*, 13, 564A, by Clearchus,
in his first book of *Erotica*.

Editor's Foreword

Having translated the three Xanthippic dialogues, I circulated copies around the academic world, hoping that some scholar would comment on their authenticity. Several months passed, during which I received only one response, from a Professor Littleton Hope-Dingwood, who had retired from the chair of Greek in a small northern university, and was now living in the country. 'I am interested,' he wrote, 'by the description of Plato's tragedy, and in particular by his use of the term "hamileter" (which should of course be *hamilleter*) to refer to the hero. The evidence is that this term was not part of Attic usage in the late fifth century BC. It is in all probability a borrowed word, of Spartan origin. The plot of the tragedy also seems to be borrowed, perhaps from Plato the dramatist, whose works we know to have been full of hesitant and unhappy characters, and written in a style somewhere between tragedy and comedy. (See H. P. de Selby, "The Lost Plays of Plato", *Epithumia*, VI, 1963, pp. 299–406.) On the other hand, the play contains definite Lacedaimonian elements. In so far as there was drama in the Sparta of Plato's day, it consisted precisely in the presentation of some cowardly and hesitant character who, through his refusal to act, provokes the lively indignation of the audience. Often the part of the anti-hero would be played by a condemned helot, and the audience invited onto the stage at the end, bringing with them whatever weapons took their fancy, to make their own contribution to the bloody *dénouement*. This is how the tragedy described by Plato the philosopher might have concluded. It seems likely, indeed, that Plato was a Spartan – possibly introduced into the family by the nurse Castallax (who would herself have been Spartan, as were the majority of nurses serving the Athenian upper class). This sheds new light, I believe, not only on Plato's relationship with his mother Perictione (who was not his mother at all), but also on the subversive advocacy of Spartan customs in such works as the *Republic* and the *Laws*.

'I have myself prepared a monograph on this theme, for which the Xanthippic corpus provides useful supplementary evidence. I should be most happy to send it to you, on receipt of £20 to cover copying (at 5p. a page) and postage. If you have any need for a translator from Greek to English (or vice versa) I can offer my services at £30 per thousand words, which is considerably less than the going rate. I also produce my own damson jam, at £1.70 for a medium-sized jar, postage and packing included.

'Looking forward to hearing from you, etc. . . .'

I put this letter to one side, as being of only marginal significance, and for several weeks no further correspondence arrived. In my disappointment I was on the point of writing in the terms suggested to Professor Hope-Dingwood, when a large envelope, covered in stamps bearing the vigilant face of Kemal Atatürk, fell one morning onto my doormat. It contained a typescript, together with the following letter, the English of which I have corrected.

Istanbul, September 10th

Respected Sir,

I was looking through my cousin's papers the other day (he having the kindness to employ me as his secretary) when I came across a copy of *Xanthippe's Republic*, together with your circular letter, which had been passed to him by a colleague. I at once recalled a manuscript which had been in my mother's possession, and in her mother's before her, and which had been given to my great-grandmother, Zeynep *hanım*, by her dear friend Leyla Azize, who died so tragically in 1905. (Perhaps you know her from the works of M. Pierre Loti.) I have had the manuscript typed and send you a copy herewith. As you will see, it bears the title *Phryne's Symposium*, and exists in two versions. The first, in Greek, seems to have come from one of the libraries of Constantinople, being written out, my cousin tells me, in a twelfth-century Byzantine hand. The second, far longer, is in Turkish, which my mother transliterated many years ago into modern script. Where it is possible to compare the versions, you will find that the Turkish is a translation, fairly free at times, of the Greek. According to Leyla Azize *hanım*, the book circulated secretly among the women of the Sultan's harem, the Greek manuscript being more and more neglected as the number of recruits from that country declined. And no doubt the Turkish version was frequently enlarged and embellished, as these poor women sought to enjoy through the written word what was denied them in the flesh. As you will see, whole sections – including the speech of Archeanassa – now exist only in the Turkish.

I enclose the typescript for your perusal, and recommend, should you require a translator, my dear friend Şule, whose London address you will find below. I beg, sir, to remain anonymous, and trust that you will accept the enclosed in the spirit of scholarship.

Şule, I discovered, was everything a translator could desire; she was also unhappily married to an absent husband. She proceeded at once with my Turkish lessons, and when the time came to translate the speech of Archeanassa, it can truly be said that *quel giorno più non vi leggemmo avante*. At last, however, the translation was finished, and I present it to the reader, remembering the lovely girl who taught me so much, and who has been recalled, alas, to the dismal suburbs of Istanbul.

PHRYNE'S SYMPOSIUM

Characters:
PHRASICLEA, a courtesan of Cyrene
DAMARETA, friend of Phrasiclea
ARETE, daughter of Aristippus, and Cyrenaic philosopher
LASTHENEIA of Mantinea, pupil at Plato's Academy
XANTHIPPE, widow of Socrates
PHRYNE, Athenean courtesan
POTONE, sister of Plato
PERICTIONE, Potone's daughter
CASTALLAX, nurse to Potone and Plato
ARCHEANASSA of Colophon, hetaera

(For other classical references to these characters, see the account at the end.)

Until the turn of the fourth century BC, literate Greeks assumed that love, like war, was the business of men – Aristophanes, as always, dissenting. It was admitted that women could enjoy sexual pleasure, and might be esteemed as wives and mothers. But the secrets of *eros* were held to be beyond their comprehension, and even the passionate women of Euripides are motivated more by desire and shame than by love for their menfolk.

In the course of fifty years all this changed. By the time of the New Comedy of Menander, love between man and woman had become the central motive of the stage and the stock theme of lyric poetry. Out of nostalgia for his younger days, Plato continued to write works in praise of homosexual love. But the greatest of them – the incomparable *Symposium* – recommends that we transcend erotic desire, rather than yield to it. By the time he came to write the *Laws*, Plato is vigorously denouncing the homosexual act, and blimpishly legislating against the criminals who would indulge in it.

What accounts for this change – a change not only in the emotional life of Plato, but in the public culture of which he remained the greatest representative (even though a frequent object of ridicule on the comic stage)? The question has puzzled classical scholars since Goethe, and none has found a wholly satisfactory answer. One reason for this failure, I am persuaded, is the vast accumulation of recent scholarship, and the dustiness of the classicists who strive to add to it, and who reach the point of doing so only at an age when the fire of *eros* has dwindled to a faint glow among the ashes.

Things have not always been so. In the great days of British philhellenism it was the fashion among scholars to die young. As is confirmed by countless instances among artists, poets and composers, premonitions of an early death may lead to a heightened creative power. In the interests of scholarship, therefore, our forebears would frequently peg out in their early twenties. Some, like Kenneth Freeman – whose unsurpassed *Schools of Hellas* was written as a fellowship dissertation in Oxford – died of natural causes; others achieved their goal through skilfully contrived accidents.

One such was E. F. M. Benecke, who, in 1895, at the age of twenty-five, managed to fall from a mountain in Switzerland. A 'Fragment Printed for the Use of Scholars' appeared over his name (published by Swan, Sonnenschein and Co.) in 1896. Variously titled, as *The Position of Women in Greek Poetry*, and *Women in Greek Poetry*, this impassioned work of investigative scholarship put a new name to the transition from boy-love to the love of women, and the name is Antimachus of Colophon (another of the work's many titles). None of Antimachus' writings survive. But we know that he composed an extended love poem to Lyde, sometimes thought to be his wife, but more probably his hetaera. The *Lyde* was objected to by the poet and scholar Callimachus of Cyrene (*Answer to the Telchines*) on account of its length and obscurity. If Benecke is right, however, it was the source and inspiration for many subsequent lyrics, including those of Callimachus himself. For the *Lyde*, according to Benecke's conjecture, was the first of those expressions of romantic love, the ἔρωτες καὶ παρθένων φθοραί, which mark the literature of Hellas in its sunset years. (As for the tradition of scholarship which attributes the great cultural shift to Anaxandrides, a fourth-century writer of the Middle Comedy, one can only conjecture that this poet, being also from Colophon – a Greek colony in Asia Minor – has been confused with Antimachus. In any case, only fragments of Anaxandrides' works survive (see T. Kock, *Fragmenta Comicorum Graecae*, II, 135f); so on what compelling evidence does this tradition rest?)

Plato, a slightly younger contemporary of Antimachus, is reputed to have been greatly interested in the poet, sending an emissary to Colophon upon Antimachus' death, with the intention of retrieving his literary remains and bringing them to the Academy. Whether he succeeded in this we do not know. What is certain, however, is that, if Plato recovered the manuscripts of Antimachus, he did not look after them very well. Indeed, it may be Plato that we have to blame for their total destruction.

In enquiring into this matter, we should remember another child of Colophon, subject of a poem attributed to Plato by Diogenes Laertius:

> Archeanassa is my girl – she of Colophon,
> Upon whose very wrinkles sits desire.
> You bastards, you who boarded her upon
> Her maiden trip: I bet she stoked your fire!

What immeasurable depths of physical obsession, jealousy and self-disgust can be read into this little fragment! But could it really have been written by the author of the *Symposium*?

PHRYNE'S SYMPOSIUM

I was on my way out of the temple of Aphrodite, where I had gone to ask a special favour of the goddess and also to pay my respects to Nanno, the priestess there, when a voice called from the shade of a fig-tree: 'Phrasiclea, will you drive past without a greeting?'

'Damareta!' I cried, and called on the slave to stop so that she could mount beside me. She came tripping across the precinct, light as a gazelle, and was no sooner in the chariot, than she had raised her veil and begged me for a hundred kisses.

'My dear Damareta,' I said. 'Suppose one of the novices should be watching, or even the priestess herself: do you think we would escape their censure, or be allowed to stand next to each other at the rite of Aphrodite Pandemos[1] next month, which I was so looking forward to?'

'Darling Phrasiclea!' she replied, 'always taking the long-term view!'

With which she kissed me on the lips and nestled against my breast most charmingly. I was going east to the grove of Anticleia, on a visit to my aunt who has a farm there; naturally Damareta begged to accompany me.

'My husband,' she said, 'is doing business in Cyprus, and today, being bored with reading, I decided to try my fortune in the temple of Aphrodite. Behold, my fortune is you. So you could not possibly deny me the favour of sitting with you on your journey, and whiling away the hours in conversation.'

---

[1] The scene is evidently Cyrene, in North Africa. Aphrodite must have had an important place in the worship of the Cyrenians, who were a trading and seafaring people, although no important temple to the goddess has yet been excavated in their city. (See the report of the first ten years of the Italian archeological mission by Sandro Stucchi: *Cirene 1957–1966*, Tripoli, 1967, and the four-volume final report on the extramural Sanctuary of Demeter and Persephone, ed. by Donald White, Philadelphia, 1984.) Aphrodite *Pandemos* is identified by Plato with the 'common' as opposed to the philosophical form of love. Aphrodite's temple, as at Cnidus (where the statue of the goddess, wrought by Praxiteles, was modelled on Phryne), was always graced with fruit trees and luxuriant vegetation. See the description in pseudo-Lucian, *Erotes*.

So saying, she renewed her caresses, until my embarrassment had quite disappeared beneath the flood of other emotions.

'You wicked girl,' I said; 'I should not wish to commit an impiety towards Aphrodite, and rather than enjoy the fate of Hippolytus,[2] I shall insist that you spend the day with me. And to pay for the pleasure of my company, I beseech you to entertain me with stories. One in particular I should wish to hear from you – which is the account of the banquet at Phryne's house in Athens, where Lastheneia and Arete and Xanthippe were present. What were the speeches they delivered? For Nanno told me that you could recite them, and for the life of me I can think of no conversation in which I would rather have taken part. Were you by any chance there?'

At which Damareta laughed and said, 'No, by Apollo! Dear Nanno must be very confused if she imagines that I could have been present at a party which took place in Athens, at a time when I was hardly conscious.'

'So how did you come to hear of it?' I asked.

'From Arete herself. For you know, a group of us meet at Arete's house from time to time, in order to discuss philosophy and to listen to the stories of Xanthippe, of which she has a remarkable store.'

'Why did I not know about this?' I asked; for I confess I was not a little vexed that so dear a friend should leave me uninvited.

'My dear Phrasiclea,' she responded, 'unmarried women are excluded. Otherwise you should have been first among the guests.'

'Why in the name of Zeus do you adopt such a rule?'

'Ah,' she said, with that furtive little smile of hers, 'we have our husbands to think of. Suppose it got around that we met with courtesans and whores: do you think they would permit it?'

'I don't see why not. After all, they usually prefer our company to that of their wives.'

'Precisely. Which lays upon us a dreadful obligation, to appear quite different from the women they secretly prefer. Think how mortified my poor Speusippus would be, should it occur to him that I viewed his embraces as *you* might, my dear Phrasiclea.'

'I swear to you by holy Demeter that I have never . . .'

'Of course you haven't, darling. But you see my point. And to make

---

[2] Punished by Aphrodite for spurning the advances of his stepmother, Phaedra. See Euripides, *Hippolytus*.

up to you I shall tell the story of that party in Phryne's house which you are so eager to hear about, just as Arete is in the habit of telling it.'

'Does she tell it so often?' I enquired.

'Oh yes, at least once a month. And I assure you it gets better every time.'

'Well, then, my dear Damareta, I shall reconcile myself to loving you just as much as I did when you first stepped into this chariot, provided you tell the story exactly as it happened.'

She kissed me, promising to relate the matter faithfully, adding nothing of her own.

Arete's father Aristippus, Damareta began, was well-connected with the philosophers of Athens. I admit, she added, that he has degenerated in recent years, and it is difficult now to recognize his barking as a version of human speech. But fifteen years ago, long before Arete was obliged to chain him to the palm tree in the garden, his reputation as a philosopher stood high, and he would correspond with other pupils of Socrates throughout Hellas. One day he decided that the time had come to revisit his old haunts; as a special favour, he proposed to take his daughter along with him, so that she could see for herself the city of Pallas Athene, and walk the streets and markets where the great Socrates had made himself heard.

The inevitable happened. No sooner had they disembarked in Piraeus, than Aristippus, catching sight of some old crony, repaired with him to the nearest wine shop. Arete waited for her father at the rooms she had taken in the harbour. At last, after three days without word from him, when the small store of money she had retained was running out, she decided to make the journey to Athens alone. She went at once to call on Lastheneia of Mantinea at the Academy, carrying a letter of introduction which she had acquired from Agido – remember her?

'Indeed I do, Damareta,' I said, for Agido had been leader of our chorus when we were girls, and my first teacher of philosophy.

Well, she continued, Lastheneia, as you know, was studying in the Academy, and welcomed Arete warmly, having already heard much of her philosophical skills. She advised the newcomer to dress in boy's clothes and, fitting her out from the wardrobe of former pupils, she led Arete on a philosophic tour of the city, carefully explaining, in the dry manner favoured by the Academicians, the social, moral and artistic failings of Arete's new surroundings, and taking her at last to the grave of Socrates, whose praises she had not ceased to sing while pouring scorn upon the city that had condemned him.

The grave was not much visited, but had a special significance for women of sound temperament, since Xanthippe had there set up a weaving establishment for the tourist trade. In fact, Arete said, the old lady had branched out rather, and was selling fruit, spring water, cakes and even wine, in the hope of making a few extra obols out of her husband's dwindling reputation.

Naturally, I was aghast at this, and accused Damareta of inventing the story, at which she put on the pertest of expressions, and affirmed that whatever tincture of invention had entered the narrative it was not her doing, and that she only faithfully related what Arete had said to her. Now it was my turn to take the initiative in kissing, and it was some minutes before we had settled down to the story.

It was evening when they arrived, Damareta went on, and Xanthippe was just packing up for the night, stowing the loom and the merchandise in a shed that stood not far from the grave. Catching sight of the girls, 'My dear Lastheneia,' she said, 'how charming you look in that bonnet, and what a fetching pair of military sandals – one might almost say that they had been made for Achilles himself. And who is your boy-friend?'

'He is not my boy-friend,' answered Lastheneia with a blush. 'In fact he is not a boy at all, but Arete, daughter of Aristippus of Cyrene, and I am taking her on a guided tour.'

'You are most welcome, Arete,' the old lady said. 'And I can show you some charming tapestries at a very reasonable price, which I wove myself, and which depict the last days of Socrates. As the daughter of a philosopher, however undistinguished, you might perhaps be interested in them.'

'I am most obliged to you,' said Arete. 'Unfortunately, however, my father ran off with our money, and is busy drinking it in Piraeus – unless he has set sail by now for one of the islands.'

And she went on to explain to the great philosopher her unhappy circumstances, adding that, had it not been for Lastheneia, she must surely have been reduced to selling her body, in order to fulfil her dearest wish and see the city of Socrates.

'And would you have done so?' asked Xanthippe curiously.

'Probably,' Arete replied. 'But I doubt that I should have got the proper price.'

Xanthippe stood for a while in thought, and then said:

'You know, Arete, I am rather interested these days in economics. And I should be greatly obliged if you could tell me what you think the proper price for such a transaction might be?'

'Enough money, I should say, to be free of men forever.'

'With all due respect,' said Xanthippe, 'I wouldn't rate you so high; though of course it is hard to judge in those clothes.'

Lastheneia, who had not ceased from blushing, now began to tug at Arete's sleeve, clearly believing that the conversation would only deteriorate. But before the two girls could set off to the Academy, where Arete had been promised a seat at one of the notoriously frugal dinners that Plato arranged for his pupils, Xanthippe asked what they were planning to do that evening, and whether they might not be free to accompany her to a feast. Lastheneia began to make excuses, but Arete, who had not had a decent meal since she stepped into the boat at Apollonia, issued a loud and imperative acceptance.

'Excellent,' said Xanthippe; 'for, although you have not been explicitly invited, our hostess is celebrating a great victory, and has let it be known that all women of philosophical disposition will be welcome to join her in offering libations to Aphrodite.'

When they enquired as to the identity of their hostess, however, they learned that it was none other than Phryne, she who had instructed some of the greatest men of Athens in the arts of Aphrodite, and in whose house no respectable woman could possibly be seen. They marvelled greatly at Xanthippe, and even Arete was at first reluctant to proceed further with this strangest of adventures.

'What troubles you?' asked Xanthippe. 'Nobody will say that you were there, and you too will keep quiet about it. And as for me, I have my own motives for accepting. In fact, if you want to know, old Socks himself persuaded me.'

'Old Socks?' they asked.

'My husband there. He took the view that important matters will be discussed, concerning which my guidance and example may be useful. And, he said, where there is a chance of dissuading people from corruption, it would be cowardly to turn aside, and to say that such matters are no concern of mine.'

This curious speech so awakened Arete's interest, that she prevailed upon Lastheneia to stay with her, so that they might accompany the old lady to Phryne's house, which of course they would not enter. So the three set off in the direction of the Areopagus, where stood the house of Phryne, bathed for the occasion in the light of torches which they could already glimpse from afar.

To Arete's disappointment Xanthippe did not speak upon the journey. Instead, becoming absorbed in her thoughts, she fell behind them as they went. And when the girls began to wait for her, she bade them go on ahead, so that, arriving at Phryne's open door, they found themselves in a somewhat ridiculous position. For they were met immediately by a servant who, giving them no choice in the matter, took them to where the company was reclining and about to dine. At the sight of two boys a cry of indignation arose, and for a moment all was confusion. At length Phryne – surely, Arete said, one of the most beautiful women in Hellas, and majestically attired in a robe of sea-green Lydian silk with turquoise ornaments – bade her guests be silent, and welcomed the newcomers.

'I am surprised at you all,' she said, her great black eyes flashing with merriment, 'that you should have been deceived by so simple a hoax. And I am even tempted to doubt your familiarity with the matter we are assembled to discuss, that you do not recognize beneath the disguise of a tunic, the fateful inheritance of a female body.'

At which Lastheneia attempted to flee from the room, and would have done so, had not Arete seized her by the sleeve and held her fast.

'And if I am not mistaken,' the courtesan continued, 'it is the badge of the Academy that this young darling has sewn over her breast, and she comes as an emissary from the philosopher himself.'

Stuttering with confusion, Lastheneia protested that Plato knew nothing of her whereabouts; and she implored her hostess with tears in her eyes never to let it be known to her master that she had been seen in the house of Phryne.

'Well,' said the courtesan, with a haughty frown, 'whatever you learn in that dismal establishment, I see that good manners form no part of the curriculum.'

At which Lastheneia, quite overcome, hid her face within her tunic.

'Most illustrious Phryne,' Arete said, stepping forward to shield her friend, 'please forgive two young seekers after truth who have come uninvited to your symposium, and who are ignorant of the ways of society. Surely we should never have dared to set foot amid so brilliant a company, had we not been urged to do so by Xanthippe.'

'Xanthippe, by Zeus!' cried Phryne, whose displeasure vanished at once, 'and is she with you?'

'Alas,' said Arete, 'we have mislaid her. She was following behind, lost in thought, and bid us go forward.'

'Go at once,' said Phryne to the servant, 'and see if you can fetch in Xanthippe. And you, my dears, are most welcome.'

With which she beckoned the maidens forward, and asked them their names. And when Arete declared herself to be the daughter of Cyrenian Aristippus, straightway the courtesan kissed her and bid the girl lie, for her dear father's sake, at the head of the table. And now even Lastheneia was smiling, seeing Arete blush on her mother's behalf.

The girls stared at the marble hall in wonderment. Flickering torches cast their light across a porphyry table, upon which hors-d'oeuvres of seasoned fish, roast quail, partridge, and spiced lentils were scattered. Ladies of every age reclined at the table's edge, their bright jewels catching the torchlight and scattering it around them like the light of a thousand fireflies. Behind the guests were statues of naked heroes, and in the background elaborately woven tapestries depicted the great tales of love. All was of such splendour that the girls did not dare to take their place among the company, but stood clutching each other until two servants approached them, washed them, and on the orders of Phryne, attired them in the finest women's robes.

As the girls were conducted to their couches, the servant returned at last with Xanthippe, who carried a large wooden box under one arm. Phryne rose to greet her, saying, 'I am as surprised as I am honoured, my dear lady, that you should attend my victory celebration. For although we are not well acquainted, I have heard many reports of your discourse, and assumed that such a woman could hardly approve of my career, and must certainly shun such gatherings as this one.'

To which Xanthippe replied:

'It has always been my ambition, Phryne, to meet the women who are gathered here tonight. And if the wine is good, and the speeches lively, I am sure I shall enjoy myself.'

Phryne bid the servant relieve the old lady of her box, at which Xanthippe said, 'Be careful of that; put it down somewhere cool.' On being asked what it contained, she declared it to be a case of anchovies, which she had obtained at rock-bottom price from a woman in one of the nearby back-streets, and which she hoped to sell piecemeal on the morrow.

'And these wicked girls,' said Phryne, 'made out that you were imitating your husband, and standing somewhere lost in thought! I might have guessed that no woman would be so careless of her time.'

So saying, she conducted Xanthippe to the table. And there were present, besides hetaerae and courtesans, several respectable ladies of Athens, including Potone, sister of Plato the philosopher, who had come with her daughter Perictione; also Lydia, wife of Apollodorus the teacher of rhetoric, and Myrtis, wife of Aeschines. Arete marvelled greatly at the presence of such women; but her wonder soon dwindled when Phryne, having bidden the company to silence, rose to her feet to address them.

'Ladies,' she said. 'Most of you are neither wholly respectable like Potone, nor entirely disreputable like myself, but somewhere in between – a possibility which men, to our sorrow, are unable to recognize. But all of us, reputable, disreputable and demi-reputable, recognize the need, from time to time, to compare notes about the matter which most concerns us, and to do so under conditions of strictest secrecy. Before our proceedings begin, therefore, let me remind you of our sacred pact, which enjoins us never to speak of our meetings to those who do not attend them, and to hide nothing from each other once the wine has been poured. And this goes also for our charming newcomers, the one from the Academy, the other from Cyrene in distant Africa; and for our distinguished guest, the renowned Xanthippe.'

At this point I could not forbear from interrupting.

'Are you telling me, my dear Damareta,' I asked, 'that Arete has broken a vow of silence, betraying the secrets and endangering the reputation of such women as Potone and her daughter?'

'Darling Phrasiclea, did Arete take such a vow? All this happened many years ago in Athens. Xanthippe is long since dead, Potone too, and as for Perictione, the last I heard she was dancing in a night-club[3] in Persian Lydia.'

---

[3] Damareta's word is νυκτέϱανος; it is difficult to know exactly what kind of establishment she had in mind. Pamphila (*Memorabilia*, 76, iii) mentions a Xanthippic dialogue between Archeanassa and the younger Perictione, set in Colophon; this work would no doubt cast light on the matter.

'All the same,' I protested, 'one really ought to be a little more careful in relating scandal: it only gives weapons to the enemy.'

Damareta laughed at this, saying, 'If you are referring to men, I have yet to find one who is capable of believing the story I am about to relate to you. As you well know, their conception of scandal is distinctly primitive.'

After a while she satisfied me that there was no great harm in narrating the events of Phryne's symposium. Besides, I was by now so impatient to hear the speeches, that I needed little persuading. Since the chariot had passed the city gate, and we were bumping along the dusty track that leads to the grove of Anticleia, I proposed that we pause awhile, to enjoy the view over the vineyards and the golden cornfields in the valley, down to the distant sea at Apollonia. Damareta readily consented, and we stood together, watching a trireme as it made its leisurely way across the bay. I had brought with me dates and dried fishes, intended as a gift for my aunt. I sent the slave for bread and wine to complete our meal, and when we were comfortably seated beneath the shade of some palm trees, Damareta returned to her story.

'Let us begin with refreshment,' Phryne continued, commanding her guests to eat as much as they could of whatever took their fancy, since the whole cost of the meal was being met by her latest protector. Straightway a maiden entered, bearing a silver ewer of water which she sprinkled over the guests where they lay, and then other maidens bearing wreaths, double-woven from sprigs of living myrtle, which they placed upon the heads of those assembled so as to dignify their motley faces. The table glistened in the rays of the lofty torches, and the starved eyes of Arete widened as the dishes descended on the polished marble. First came a nail-studded charger of bronze, laden with a gleaming eel – a conger eel, no less – its mouth bursting with sorb-apples. And then a dish bearing a steamed turbot as large as a cartwheel, sown with sprigs of parsley, garnished with the tenderest squid and soft-tressed sepia, and anointed with sweet oil of walnuts. From guest to guest the train of servants passed, carrying snow-white rolls of wheat, fragrant fennel-cakes and side-dishes of hump-backed prawns, baked brown before the fire. And when the ladies had eaten their fill of fish, straightway the table groaned beneath a stall-fed porker stuffed with chitterlings, and a milk-fattened cosset-kid, embalmed in caper sauce and laid around with sausages of mule-meat.

And there were side-dishes of jugged hare and roasted partridge, of forcemeat, brains and livers, of snouts and ears and pettitoes. When these had been tried and praised, the table was set with a fair white beestings-pudding, bowls of yellow honey, sweet sesame biscuits, and cream so thick you would have mistaken it for cheese.

The dishes were cleared at last, the guests were washed with orris-mingled soap and soft warm water, and the wine-coolers set upon the table. Phryne rose again to her feet, compelling with genial authoritative eyes the attention of the company.

'Dear ladies,' she said, 'let us proceed now to our business. I ask all of you to pour a libation to Aphrodite. and I invite the beautiful Perictione to sing the hymn. If, in addition, she wishes to entertain us with some specimens of her dancing, I have no doubt that the company will be most grateful. And then, with myself as *archousa*,[4] we will begin our speeches about love, proceeding from right to left around the table.'

The two girls looked at each other in alarm. Arete was on the point of begging to be excused from the proceedings, when a hush fell on the company and the young Perictione offered her hymn to 'glittering-throned immortal Aphrodite',[5] afterwards charming the company with her dances so that they burst out in applause and endeavoured each to

---

[4] The symposium was a male institution, conducted in the men's room (the *andron*), and presided over by the *archon*, armed with a baton, who controlled the flow both of words and of wine. The rare feminine of *archon* – *archousa* – occurs also in Plato, *Republic*, 457c.

Greek cities granted to women their own institution – the religious festival of the Thesmophoria – from which men were excluded and at which women were reputed to drink considerable quantities of wine. (See Aristophanes, *Thesmophoriaszusai*, 627–33.) Apart from the present text, there is no record of an all-female symposium.

[5] Should the first word of Sappho's most famous surviving poem be 'many-minded' (Ποικιλόφρον) or 'many-throned' (Ποικιλόθρον' – alternatively 'glittering-throned')? Let us hope that the text of *Phryne's Symposium*, which gives the second of those readings, will bring this particular controversy to an end.

Perictione's singing of this hymn might raise a few scholarly eyebrows none the less: it is, after all, a highly personal utterance, requesting the goddess's help in a particular erotic adventure. On public occasions it would surely have been more proper to sing one of the liturgical hymns to Aphrodite, such as the famous Homeric hymn which has come down to us and which is quoted by other speakers at Phryne's symposium. On the other hand, the liturgical hymns were rather long, and I can only assume that the brevity of Sappho's masterpiece meant that a young girl like Perictione could easily include it in her repertoire, despite the fact that it is written in Lesbian dialect.

capture the girl's attention and entice her across. One of the older harlots swore that the girl was at least the equal of her namesake, Potone's mother, and when she finally sat down beside Xanthippe, all praised Perictione's discretion at planting herself beside so old and ugly a creature, and applauded as she pressed her kisses on that withered cheek.

So nervous was Arete that at first she could take no note of the speeches. It was not until her goblet had been filled for the fourth time that she was able to concentrate on what was being said. A young hetaera was speaking, somewhat platitudinously, arguing for the superiority of woman's love over man's, and uttering much blistering invective against the infidelity and perfidy of the inferior sex. She concluded that the gods, in designing this second-rate creature, could have had no intention save to provide us with an example of depravity, so that we should strive to resemble it as little as we may.

The next girl was already too drunk to speak, so that the lot fell to Lastheneia, who began by protesting that she had come unexpected and unprepared and that she was unused to speaking in public.

'Come, come,' said Phryne, 'you are not going to tell me that rhetoric too is excluded from the curriculum in that wretched place.'

'Indeed it is,' said Lastheneia, with a trace of indignation, 'and rightly so.'

'Why rightly?'

'Because rhetoric is the art of persuasion. Its goal is not to prove the truth of a doctrine, but merely to persuade others to accept it, whether true or false. In this it is the opposite of philosophy.'

'Whose goal, I take it,' said Phryne, 'is to say what is true, regardless of whether you can persuade anyone to believe it.'

'Exactly.'

'Well then, let us have a specimen of this philosophy, for I am sure the ladies here are as impatient to hear you as I am. But do you first drain your goblet, which has been standing untouched since the libation.'

Lastheneia looked down at the wine, seeming to notice it for the first time. Then snatching it up with an expression of one who grasps a thistle, she drained the goblet in one draught and replaced it on the table. Slightly flushed and looking rather comely, despite her cropped hair and trembling cheeks, she began her speech.

LASTHENEIA'S SPEECH

Many things have been said by the last speaker concerning the alleged inferiority of men as lovers. But can we not point to a hundred examples of their fidelity and devotion? Consider Orestes and Pylades, who sailed together, as it were, on the same vessel of life, Pylades even calling upon his own head the Eumenides, who hounded his friend. Or consider Achilles son of Thetis, who chose to avenge his beloved Patroclus, even though his divine mother had warned him that, slaying Hector, he would himself die before the walls of Troy. Our young men are not taught to imitate the strength and swiftness of Achilles, for these they can never match. They are taught to imitate his love, so that going side by side with their friend into battle they may the more willingly die for the sake of the one who is dearest to them. Such indeed are the men of the Sacred Band of Thebes.

But it is not only in military exploits that men show their capacity for faithful attachments. In poetry too they express their undying concern for those they love, as Theognis for Cyrnus, whom he overlooks as the kindly sun overlooks the earth. And who more famous for the intensity and fidelity of their love than the philosophers? Who among us women can match the love of Parmenides for Zeno, of Socrates for Alcibiades, and Plato for Socrates? What woman indeed is capable of the devotion of a Plato, who wrote down every word of his master's discourses so that his memory should live for ever, and who went with him through every danger, even staying at his side, at great risk to himself, when he drank the hemlock – the only one who dared to do so?

Here Xanthippe was heard to gasp, and was about to speak when Phryne, with a sign, bid the old lady await her turn.

Not only that, Lastheneia continued, looking yet more flustered, but, having done all he could for his dearly beloved, Plato decided that no credit should come to himself, but on the contrary that everything should belong to Socrates. Hence, when writing of his master's death, as of his life, he modestly claims not to have been present, and in this way conceals not only his heroism, but even his love, for his beloved's sake. Is this not the perfection of love, to negate itself so that the beloved gains immortality?

But now, what is this love, which dwells in such superior souls as Plato's? Is it desire for the pleasures of Aphrodite? Such we might think was the nature of all love, if the last speaker is to be believed. But here, briefly, are the reasons against such a view:

(a) All desire is a lack, which must be completed by the object desired. Hence to desire the beloved is in a sense to be deprived of him.

(b) Desire is sensuous, whereas love is intellectual.

(c) The desire for pleasure can be satisfied in many ways, and by many objects. Love, however, has only one way, and its object is one.

(d) The object of desire is fleeting; no sooner is it possessed than it ceases to be desired, and desire goes its way in search of novelty. The object of love, like love itself, is eternal, which is why love outlasts the death of the beloved, and why all fleeting things may be sacrificed for love's sake.

(e) (I think; or is it (f)?) This means that love has as its object not particular things like – er, well, like particular things – but, yes, universals, I mean the forms, that's it, the forms themselves, to which we aspire through love, as we aspire to them also through mathematics and philosophy and . . .

'Knickers,' said Phryne suddenly, at which Lastheneia stuttered to a halt and looked up at her hostess in confusion.[6]

'I only meant,' Phryne went on, 'that you should drink a little more wine, my dear. Your speech is far too dry.'

Lastheneia looked down at her goblet, which the servant had already filled. With a resolute expression she seized it, drained it, and cleared her throat.

Let me, then, come quickly to the point, said she, and introduce you to quite another love than the one described by the last speaker, the love which we may call Platonic, and which is the highest form of love that mortals may know. Whether women experience it we may reasonably

---

[6] The word used by Phryne is βραχύλινοι – 'short linens' – though precisely what garment she had in mind I do not know. The Turkish has *külot*: a word which shows exactly how, and in what part of the anatomy, the Turks have been influenced by their centuries-old connection with the French. This is almost certainly a mistranslation, however, since Greek women did not wear undergarments of the kind familiar to us. Vases show female acrobats and jugglers wearing drawers; otherwise the free-flowing *chiton* seemed to suffice. (Incidentally, the Turkish word has entered modern Greek, as κύλοτα. As to the ease with which the three garments – *Külot*, κύλοτα and *culottes* – may be charmed from the wearer of them, see H. P. de Selby, 'Orpheus in the Underwear', *Epithumia*, forthcoming.)

doubt; but that men feel it for one another is indisputable, and it is in this that they are our superiors and tutors. Love begins in the attraction towards beauty: it is beauty and not pleasure that draws us on, and this anyone can understand who has eyes to see and a heart to feel. For, however expertly the young girl danced, she would not have held your eyes, ladies, not for one second, had she not also had in her face and body – but especially in her face – some of that beauty which makes her unmistakably the niece of, I mean the daughter of Potone.

Now what is beauty? Here I must distinguish five senses of the question. (a) . . .

'Oh no you don't,' said Phryne, rapping the table with the *archousa*'s baton. 'We're in civilized company here. None of your alphas, betas and gammas. As darling Antiphon used to say . . .'

'Not Antiphon the sophist?' cried Lastheneia with a gasp.[7]

'As darling Antiphon used to say, an argument should flow like love itself, beginning in those tender explorations, and moving ever onwards, guided by the light of sweet desire, to the point of climax. However, let me not anticipate what others may wish to say. Proceed, young lady from Mantinea.'

'How did you know I was from Mantinea?' asked Lastheneia, with another gasp.

'How apart from your charming Arcadian accent, you mean? Isn't it obvious? You have fallen hook, line and sinker for the stuff put about by the fraudulent priestess there, Diotima, who is in fact a distant cousin of mine.'[8]

'Who?' asked the girl.

'Diotima,' Phryne replied. 'You mean you have never *heard* of her? What can they teach you in that place?'

Here poor Lastheneia was at such a loss that she sat down and hid her face in her sleeve. But her neighbours, leaning across to comfort her, lifted the goblet to her lips, and soon she was on her feet once more, swaying slightly, her pretty brown eyes shining, and with a hot wine-flush burning along her cheeks.

---

[7] Presumably not, if Antiphon the orator (who was executed, as the records suggest, before Phryne was born) was identical with Antiphon the sophist. Of course, it is just possible that Phryne is referring to Antiphon, Plato's half brother.

[8] It is highly unlikely that the Diotima mentioned by Socrates in Plato's *Symposium* should still have been alive in Phryne's day. On the other hand, Phryne and Socrates are clearly referring to the same person.

Now what is beauty? she began again. Is it something that the animals know? Do animals stare entranced at their chosen mates and contemplate their form with pleasure? By no means, ladies. Nor do they, as the Orphics pretend, know the charms of music, the dignities of architecture, the thrill of painting or poetry. Nor do they look on the work of the gods, and enrich their souls through contemplation of its ineffable mystery. In all these things they are unvisited by the Muses, and without the organ of delight. Only reasonable beings are awake to beauty, for only they, studying appearances, can perceive the ideas that shine in them.

Therefore I say to you, ladies, that *eros*, which awakens only to the thrill of beauty, is far indeed from the promptings of sensual desire, of which animals have their fill. In us the animal is cunningly mingled with the divine. In our nature, woven together as in a tapestry, are the coarse threads of sensuality and the pure gold of *eros*. And I would say to you, ladies, that it behoves you to unravel that tapestry and gather up the threads of gold that hide in it, so as to form the globe of light which will illuminate your longing.

This, ladies, is how we should consider love, which is not, as so many poets would have it, a god, but rather a divine spirit, a daimon, which travels freely between the sensuous world in which we live and the realm of heaven, bringing the light of reason down into this our temporary dwelling place, and causing us to see in the eye and the cheek of the beloved some faint but unmistakable glimmer of eternity.

What is it, then, to which love aspires? Beauty cannot be possessed, but only contemplated, and the study of beauty neither consumes nor tarnishes it. If love flows from reason, therefore, it cannot aspire to possess the beauty which excites it: for such a desire would be irrational. Nor does it seek to possess the beloved in any other way: for the beloved is a mortal individual and all the possessions of reason are eternal and universal. Therefore, for the true lover, the beloved is a gateway to something higher and richer, which the lover glimpses in the beloved's form. This higher and richer thing, ladies, is beauty itself, by which I do not mean the beauty of this or that particular body, but the feature that they share, and which draws us to its every instance, just so long as we are rational, and our soul has been purified of the body's base desires. The true lover, who has unravelled the threads of sensual desire and contemptuously discarded them, who has begun to study not just the face of his beloved, but the reason that shows in it, who loves not the beauty of his beloved only, but beauty as such, so that escaping from the mean and meticulous slavery of a single instance he begins to contemplate the great ocean of the beautiful – such a lover, whose being is all aglow, if I may put it so, with the golden light of *eros*, begins at last to find what his soul has all along been hungering for, which is the knowledge of eternal truth, of Being itself.

And there are incontrovertible arguments, ladies, which – were I to rehearse them before you – must infallibly persuade you that the realm of Being, which we glimpse in the experience of beauty, was once known to each of us, in that previous life when, winged with wisdom, the soul travelled in the blessed regions whence it fell. Our earthly life is one long forgetting, ladies, one long betrayal of the mysterious union with Being that defines and furnishes our home. Yet, even in the sensuous world which so distracts us, we glimpse the condition that is ours by nature, and towards which we unceasingly and unknowingly aspire. Thus it happens that, when we behold a god-like face that truly expresses beauty, there comes upon us a shuddering and a reverence as in the presence of a god, and, but for fear of the world's opinion, which has no patience for what it deems to be a kind of madness, we should offer sacrifices to our beloved as to a holy image of the deity itself. And, with the passing of this shuddering, a strange sweating and fever seizes us: for by reason of the stream of beauty entering through our eyes there comes a warmth, whereby the soul's plumage is fostered; and with the warmth the roots of the soul's wings are melted, which for long had been hardened and atrophied so that nothing could grow. Then, as the nourishment of beauty is poured into the stump, the soul's wings spread as they once spread in that other world: and what pain and trouble this causes us, ladies, I need not tell you, as we fret against the body's prison and seek, through the experience of beauty, to be joined again to that higher sphere. It is this, rather than the desire to propagate our species, or the still baser desire to possess the beloved's body, that causes the passions of *eros*, which are well likened to the agonies of death, when the soul strives to free itself for ever from its earthly tethers.[9]

[9] It is clear from this paragraph that the *Phaedrus* was used as a textbook in the Academy. (See *Phaedrus*, 250E–251D.) Since the second half of the *Phaedrus* is about rhetoric, it was both provocative and misleading of Lastheneia to deny that the subject was taught in Plato's school. As to the rest of the curriculum – a matter discussed between Xanthippe and Plato himself in *Xanthippe's Laws* – see the exhaustive study by G. C. Field, *Plato and his Contemporaries*, London, 1930, Chapter 3.

And that, ladies, is why men are so much the better lovers. For when a man loves a man, how easy he finds it to set aside the merely sensual emotions, to unfold the wings of the soul, and to embark on the great ascending flight towards his goal. Men have courage, ambition, knowledge of an open world: is it not natural to them, therefore, to move out of the darkness and comfort of mere sensuality, into the rational sphere of dialogue? By contrast, when a woman loves, she finds it difficult to separate her feelings from the comfort of her lover's body – the feeling of warmth and intimacy, of being protected by his superior strength. The woman seeks therefore to ensnare and entrap her beloved, to bind him in the here and now, to make him hers in body – for little she cares whether he is hers also in soul. And because it is the individual that matters to her, the woman is not released by her love from the world of particulars but on the contrary bound more firmly to it, so as never to ascend to the realm of universal truth which is the object of her soul's true desiring. And when women complain, as did the last speaker, of the fickleness of men, contrasting it with their own imagined constancy, they but record their error, in attaching their love to the sensual world, whose principle is change and whose meaning, therefore, is inconstancy. Better by far to learn from the superior sex, so as to tutor our love, to direct it away from the works of Aphrodite, and to point it, at last, towards the divine sphere of Being, where resides the knowledge for which our spirit yearns.

On that note did Lastheneia sit down, though 'sit' is not quite the word for it: rather, she staggered and swayed towards the table, and finally collapsed backwards in a heap, while the company responded to her speech with muted applause.

Phryne, whose face had not ceased to flicker with impatience as the girl academician spoke, now rose again to her feet.

'Ladies,' she said, 'it is the *archousa*'s privilege to speak out of turn, and I cannot forbear, having listened carefully to the discourse of the learned Mantinean, from framing a reply. And I do this, knowing that I reply not for myself only, but for all of you, who will not, I am sure, readily accept the specious piety with which my predecessor has wrapped the great gifts of Aphrodite, only to bury them. Besides, the time has come to speak of my victory, in honour of which we are here assembled, and the details of which I have yet to reveal.'

At which all the company raised their goblets and cried 'The victory!', beseeching Phryne that she tell the story at once.

PHRYNE'S SPEECH

Shortly, my friends, you will hear it. But first I must lead you once again into the mysterious regions where the Mantinean has pitched her argument, so that you may know what kind of victory it is, of which I am to give an account. For if the Mantinean were right, those conquests of which we women are capable would be no conquests at all. How, pray, do you vanquish a man by scanning his features in search of the universal and the eternal? Surely any self-respecting man would laugh at the woman who fawned on him in such a way. Nor is the Mantinean herself convinced, if I may express an opinion in the matter, by what she has said. Her words may console her for the lack of the love she craves, but they do not describe some higher and nobler alternative. I am willing to bet that, were a god to look into her heart and tell what resides there, he should find a love like yours and mine, focused on some individual man, desiring him as we do. And the proof of this will not be hard to find, even without the help of a god.

(Poor Lastheneia, who had roused herself from her neighbour's lap and flung away the hand which had been cooling her brow with rose-water, began to stare at her adversary with trembling lips. She made as if to speak, thought better of it, and, having drained off another goblet, sank back on her couch with closed and feverish eyelids.)

But to that matter too I shall return, Phryne continued. My subject is not the Mantinean's love, nor my own love, but love in general. Love in general, however, can be understood only through love in particular. I shall therefore describe certain details of my loves, and beg your indulgence, dear ladies, if in doing so I offend your sense of decorum and appear to speak like a man. Yet although, as Pasithea said, men are our inferiors in matters of love, their boldness in speaking of it – which is but the side-effect of their clumsiness in feeling it – is not always to be despised. Let me then begin by telling you my story.

I was born in Thespiae in Boeotia, in the year that Socrates was put to death at Athens. I was still a child when my father, who was a merchant, was lost at sea, and I and my mother moved to Styra in

Euboea. There we lived alone with an old servant, depending on my uncles for support. We kept a frugal household in the country, growing olives and cucumbers for our table, earning extra obols with our weaving, living in justice with our neighbours and piety towards the gods. My mother taught me to read and write, and to love the poets of Hellas. How content we were I need not explain to you, my dear friends. For you surely remember those years when the world seemed on every side to offer its protection, and when the storms which lashed the house in winter served only to increase the warmth within:

> Boreas blows not through the tender maiden
> Who stays with her dear mother in the house,
> Unlearned in the works of golden Aphrodite . . .[10]

How brief are those years of innocence, and how soon do the winds of fortune break down the shutters of the soul! My poor mother died, and I was sent, alone, grieving and full of dread, to a cousin's house in Athens. I was seventeen and my uncles had contracted for my marriage to a wealthy merchant, hoping to recompense themselves thereby for the expense of my upbringing.[11] What confused thoughts I had of love in those days, dear ladies, and how I dreaded the marriage to this unknown and unseen man of wealth and power! Day and night I kept to my room, weeping bitterly for my dear mother, and praying to Artemis to deliver me from my promised fate.

My cousin was older than I, her husband older still, with two sons by an earlier marriage, one of whom, Peleus, still lived in the house.

---

[10] Hesiod, *Works and Days*, 519–521.

[11] Unlikely perhaps. For Phryne was not of Athenian birth, and therefore could not enter into a fully legitimate marriage with a citizen of Athens. This law, introduced by Pericles (who thereby could marry his beloved Aspasia only as a 'left-handed' wife), was, however, increasingly evaded. It is possible that, by the time of Phryne's youth, some easy means had been found to circumvent it. See Alfred E. Zimmern, *The Greek Commonwealth*, Oxford, 1915, pp. 337–9. On the other hand, the evidence of Demosthenes' speech *In Neaeram*, 88ff, suggests that the Athenaeans remained too jealous of the privileges of citizenship, to relax the conditions for acquiring it – one of which being the possession of Athenian descent on both the paternal and the maternal side. As Roger Just has argued (*Women in Athenian Law and Life*, London and New York, 1989) the state's anxiety over citizenship lay at the basis not only of Athenian marriage laws, but also of many of the legal disabilities suffered both by women and by metics.

Often, in those brief moments when the doors of the women's quarters (*gynaikon*) stood open, I would notice the compassionate glances which Peleus cast in my direction, and I was grateful for them, seeing that my grief did not go unnoticed in that otherwise unloving household. It will not surprise you, dear ladies, that sometimes I would linger in the *exedra*, hoping to exchange a word with him, or that I began to leave my room more often, sitting sometimes in a corner of the *aula*, staring expectantly into the middle distance. Not that any thoughts of love had crossed my mind. But my situation emboldened me, and when I caught sight of Peleus – who was strong, well-built, with an expression of comely resolve – I gazed upon him as Nausicaa upon Odysseus.

Peleus seemed at first to take no special notice of me. After a while, I again began to keep to my room, grieving more bitterly, my spirit in disarray. One day, however, when I was reading, the tears dropping from my eyes onto the papyrus, I looked up to see a form standing beneath the lintel. I could not tell whether it were man or woman. But when Peleus stepped forward, with the noble firmness of gesture which characterized him, I cried out in alarm and pleasure, and began to tremble where I sat.

'My dear gentle cousin,' he began, 'it grieves me to see your deep unhappiness; and I hope that you will confide in me, so that together we might look for a solution.'

I assured him that the matters which troubled me were irremediable, but thanked him kindly none the less for his concern.

'If you mean your poor mother's death,' he replied, 'then you are of course right that it cannot be changed. But I do suspect that you are referring to something else – something which lies in the future rather than the past, and which therefore may still be remedied.'

My heart thrilled to hear these words; I let forth a sigh which Peleus, I do not doubt, was quick to interpret, though its meaning was a mystery to me, and the papyrus slipped from my hand onto the floor. He stooped to retrieve it and, noticing the golden curls on his neck, ladies, I felt for the first time the power of the goddess in whose honour we are tonight assembled. I wanted to touch, to caress, to kiss, and to be touched, caressed and kissed in turn. And this desire seemed to me quite innocent, a natural extension of the affection that any girl might have for a young and sympathetic relative, who offers sudden comfort in her time of trouble.

'You are silent, my dear cousin,' he continued, 'as though you would have me name the cause of your unhappiness.'

'I am ashamed,' I said, and though my tears had ceased to flow, I do not doubt that my cheeks were the colour of shame.

'Why be ashamed, cousin, when it is others who wrong you, not you who do wrong?'

'I am ashamed before you, cousin, that I do not accept, as a girl should accept, the wise decrees of loving relatives.'

'Loving relatives, indeed, who could give a girl in marriage to a man she has never seen!'

'But a man, cousin, whom they judge to be kind, affectionate, and in every way suitable, and whom I must therefore study to love.'

At this Peleus let out a cry of indignation and began to pace about the room.

'Kind, affectionate, and suitable indeed! Let me tell you, dear cousin, what kind of a man is this Evarchus to whom you are promised in marriage.'

'Ah, cousin,' I cried, 'do not unduly alarm me!'

'It is better that you should know,' he went on, 'so that together we may plan to save you.'

And at those words, my dear ladies, I felt for the first time since my poor mother's death, a ray of hope for the future, and a little spark of warmth amid the cinders of my heart. Peleus went on to give such a picture of Evarchus that for many days I quaked at the very sound of his name: a wanton, cruel, degenerate drunkard, mad in his lust as in his constant quarrelling; fat, sweaty, malodorous and indecent, without a trace of culture and wealthy only by the accident of birth, which had endowed him with a fortune that he was rapidly and ineluctably squandering. Married thrice already, to women whose disappearance had been only imperfectly accounted for, he lived with a fierce concubine from Egypt, who had presented him with a brood of licentious bastards that no man or woman could control. In short, my dears, Peleus did not merely plant in me the seeds of alarm; he caused me to fall on my knees in terror and beg him by holy Artemis and all the gods to save me from the fate that awaited me, or else to help me then and there to death.

He clasped my hands, stroked my hair, and, gently raising me to my feet, spoke golden words of comfort.

'My dear cousin,' he said. 'If I were but half a man I should do my best to save you. And stirred to my depths as I am by your gentleness and beauty, I could see you given in marriage to such a creature only on the day of my death. Therefore be of good cheer, and obey me in all that I have planned for you.'

So saying, he kissed me lightly on the forehead and left the room. How impatiently I waited for his next visit you may well imagine, ladies; just as you may imagine my distress to find him taking no opportunity to cross my path. I slept ill that night, visited by many an evil dream, and again by dreams of a kind that I had never known before, in which the breath of Peleus played about my face and neck like a soothing breeze in summer. I sat down to my weaving next day, hoping and dreading in equal measure; and, finding no Peleus in the house, my dread for a while prevailed. My cousins, observing my loss of appetite, supposed that I was ill, and counselled rest and seclusion – to which I willingly agreed. And once back in my room I flung myself upon the couch and gave vent to my tears, beating my head against the pillow, until at last, in utter weariness, I gained the brief refuge of Morpheus.

When I awoke, Peleus was standing beside the couch, looking down on me with such warm desire that I was blinded by him, and hid my eyes.

'Dear cousin,' he said. 'I have arranged everything for your rescue. Take what you will need and, when the moon rises, wait for me inside the gate to the servants' quarters. Be of good cheer, for I shall be beside you; and whatever befalls us, it can only be better than the fate which they decreed.'

I took his hand and held it to my cheek, so as to bathe it in my tears of gratitude. And there were tears too in his eyes, as he took his brief leave of me.

He was waiting in the street, and opened the gate just as soon as he heard my footstep within. I trembled as I followed him: for what freeborn girl would enter boldly into so rash an adventure? Yet my heart was soaring with joy and resolve. The cottage we came to was old and ill-cared for, standing amid ruins left unrepaired since the war. Inside, however, it was neat enough, and he had put together some scraps of furniture, with a rather fetching ignorance as to what a woman's needs might be. He gave me ink and papyrus, and told me to compose a letter to my uncles, saying that I was returning forthwith to

Euboea, and would be sailing in the ship which followed the one that brought my message.

'But I cannot go home!' I protested, 'they would kill me!'

'Exactly,' he replied. 'I have therefore arranged for a ship to follow the one that bears your letter, carrying the huddled form of a lady who, once out at sea, will leap from the prow into the waters. After a fruitless search the sailors will proceed to Styra, bearing the sad news of your death.'

'And who is this lady, who is to sacrifice herself for me?'

'No lady at all,' he replied, 'but my slave Ducetius, an excellent diver, who will quickly regain the shore, where I shall be waiting to grant his freedom.'

'And thereafter I am to stay here, a dead woman, who never dares to show her face?'

'My dear cousin: as you know, in this Athens of ours, it is not dead women but living women who dare not show themselves. Be patient, therefore, and when the time is ripe I shall lead you forth from this temporary prison – which is in truth less of a prison than the room you have left – and make you my bride.'

The vagueness of the plan made less impression on me, ladies, than the glorious promise of its goal, towards which all my own desires already tended. For what woman, rescued by an ardent and handsome protector, can easily withhold her love? And when Peleus crowned his words with a flood of kisses, I bathed in them as a nymph bathes in a fountain, radiant with the promise of desire.

I had no company but that of an old servant whom he had provided. But each day he visited, and I impatiently awaited him, weaving meanwhile, or reading; sometimes composing verses and songs of my own. Like a dog, I attached myself to him completely, counting the hours until he would next appear, and sickening with grief should he be only a moment late. Two weeks passed, and I had read the whole of Aeschylus and half of Thucydides before daring to broach the question which concerned me.[12]

'My dear Peleus,' I said to him one evening, after he had set down a basket containing the cheese, bread and olives which were to be our meal. 'Can it be that you have encountered some difficulty that you are

---

[12] An amazing feat, if she is telling the truth, since seventy or more plays of Aeschylus were extant in Phryne's day.

reluctant to reveal to me, hoping in your kindness that it may be overcome without my knowledge? For, although I promised you to be patient, I cannot help remarking on the fact that our marriage has not been first among the topics to which our conversations have tended.'

'Dearest Phryne,' he replied. 'Full well do you know how difficult it is, even for so faithful a husband as Orpheus, to bring back a wife from the underworld. But I am on the point of success, and await only one small detail, which I hope may shortly be accomplished.'

'And what is that?' I asked.

'The marriage of Evarchus,' he answered.

'Evarchus!' I cried; and at the sound of this name the shameful reality of my predicament was borne in upon me, as on a flood. For indeed Peleus was right. I could not appear in public while Evarchus' claim on me was yet alive. My heart sank at the thought of the months I might have to wait. But Peleus reached over to stroke my hair, assuring me that already Evarchus had overcome his grief for the lost Phryne, whose form he had but glimpsed through a key-hole, and was paying court to the family of a richer and more suitable girl.

As he spoke, however, I could not help noticing a certain distracted expression, which stole across his features, cancelling the handsome resolve which was accustomed to shine in them, as a cloud cancels the sun. How often, as the days wore on, was I to catch sight of this new expression, which sent a chill through my body, ladies, as though the light and warmth by which I lived were suddenly extinguished. It seemed to me that Peleus had other thoughts in mind than those he confessed to, and this impression stirred a dread to which I could attach no name.

Nor was I wrong. For that night, as I was preparing myself for bed, having dismissed the slave and sprinkled a libation of water to Artemis, I heard the key turn in the lock of the outside door. It could only be Peleus, and my pleasure at the thought of seeing him was mingled with apprehension at his designs in visiting me so late. Hastily completing my prayer, I threw my tunic about my shoulders, and faced the door through which he must enter.

Enter he did, ladies, and not the room only. I hardly need explain to you how I struggled, not with him so much as with myself, wanting what I feared and fearing what I wanted. Like Creusa in the play, I called for my mother, whose shade must surely have died again in Hades, hearing her daughter's cry. But at last his mouth, closing upon mine, extinguished my protests, so that 'all shamelessly he bedded me, forcing Aphrodite's joy'.[13]

Injustice, my dear friends, has many forms. Young Aristotle interrupted our lesson the other day in order to recount a lecture of Xanthippe's upon this subject, which I beg to mention in that distinguished lady's presence, because it is so very pertinent to our theme. According to Xanthippe, Aristotle said, there are the small injustices, in which we take what is not our own by force or deception. And of these theft is the prime example. From such small injustices the victim may recover, when her right is reasserted and her property restored. But there are graver injustices, such as calumny and slander, which the victim does not so easily overcome, since they may alter her reputation forever in this world. And even if she should see herself vindicated at last, some taint will always remain of the evil tittle-tattle that injured her. Most serious of all, however, are those injustices that destroy the very being of the victim, so that afterwards she is bereft of the life and thread of her will. Murder is one such injustice; but as great, to my thinking, is the wrong we suffer, when we are compelled by force to Aphrodite's altar. And never is the injustice greater, than when love stirs in us for the criminal, and those forced embraces are sweetened by our own desire for them. For truly the work of Aphrodite is a divine work, and nothing of the old remains thereafter.

All my innocent endeavours, my attempts in the face of misfortune to retain the thread of personality, which points clear and certain from past to future, telling me, even in the midst of grief, that I am what I am and will be what I was: all this was destroyed in a moment by Peleus. And yet, even as my life fell in ruins about me, I loved and wanted him. When, after the first storm had swept through me, and I returned to my senses, my tears of desolation were mingled with the sighs of fresh desire. Peleus would have wronged me far less, had I not been already his.

My dear friends, I know that you are awaiting the end of my story, and those philosophical reflections which, for such ladies as yourselves, are the true purpose of narrating it. So I will be brief. Know then that, for many days and nights thereafter, 'desire that loosens the limbs'[14] subdued me. And although I reproached Peleus, that he had

[13] Euripides, *Ion*, 891–6.

[14] Archilochus, Fr. 196.

seized by force what I had longed with all my heart to give him freely, I still believed that he would find the way to bring me forth from my temporary prison as his wife.

As the weeks wore on, however, I began to notice that he evaded my questions, and looked increasingly distracted whenever our conversation turned to the future. And when one day he came to inform me that he was leaving Athens on business, and would be absent for a month, a dreadful premonition stole over me. I looked into his eyes, and saw that his soul flitted away from my glances like a hunted fox, seeking some cover into which I could not venture. And I forbore from telling him that, wife or harlot, I was to be the mother of his child.

Well, ladies, I had the time during his absence to meditate on my condition. And truly it was not an enviable one. For what free-born woman would choose the life of a metic, with neither lawful husband nor legal guardian, pregnant, propertyless, friendless and officially dead?[15] I realized then that I must act on my own behalf. I therefore took some of the money that Peleus had left for my maintenance, and sent the old servant to buy clothes – boys' clothes, of the kind that our two guests, she of Mantinea and she from Africa, were wearing when they arrived. With industry and skill we succeeded in creating a plausible pastiche of manhood, and the newly created Phrynis, his hair hidden within a shepherd's bonnet, ventured forth into the streets of Athens, there to mingle with his fellow men.

My first act was to enquire at my cousin's house for news of Phryne. I gave out that I was from her family in Styra, and that, having received no word of her for some weeks, I wished anxiously to know whether she were still alive. Could it be, I asked the servant, that she had met her father's fate upon those treacherous straits? Without answering, the domestic disappeared into the house and returned with my cousin's husband, who was foaming at the mouth in anger.

[15] Resident aliens (metics – μέτοικοι) could only exceptionally own property on Athenian soil. Under the laws of most Greek cities, a woman could neither sue nor be sued in the courts, and therefore required a guardian (κύριος) through whom to exercise her legal rights. Moreover, as mentioned above, note 9, metics could not enter a legally binding marriage with an Athenian citizen. These disabilities notwithstanding, both metics and women could lead prosperous and independent lives in fourth-century Athens: see David M. Schaps, *Economic Rights of Women in Ancient Greece*, Edinburgh, 1979. Phryne's guardian, before her 'death', would have been an uncle in Styra. She goes on to solve the problem posed by this fact in characteristic manner.

'What is the meaning of this?' he shouted, barely looking at me, for which mercy I was particularly glad. 'Who are you, young man, to be prying into matters about which the whole of Styra is in any case very well informed?'

I took a step or two backwards, and endeavoured to conceal my face within the loose collar of my tunic.

'I am a cousin of Phryne on her mother's side,' I declared in my huskiest voice.

'I very much doubt it,' he continued, 'for we are not on speaking terms with Phryne's family. They hold us responsible for her disappearance. And I'm damned if we are going to look for the slut.'

'But did she not drown at sea?' I asked.

'First I've heard of it,' he said. 'Though I can't think of a better fate for her.'

'I see,' I muttered, my suspicions growing with every word. 'But her uncles received a letter, saying she was travelling home rather than marry the man who had been chosen for her.'

'A likely story! Listen, young man, I don't know who you are or where you get your information, but either you are the victim of some deception, or you are yourself trying to create one. Phryne's uncles claim to have heard nothing from her, and so far as we know she has decided to become a whore. Indeed, my son Peleus swears he saw her only the other day, plying for trade in the Agora. I say, what's the matter? You're not going to throw a fit, are you?'

It was a god, surely, who helped me to remain standing, swaying slightly and muttering beneath my breath. But my spirit collapsed entirely.

'Just a minute,' he said. 'Your face is familiar, I could swear I've met you somewhere before. By Zeus, I remember! You're the rascal who cheated me last week, charging two drachmas a sack for half-rotten haricot beans!'

He beckoned to the servant to come forward, and I made off at once, so overcome by shame that I forgot all discretion, and ran as a woman would, one hand at my breast.

I lay on the couch where I had been sacrificed. Sometimes I slumbered fitfully; at other times I stared about me like a creature half mad, seeing monsters in every shadow, and hearing the wings of furies as they beat around my head. I called on the gods to avenge me; I invoked my mother's spirit, and the spirits of all my dead. I cried aloud, I wept, I tore my garments and poured ashes in my hair. And so I remained for several days, dead to the world.

And then my thoughts turned to Evarchus. Of all men living, it seemed to me, he alone could be my avenger: none other had been wronged by Peleus' action – apart from those, like my uncles, who would place the blame on me. Would not some vestige of masculine pride cause Evarchus to prepare a punishment for my seducer? I thought of this, my emotions in disarray. And with my little experience of life, having acquired my knowledge of the soul from Aeschylus and Euripides, I imagined that the world would rise to my emotions: justice, vengeance and piety stepping onto the stage in human form. Such is the result of an exclusively literary education, my dears. It took me several years to realize that the only harm that can come to the seducer comes from his victim, and that usually she loves him too much to see the action through.

It is a measure of the destruction that had been wrought in me, ladies, that I should turn in my sorrow to Evarchus, whose very name had caused me, some weeks before, to shrink in terror. Yet this is the crazy plan I formed. I sent the servant to enquire after him, and, when I had his address, ventured forth myself, in my masculine disguise, to seek vengeance for my cousin Phryne.

In all this sequence of events, ladies, nothing astonished me more than my encounter with Evarchus. The man into whose presence the servant ushered me was not the fat, sweaty lecher whom Peleus had painted, but a noble and dignified youth, with kindly eyes, a studious brow, and a faintly sorrowing expression, who looked at me with sympathy as he bade me tell my tale. Just such a man, in short, as I should willingly have married, had Peleus not already made me his.

And here, ladies, I must express my difference of opinion with the girl from Mantinea, who argued, you will remember, that the goal of *eros* is not to possess the other, since beauty cannot be possessed, nor in any other way to reduce or consume him. And yet those who know the work of Aphrodite will surely agree that possession is the correct word for the state in which men hold us, when we are bound to them by the goddess's laws. That which we might have given we may no longer give elsewhere; and our will and our desire are yoked to another. True it is, that we do not aim for this condition; but Aphrodite aims on our behalf, and this is her goal, and the goal of her son Eros too. That is why, being possessed, we too aim to possess – to enslave our enslaver, lest he abuse our love.

You may well understand, my friends, that I had no words to speak my tale of woe to Evarchus. I could only stare at him, pale, speechless and betrayed.

'My dear young man,' he said. 'I fear you are the victim of some dreadful calamity. Have the goodness, I beseech you, to speak of it. Who knows whether there might yet be a remedy.'

And at these gentle words, no longer able to contain my tears, I flung myself upon the couch that lay against the wall.

'I see,' he said at last, 'not a young man at all. Let me look at you. I say – you're not the young lady from Chios, are you?'

I shook my head.

'Phew! That's a relief. Delos? The boat to Syros? – No, I'd recognize that one. Sunium? Piraeus?'

And at each shake of my head, his expression of relief and puzzlement deepened. Swallowing back my tears, I addressed him finally with the only words that were left to me.

'I am Phryne,' I said; 'she of Styra, who was to be your wife.'

He looked at me for a moment, and then said,

'There must be some mistake.'

'Are you not Evarchus?' I asked.

'Well yes,' he answered, 'I suppose I am.'

This less than forthright reply caused me to hesitate. However, bursting into a warm and candid smile, he went on:

'Of course I am. Evarchus. That's me. Yes. Evarchus. But I was not aware, I mean, I had not the honour, that is to say, no one had troubled to inform me that I was to be married.'

'I see.'

'Are you sure you haven't mixed me up with Evarchus the corn-merchant, in Melite, near the Pnyx?'

'Is he fat, malodorous, with an Egyptian concubine and a menagerie of repulsive children?'

'No, not really. That is to say, she is from Cyprus; and so far as I know there are no children. He *is* somewhat on the large side. But if he smells, it is probably in the way some animals do, out of shyness, you know. Once you get to know him, he's rather sweet.'

'You know him well?'

'Oh, so-so. Anyway, it sounds as though he's your man.'

Everywhere I turned, it seemed, the ground gave way beneath me. I could not be certain that the man before me was not my intended husband. Yet nothing in his manner betrayed any knowledge of the fact. As I discovered in time, ladies, it is in the nature of men to deny the existence of a woman, rather than acknowledge an unwanted obligation. I wept again, tears of frustration and despair.

'I say, steady on,' he said. 'Let's see if we can't sort this out. Why don't you tell me the whole story?'

Because his voice was kind and I was desperate, weak woman that I was, I told him – not everything, but the outlines. He nodded sympathetically, often beating his fist into the palm of his hand, and swearing to teach that Peleus a lesson. When I had finished he stood in silence for a while, his fingers pressed to his brow in thought.

'You know something?' he said at last. 'I rather admire you. I really do. And if that Peleus has got any sense, he will surely marry you.'

'Do you imagine I could be his wife,' I asked in astonishment, 'after the foul trick he has played on me?'

'I don't see why not. It is in the nature of men to play foul tricks on women – and vice versa, I might add. If you let that stand in the way of marriage, you will be a spinster for life.'

'Indeed,' I said, 'that is precisely what I intend.'

'And your child?'

'I shall leave the poor thing in the temple of Zeus, as befits a creature who has only the gods to protect him.'

'Yes, I suppose that is the correct solution,' he said, looking somewhat lighter. 'And then?'

'How can I think so far ahead, when my soul is boiling at this injustice?'

'Consider Achilles. He had the whole plot of the Iliad worked out, just as soon as Agamemnon offended him.'

'Achilles,' I answered, 'was different.'

'In certain ways, perhaps. But you know, I was reading a most interesting pamphlet only yesterday, which argued that the real cause of Achilles' rage was *eros*, and that he avenged himself on Agamemnon, not as a man but as a woman would. It was very learned, and made some fine comparisons with the Calyce of Stesichorus, a most interesting poem, which I am sure you must know. Come to think of it, the Calyce is more suited to your case, in a way. I am thinking especially of the lines which begin . . .'

'I am really not in the mood for literary criticism,' I said, interrupting him.[16]

'Of course not. Sorry. So let's talk about your problems. If you are not going to marry Peleus, then clearly it would be better to avoid him. That way the gods might grant you another chance.'

'How can I avoid him?'

And I confess, ladies, that even though I hated Peleus then and despised him, the thought that I should never see him again stirred in me a profound desolation. And – yes, why do I not confess it? Even as I sat there brooding miserably upon my ruin, the image returned of those sweet hours of pleasure, in which the goddess bound us each to each like twisting vines. I did my best to drown these memories, while Evarchus unfolded his plan.

'I have a house,' he said, 'just below the Acropolis in Collytus – not a bad district, safe, salubrious, within easy reach of markets, theatres and so on. As luck would have it, I have no present use for it, and it needs a tenant. In fact you would do me a favour by living there: you might think of tidying it up, maybe doing some decorating. I could make you a small allowance – what do you reckon, three drachmas a week?'

I shrugged my shoulders contemptuously.

'Yes, three should see you through. And I'm sure we could dig out a spare slave for you: there's a few gathering dust in the shed behind the house, and they could do with a bit of exercise.'

'I should be most grateful, sir, if you could tell me where this is leading.'

He looked at me from his innocent blue eyes, and then stopped in his tracks as though struck by a thunderbolt.

'Great Zeus!' he cried. 'You don't suspect me of . . . You don't imagine that . . .'

'I simply would like to know what follows, when I have been hidden for the second time, and have abandoned my poor child to the mercy of Zeus. Do I stay in that house forever?'

'By no means, Phryne – may I call you Phryne?'

'I suppose you may.'

---

[16] It is a great pity that Phryne was not disposed to continue this literary conversation, since we were clearly about to be given a fragment of the lost *Calyce* of Stesichorus, summarized in Athenaeus, *Deipnosophistae*, 14, 519D.

'By no means, Phryne. You may come forth at last, with a new name and a virgin reputation, like Creusa, to become a queen.'

'And to live with some other man than Peleus?'

'Eventually, yes. Why not?'

'You don't see why not!' I exclaimed, and he looked at me curiously.

'Now listen, Phryne. First, you say you can have nothing to do with Peleus. Then you imply that you can have nothing to do with anyone else. Is this not a contradiction?'

'I see no contradiction.' And indeed, ladies, at the time I did not.

'Sir,' I went on. 'I have wasted enough of your time, and am grateful to you for your kind advice. I pray that you will not be offended if I choose to ignore it.'

I made as if to leave, but with a surprising gesture he stepped across my path.

'I'm sorry,' he said, 'I can't let you go like this. It is my duty to prevent you. Caught as you are between your hatred of Peleus and your love for him, you will most certainly do something foolish, and destroy both yourself and the child which you are carrying.'

I hesitated, and he pressed his advantage home.

'Return to the house in which he installed you, and disaster must ensue. You will embark on some ghastly Euripidean murder, for such, I gather, is the fashion; or he, dreading discovery, will murder you and the child. You cannot return to Euboea; nor are you welcome in your cousin's house. You have no friends in Athens, save one, if I may count myself your friend. And as for Evarchus – the, er, true Evarchus I mean – do you think he would be pleased to discover you are still alive, and himself pipped at the post for the most beautiful girl in Hellas?'

'Alas!' I cried in my helplessness.

'One place alone in the whole of Athens, the whole of Attica, can offer you protection, and to that place, out of compassion for you and the child, I give you the key. No strings attached. So why refuse?'

Well, my dear ladies, I allowed myself to be persuaded. And in truth, had I not done so, a rather brilliant career would certainly have been cut short after the very first steps. Indeed, I believe that a god decided for me, having the future good of Athens at heart. It was therefore in the spare house of Evarchus, whom I may truly call the false Evarchus, in order to distinguish him, you understand, from the true one, that I henceforth made my home.

And now, ladies, I come to the crux of my story, which is taking rather longer than I intended. Two dreadful experiences awaited me, as they await all women whom the goddess has chosen for our profession. First, with numb and fainting heart, I left my boy upon Zeus' altar, praying to the god of hospitality that the poor mite would find protection. And having done this thing, I divided myself in two, separating the mother of the gentle Achilles from the woman who had abandoned him, and who would henceforth trust no man beyond the terms that she could dictate. And yet, my dears, there is not an hour that passes of the day or night, when my thoughts do not return to that sweet unseeing face, and to those little hands, so wondrous in their miniature perfection, as they vainly clutched at the fingers that discarded them. And still my poor breast yearns for those lips that never suckled there.

Here Phryne paused with a sigh. A slight breeze, passing through the hall, caused the torches to glow more brightly, illuminating the faces that gazed speechless upon the speaker. And Arete marvelled to see the tears of whore and courtesan, as each heard again the piteous cries of some abandoned infant. At last, having drunk deeply from her goblet, Phryne resumed her story.

So now let me tell you of the second dread experience, though surely you have guessed at it by now. I found that I was not indifferent to the kind voice and manly form of my protector. And although he spoke still, on occasion, of my resurrection, and of the untarnished name that would be mine by adoption, I saw that he neither believed in such a future nor greatly cared. This false Evarchus had protected me for his own dishonourable purposes, and the new Phryne was not only aware of the fact, but willing to meet him on terms. He was a wealthy man, and before yielding to him, I was determined to secure my independence, begging, borrowing, wheedling and using all those arts we women know so well, in order to fill my coffer. This done, I led him to my couch, expecting the same unthinking violence I had received from Peleus. To my surprise, however, he hardly dared to touch me, and it was I who was forced to lead. Nor was it unpleasant to be possessed by this body full of trepidation. Here, ladies, began my career as a teacher. And I may say, with due modesty, that my evening classes for adults have been of far greater benefit to this Athens of ours, than the day-schools for boys, for all that the Mantinean may say to the contrary.

My experience with Evarchus was terrible, for the very reason that it was pleasant. I realized that Phryne could belong to more than one man: and if two, why not three, five, a dozen, a score? A line had been drawn forever across the innocent life that was mine: having abandoned my love-child, and found pleasure with a man who was not his father, I had ceased to be counted among my race, and was alone in the world.

Well, ladies, you know that I made a success of this solitude that Peleus forced upon me. But before dwelling on my present circumstances, I wish to relate another episode of my early days, since it will illustrate the philosophical thoughts that you are impatiently awaiting. Although I had found comfort and pleasure in Evarchus' arms, I was not so hard a woman that I did not grieve over my great misfortune. And often I would think of Peleus and our days together, so that gradually, as I became accustomed to my new life, my bitterness receded, and tenderness returned. I longed to relieve my feelings to Peleus: I wanted to accuse him, to humble him, to tell him of his abandoned child; above all I wanted him to ask my forgiveness, and who knows whether I might not grant it, after suitable penance for his crime?

One day it came to my notice that Peleus was in Athens, from which city he had been absent for over a year. I sent a note to his house, informing him that an old friend was briefly in town, and wished to meet him in person, with a message for him alone. I gave my address, and a time when I knew that Evarchus would be away on business. And I waited impatiently in the *aula* for the miscreant to be ushered in. Seeing me, ladies, he fell on his knees in astonishment.

'Phryne!' he cried. 'My dear, my long-lost Phryne! I thought you were dead! I thought – yes – I feared you had done away with yourself!'

I looked at him scornfully.

'You imagine I would kill myself for so slight a worm as you?' I asked.

'Not for my sake, no. It never crossed my mind,' he went on in passionate tones. 'But when I looked for you in our little hideout and found that you had departed; when I discovered that you had come, thinly disguised as a boy, to our house, and that my father, recognizing you, had cast me for your benefit in a villain's role, what was I to imagine? I searched all Athens for you, resolved to go down on my knees, as I go down now, and beg your forgiveness for my cowardly delay, which I would end at once in marriage, with or without my father's consent. Alas, I could not find you. I returned day and night to our little cottage, sick with remorse. How many tears have I poured onto the couch there, vainly calling on the gods to restore the lovely form that once had lain in it! I left Athens at last, wandering from shrine to shrine, invoking the help now of this god, now of that, until after a year of penitence my prayer was heard, and I was brought before you. Thanks be to great Apollo. Alas, however, I am come too late! For here you are, installed amid such luxury, and I can only imagine that you have married another, far wiser, richer and happier than I.'

Don't ask me, ladies, whether I believed this speech, any more than I believed that the false Evarchus was not also the true one. I had learned to look on men as they do on us, as creatures to whom reason was given, only so that we might bend them to our will. And their words had become, for me, ambiguous signs of the spirit, to be interpreted only with caution and with a view to enhancing one's power. Nevertheless, while I did not trouble myself to ascertain whether it was truth or falsehood that flowed from those lips, I could not forbear from studying the lips themselves, and remembering their kisses. I fell into a dream, and smiled down on him, so that he too became part of my dream, and 'the goddess put sweet desire in my heart.'[17]

At length I bid him rise and listen to my story. I told it to him with many detours and embellishments; in a nutshell, however, it was this: I had fled our cottage, I said, in shame and humiliation, travelling to Styra and my mother's grave, which I fully intended to share with her. Arriving, I found myself heir to a considerable property, which had come to me from my mother's aunt. And with this property I had acquired a new and trusted guardian – a long-lost brother of my mother herself, before whom my uncles were forced to bow. My uncles could no longer dispose of me as they wished, and would be forced in any case to respect a woman who could pay an army of mercenaries to defend her. In due course, after much agonizing at my mother's grave, I was dissuaded by the priestess of Cybele from my impious purpose. I decided to live, to bring up the child, and to found a hostel for abandoned women in Styra. The child was born, but died

[17] Homeric *Hymn to Aphrodite*, 143.

almost at once, I said, of distemper – at which Peleus made a most creditable show of grief. The hostel too was a failure, since the priestess began to use it as a recruiting ground for corybants. Nevertheless, the project restored my desire to live, and I returned after a few months to Athens bringing my new guardian with me. To complete the deception I had fitted out a slave in this role, and now introduced him with all ceremony to Peleus, as my dear uncle Apollodorus. Thanks to my wealth, I went on, all the disabilities of a metic had been cancelled by the *boule* itself.[18] I was rich, independent and unwed. But I found that I could not begin my new life without first setting eyes upon the man who had ruined me.

'Not ruined, Phryne!' he cried. 'I beseech you to come to me again!'

'As your mistress?' I asked, with a sarcastic smile.

'As my wife!' he cried.

'Then, my dear Peleus,' I said, 'let us take our fill of love, and discuss the arrangements.'

You might say, ladies, that I had got things in the wrong order here. But Aphrodite, in her wisdom, saw further than I did. Never before, ladies, and seldom since, have I enjoyed the goddess's work as I did on that night, and on the night that followed – when, however, it was Evarchus who shared my bed. And yet how is this possible? For of course, I did not merely despise Peleus, I was scheming against him, as I schemed against Evarchus too. And in some measure it was the promise of triumph that heightened my desire.

Within a week I had transferred to my coffer all that Peleus possessed in gold and jewels, in exchange for a worthless sheet of papyrus, signed by 'Apollodorus', conveying the house and its contents to Peleus. This bargain, from which he imagined himself to be greatly the gainer, was ancillary to a marriage agreement, which 'Apollodorus' also executed, to be conveyed in due course for signature to Peleus' father. Marriage or no marriage, however, I now had enough money to live as I wished, and Peleus nothing but a useless sheet of papyrus, and

---

[18] Did the *boule* (the supreme Council) have this power? Certainly Pericles had wished for it; but the actual status of metics is still a matter of great controversy. By the end of the fourth century BC there were some 10,000 metics in Athens, including several prominent independent women.

Only the full assembly (the *ecclesia*) could grant citizenship (see Demosthenes, *In Neaeram*, 88f), to which Phryne, as a woman, would not have been entitled in any case. Presumably Phryne is implying that her children by Peleus would have the right to it.

the future humiliation of learning that the house I had pretended to confer on him, belonged in fact to his rival.

Rather than bore you, dear ladies, with the details of my two affairs, let me say only that they ended at last without violence, myself installed elsewhere, mistress of a rather sweet though undistinguished teacher of rhetoric. Evarchus and Peleus were so impoverished by my stratagems that they were obliged to live together in the house that I had vacated, Evarchus having sold his remaining property and Peleus (who, unlike Evarchus, had some skills as a businessman) earning enough for their upkeep. They lived together amicably enough, for, as you have no doubt guessed, my dears, they were not unacquainted, and their scores against each other were by now roughly equal.

I come at last to my answer to the girl from Mantinea. When I lay with Peleus on that night of pleasure, what compelled me? Whatever it was, it is this force that we honour in the names of Aphrodite and Eros, and which is the making and undoing of our sex. So let me say that, whatever drew me to Peleus, it was not his virtue, for I well knew that he had none. On that night I saw him for what he was, and what in truth I had long suspected: a man who was neither brave, nor honest, nor just, and who, if he appeared clever, was clever only with the cunning of a fox. And I was resolved to prove his lack of wisdom, and to triumph over his injustice. The man that I held in my arms had all the vices, and was a poor specimen indeed of a rational being. Nevertheless, although my love for him was mixed with pain, and both pain and love had dwindled, love him I did in that moment.

But now, the Academician will say, if it was not virtue that drew me on, was I not merely the victim of the lust that drives the animals, and which causes them, they know not why, to offer a particular part of their anatomy to passing members of the other sex? After all, she will argue, on the very next night I lay with Evarchus; how, then, can the object of my desire have been either Peleus or Evarchus? And how can my pleasure have depended upon anything but the generality of their sex – that object which, though it never ceases to arouse in us, dear friends, the greatest wonder and amusement, is, when all is said and done, but a mobile sausage, though of a kind that could be displayed on no respectable table? In which case, the Mantinean will say, neither Eros nor Aphrodite had a part in it, any more than they have a part in the scratching of an itch or the quenching of thirst at a stream.

But here, ladies, is the most wondrous thing, and I bid you reflect on it, for it illustrates to my thinking the way in which the most ordinary matters are full of paradox. On the first night it was precisely Peleus I wanted, on the second night Evarchus. And supposing, as I prepared myself for Peleus, Evarchus should have stepped between us and Peleus declared, 'Here, take my friend, for he is well-endowed as I am' – do you not suppose that all desire would instantly have frozen in me, and that I should have at once turned away in outrage? Of course. Yet had I been thirsting for water, would not one stream serve as well as the next? And is not one brush as good as another for scratching the itchy part?

Nor is it only in our first preparations that we respond so exclusively. When the rites of lustration are accomplished, and we have, with all decorum, entered Aphrodite's precinct, there to give way to our desire, fondling, kissing and caressing as the goddess prompts, do we suppose that it is just any body that we touch, or that another body would serve us as well? By no means, ladies. Holding the sceptre of Peleus it is Peleus I hold, and not some instrument of pleasure. And although Peleus resemble Evarchus in this part as closely as you will (which I recall was not the case, being more Ionic in style beside the Doric of his rival), it is not merely senseless but in some way disgusting to suggest that the sceptre of Evarchus might have served the present purpose. The very excitement of the flesh with which I receive my lover's body is directed upon *him*, and on no specific part of him. And if, from some trick or misfortune (for this too is among the deceptions that men can play on us, dear ladies) I discover that it is not my lover at all, but a stranger who has stolen my favours, then my excitement is an error, like the grief that is felt over one who is still alive, or joy at a non-existent triumph. Discovering my error, I freeze at once.

If this were not so, ladies, where would be the pleasure of a new lover – who, we may suppose, would differ little enough in his anatomical provisions from the last one, but who arouses in us a wholly new excitement, simply because he is other than the one with whom we are presently familiar? Do you think animals know anything of this, or that they experience, as we do, the great torments of jealousy that flow from it?

For here, I believe, lies the source of jealousy (which is the most mysterious of Aphrodite's gifts to us): that my lover should be aroused to desire by a person who is other than me. If desire were for the generality of the other sex, then each new desire has the same object as the last, and my lover's emotion in my arms is no different from his emotion in the arms of my rival. In such a case, jealousy would be senseless: for how could I resent my lover's feeling precisely what I wish him to feel, which is desire for the sex that is mine? Since I, like my rival, am not the object of desire, but merely its occasion, why have either of us cause for grief?

Yet jealousy, my dear ladies, is far from senseless; on the contrary, as I hope to show to you in a moment, it is the proof of love. For jealousy tells us that what we seek through the work of Aphrodite is not the abstract idea of beauty as the Mantinean describes it, nor any other abstract or general thing, but the particular man himself, in order to possess and be possessed by him. Hence my lover's desire for another is not merely an instance of the desire that he shows towards myself: on the contrary, it is the very negation of his desire for me, the poison of my own desire, and a threat to my existence as his beloved.

But the mystery, ladies, is by no means solved. For when we ask what he is, this individual whom we seek through the work of Aphrodite, we can find no answer. I grant that the philosophers divide the world into particulars and universals, and do their best to persuade us, like the Mantinean, that only the second are really real. But there are particular carrots, particular cucumbers, particular sausages – and none of these, I warrant, is an object of desire. The particular cucumber serves as well as any other that resembles it, and in this the philosophers are surely right, that the particular is subsumed by the universal, and derives its reality from its form. The individual, however, is precisely that which cannot be substituted, as one man cannot be substituted for another in the act of love. Our world is full of particulars. But it is short on individuals: indeed, apart from gods and humans – and perhaps those things like works of music and poetry in which the human personality is distilled – I find nothing in the world that is indispensable, immeasurable, irreplaceable as individuals must be. And that is my reason for agreeing with the Mantinean, that the animals know nothing of love, and that only rational beings are subject to its power. For only rational beings have an idea of the individual other, and only rational beings can exemplify it.

Here, ladies, I will give you the fruit of my years of meditation on the act of love, and all that it has meant to me and my pupils. It is certain that rational beings alone are virtuous: but it is not virtue that we desire in the throes of Aphrodite, even if we wish for virtue in our lover, so that our love should be secure. It is certain too that rational beings alone aspire towards the truth: but it is not truth that I seek through my lover, who may be deceiver and deceived as my dear Peleus was to me, at the very moment when most I coveted his embraces. One thing alone fits the rational being for desire, and this is his existence as an individual. He alone of all creation is what he is, and not another thing. He alone is irreplaceable, an end and not a means, and desired as such. But this is true of him, however vicious, however unwise, however ugly. Aphrodite herself, the poets tell us, is the wife of a cripple.

But in what did the individuality of my Peleus reside? As he spoke to me his smooth deceiving words, I watched his lips and wanted him – I wanted him *in* his lips, as later, when we lay together, I wanted him in his sceptre too. Yet what made this flesh a part of him? And what caused Peleus to shine in it? My answer, ladies, is that a rational being, even one so base as Peleus, is conscious of himself and of his body, and that this consciousness binds soul and body together, making one the image of the other. I can find no adequate words for this fact, and bequeath to Xanthippe the task of rendering it more clearly. If I were to try none the less to speak my meaning, I should say that, when I speak to Peleus and when I touch his flesh, I speak to and touch the thing that Peleus knows as 'I'. It is the 'I' of Peleus that comes to his lips as I touch them, and which feeds at my fingertips like a fish that feeds on the surface of the sea. My fingers enter then the 'I' of Peleus, and his lips the 'I' of me.

And if we are to say what the lover wants from her beloved, here lies the answer. She wants to enter his consciousness, through the consciousness that he has of his body. She wants to become part of the body that he feels, just as his body becomes a part of hers, and irradiated by her consciousness. The two lovers seek to know each other's body, with the very same intimacy that each knows himself.

And herein lies the danger of love. For in love the citadel of the body, wherein our will and personality take refuge from the world and strive to maintain themselves against it, is overcome. The self is invaded by the other, and in a certain manner enslaved by him. The pleasure of love is the pleasure of stirring another's body as he stirs it himself. The great force of Aphrodite is the force of my lover, who has become incarnate in me, and therefore irresistible. Is it surprising that this experience attaches us to our lovers, so that we can hardly live apart from them, and view all their desires with a desperate jealousy?

That, surely, is why we feel shame: 'shame and justice,' as Protagoras used to say, 'the two gifts of the gods.' It is shame which protects us from the force of love, and which protected me from Peleus. Shame is effective, however, only when justice inhabits the other, and persuades him not to take by force what he cannot gain by persuasion. Without shame, there would be open war between mankind and *eros*; we should strive to destroy the experience of love, to live in a world where we copulate casually and meaninglessly as the animals do, rather than face this dreadful force without protection.

But here too lies the triumph of love, that it can humble even the proudest of rational beings, and show that, however well-fortified is reason, it is never stronger than the flesh. And now, ladies, I come at last to my victory . . .

'The victory! The victory!' cried the guests once again and, holding out her hand for silence, Phryne paused to smile at them.

How soft and knowing and god-like was that smile, thought Arete: the smile of one who, surveying her worshippers from some point of high detachment, stirs them unscrupulously to love. And indeed, Arete said, there could be no better model for Aphrodite than this perfect shape of woman, in which Olympian disdain and child-like provocation seemed to mix inseparably like the dancing strands of a flame. Would that the hand of some cunning sculptor might transcribe her perfection into marble: what a gift would this be for the temple of Aphrodite, and what blessings would the goddess bestow upon the donor! Her ivory fingers stroked the air, while her eyes, brimming with a calm emotion, bound every rival glance in chains of sympathy.

'Well, ladies,' Phryne said at last, 'my triumph was no petty one. Indeed, it was over one of the proudest, the frostiest, and the most disdainful men of Athens, who would turn from me at every gathering and pour slander on my name, rather than admit to the faintest flicker of desire for me. He is, I think I can reveal, a distinguished man, a man of letters, and one of the few to have escaped my instruction. Indeed, he was a living insult to my professional standing, who poured public scorn on my languid glances, and deigned not to answer my tantalizing words. And the more he scorned me, my friends, the more I wanted him, so that I was reduced at last to following him in the streets most shamefully, in the hope that by some good fortune he would turn and meet my eyes.

'At last my opportunity came. It was two weeks ago, during that dreadful rainstorm, when I happened to be walking alone in the neighbourhood of his house.[19] What more natural than to run for shelter to his porch, and thence to the study where, as luck would have it, he lay on the couch beside his books and tablets, stylus in hand, staring heavenward with his lovely god-seeing eyes, alone, self-contained and irresistible? And what more natural, having arrived there, and pleaded for his hospitality, than to sit beside him, making sweet talk of philosophy until he, astonished at my wisdom, let fall his stylus to the floor? In short, dear ladies, I at last triumphed over that proud spirit and possessed him there, most gloriously, on the very couch which had been the birthplace of his greatest works. Therefore, I invite you to drink with me to this triumph, and to the eager love which sprang from it, and which now binds him to me and me to him eternally, in the godliest of unions. To Aphrodite! And to her victory on Phryne's behalf!'

And at that all the women save Lastheneia, Potone and her daughter raised their goblets, crying the name of the goddess and drinking the good wine to their heart's content. But soon the cry went up: 'Who is he? What is his name?' at which Phryne, extending her arm for silence, broke into a smile.

'Why,' she said, 'I almost forgot. And so that you shall know how great was my triumph, and what a wondrous goddess is she who secured it, I shall cast all discretion to the winds, and reveal that my lover, and your absent host, is none other than the great Plato!'

At which Lastheneia screamed aloud, started to her feet and threw out her arms in outrage. Some cheered and stamped, others repeated the name in wonderment, and soon the whole room was in an uproar,

---

[19] Phryne's story is related in a somewhat confused version by Diogenes Laertius (IV, 7). In this version the intended victim of seduction is Xenocrates, Plato's pupil, and later head of the Academy: '[it is said] that once the notorious Phryne tried to make his acquaintance and, as if she were being chased by some people, took refuge under his roof; that he admitted her out of ordinary humanity and, there being but one small couch in the room, permitted her to share it with him, and at last, after many importunities, she retired without success, telling those who enquired, that he whom she quitted was not a man but a statue.' (An interesting comment, from the most famous statue in the ancient world.)

Ancient authors liked to imagine the Academy as a target for loose women: thus Aeilian (13, 12) writes of Callisto, a courtesan who specialized in making passes at Plato's pupils.

with Lastheneia striving to throw herself across the table so as to sink her teeth and claws into the triumphant Phryne, crying,

'You corrupter of souls!'

Hearing these words, her neighbours strove to restrain her, and the company fell uneasily silent, fearing that Lastheneia would never be forgiven so passionate a breach of the decorum to which the great Phryne was accustomed. But all heard with astonishment, as the courtesan, her smile undiminished, addressed them in taunting words.

'Did I not tell you, my dears, that jealousy is the infallible sign of love? And if any of you wanted proof that this girl is bound to her dear teacher by carnal desires, do you not see it in her jealous raging? After all, if her doctrine were correct, I should in no way be her rival, but merely a base irrelevance in the life of that soul which she adores for reason's sake. But matters are otherwise, dear ladies, and, thinking that I have enjoyed the body which she secretly covets, poor Lastheneia falls, as all true lovers fall, into the pit of misery from which there is no emerging save by the loss of love or the recognition of error. And so great is my pity for you, O girl from Mantinea, that I shall continue my indiscretions and say that, when I refer to the great Plato, I do not mean that pretentious ass who runs the Academy – to the crows with him! – but Plato the dramatist, the profoundest poet of our day.'

At which Lastheneia sank in a fainting heap onto the couch behind her, there to remain, unmoved and unmoving, for several minutes.

As you can imagine, my dear Phrasiclea, the temperature of the symposium had risen somewhat by now, and, after enjoining the women to secrecy concerning the identity of her lover, Phryne proposed that they clear the air by singing one of Praxilla's drinking songs, you know, the one which goes:

> Oh you who look so prettily through the window,
> A maiden in face, but a nymph below![20]

And with a chorus of jolly laughter they all lapsed into a contented murmuring, awaiting the next speaker. Because Lastheneia's neighbour was too drunk to stand, the lot passed to Potone. With grave and

---

[20] Praxilla, Fr. 8, in Denys Page, *Poetae melici graeci*. Praxilla was a poetess from Sicyon, who flourished in the mid-fifth century BC; she had decided views about sexual love, believing (according to Hesychius' *Lexicon*) that Dionysus was the son of Aphrodite.

noble countenance, she slowly rose to address the table, her heavy pearls and golden bracelets creating, in the sudden stillness of the hall, a cascade of rattles like an oriental curtain.

POTONE'S SPEECH,
WITH COMMENTS FROM PERICTIONE

Ladies, she began, I am bound by chains which prevent me from speaking: chains of obligation to my husband, of courtesy to our hostess, and of duty to the gods, all of which bid me refrain from saying what I would wish to say, and enjoin me to silence.

'Come, come,' said Phryne, 'this is man's talk. There is only one rule here, old girl, and that is to utter your mind. And as for these chains of courtesy, I hereby loosen them. The others, in my experience, generally loosen themselves.'

Potone coloured slightly and went on.

Well, then, my dear Phryne. I have listened attentively to all that you have said, and hope you will forgive me if I express the opinion that it was, from beginning to end, a pack of lies. Noble lies, perhaps, uttered with sound pedagogical intention, but lies just the same. Oh, I don't doubt the existence of this Peleus and Evarchus; and as a picture of masculine perfidy the story was indeed convincing. But that a young woman should behave as you did, that she should be motivated by the feelings that you so shamefully describe, this I venture to doubt. Indeed, if I were to express an opinion in this matter, I should say that the emotions you ascribe to the young and virgin Phryne were not the emotions which really governed her, but those of her older and more cynical successor, who remembers those first embraces and reinterprets them as the embraces of a woman who has abandoned the hope of a chaste and enduring attachment.

Phryne laughed good-humouredly, and said,

'If that's your opinion, my dear Potone, all well and good. But perhaps you will enlighten us with a description of *your* first encounter with the goddess, and those more maidenly and delicate feelings which she caused to stir in you.'

'Modesty forbids,' said Potone with a blush. 'And besides, how could I, in front of Perictione here, recount the story of her conception?'

'Go on, Mum,' said the girl,[21] 'don't mind me. I heard all about it from Granny.'

'You what?'

'I'm sorry. Should I have closed my ears?'

'Indeed you should,' said Potone, 'and I order you to say not another word.'

At this the company uttered a loud boo! of protest, and banged their goblets on the table.

'Tell us what Granny said!' they chorused.

'I forbid you to speak!' Potone repeated, with a look of anguish.

'Shame! shame!' cried the company. 'Let the *archousa* decide!'

And they all appealed to Phryne, who ruled that the girl should be allowed to repeat what her grandmother had said to her, and that Potone was on no account to punish her for doing so. Moreover, she added, if it were ever learned that Potone had defied the *archousa*'s ruling, she would suffer the worst fate that could befall a lady of Athens, which was to be excluded forthwith from Phryne's secret drinking parties. At this Potone went pale, and promptly made way for her daughter. Blushing a little and holding her delicate fingers close to her lips, so that many of the older whores had to cup their hands to their ears to follow her, Perictione spoke thus:

'She was giving me a dancing lesson, and, after a bowl or two, began to tell me all about how ghastly it is the first time, and how Ariston had forced her to do it and left her quite frozen with revulsion until Uncle Glaucon was born.[22] Then one thing led to another, or rather one bowl led to another, until she said that the same had happened to Mum, that she was deeply ashamed about it, and regretted the weakness that led her to give way to Pyrilampes in this as in everything.'

'In what, Perictione?' asked her mother with a searching frown.

'In – well, in marrying you off to Dad. Oh, I know you love him; and Granny said so too. But it doesn't change the fact that, on the first night,

---

[21] It is clear from her language that Perictione has not yet mastered the dignified turns of phrase and high seriousness of tone required at a true symposium.

[22] The story is confirmed by Diogenes Laertius, III, 2, and also by incidental remarks in *Perictione's Parmenides*.

so she said, you screamed aloud, crying "Mother! Mother!" in a most heart-rending way. And to drown her guilt, and the ghastly memory of her own first experience, Granny polished off a whole amphora!'

Many of the ladies gasped at this, though whether it was the quantity of wine, or the dreadfulness of Potone's martyrdom that prompted them, Arete could not ascertain. As for Potone herself, she stared at her daughter, as though discovering for the first time that she had given birth to a Gorgon.

'Please don't look at me like that, Mum,' said the girl, whose hand had fallen from her mouth, and who was speaking ever more boldly, 'I'm only reporting what Granny said.'

'And what else did she say?'

'That you get used to anything in time, and that I shouldn't regard this beastly business as an insuperable reason for resisting my parents' choice of husband. On the other hand, she said, it would do no harm to get a glimpse of your intended first – say, by singing paeans and dancing after dinner when he is a guest – and putting discreet pressure on the parental machinery to ensure that the chosen one is not entirely repulsive.'

'And is that what you have been doing?'

'Well, I've not really started yet, Mum. But while we're on the subject and I can count on the support of these good ladies . . .'

'Hear! Hear!' cried the company, and many of the whores blew kisses across the table, applauding the brave girl who spoke, as Arete put it, for every woman in Hellas.

'While we're on the subject, I am simply *not* going to have that bumpkin Astyochus whom you brought round the other day, and if you say I'm to marry him I shall go and hang myself! So there!'

'My dear Perictione, did I say any such thing?'

'Then why did you invite him to dinner? Surely, not for the pleasure of his conversation: he didn't even know the three of Stesichorus,[23] let alone catch the allusion to Bacchylides when you spoke about the Pythian games.'

---

[23] Stesichorus was credited with dividing choral verses into the three familiar components of strophe, antistrophe and epode. Thus in the Byzantine Lexicon of 'Suidas' (the 'Suda'), we find that 'when the ancients wanted to abuse an uncultivated man they said that he did not know even the three of Stesichorus'. But see M. Davies, *Journal of Hellenic Studies* 102 (1982), pp. 206–210, where it is argued that the proverb might equally refer to three famous *lines*, or three famous *poems*, by Stesichorus.

'But you weren't there when we discussed the games!'

'Do you think not?'

'Why, you little spy!'

'Come off it, Mum. Didn't you do the same at my age?'

Speechless, Potone reached down for her goblet.

'That's it, Mum,' Perictione went on. 'Knock it back, like Granny. Zeus, ladies! I really like it here.'

With a sudden blush, the girl sat down to a round of applause. It was some time before her mother, still pale and severe, could resume her discourse.

Well, ladies, she went on, I hate to confess that, to a certain extent, my daughter is right, although her grandmother exaggerated in the matter of my screaming. If I uttered an audible protest it was largely – how shall I say? – for form's sake, and lest my mother (who had formed the habit, like this young amazon here, of spying at key-holes, and for whom the only reality was drama) should feel that the *agon* was missing. However, it was not a bed of roses, ladies. Rarely before my marriage did I meet a man, still more rarely could I speak to one alone. And if some guest had chanced to ask me for my hand (which never happened), I could but reply as Hermione did:

> My marriage is my father's choice
> And I have nought to say in it.[24]

Like most women of my class, therefore, I was married against my will; or rather, not against my will, but not with it either – in complete indifference to whether I wished the match or not.

This could not fail to strike me as an injustice, and even now I feel a certain revulsion, recalling that first night, when the *hymenaeos* had been sung, and I had been hustled, trembling, into the *thalamos*, there to appear in my nakedness before a man who was almost entirely strange to me, and whose greedy eyes surveyed their new property without the first regard for my maidenhead. In my confusion I wept, and perhaps it is true that I involuntarily called upon my mother. At any rate, I hid my breasts and sex as best I could, and turned my eyes from his. It was all to no avail, of course, and had I not fainted away at

---

[24] Euripides, *Andromache*, 987–8.

the touch of his breath upon my shoulder, I should most assuredly have struggled until my strength was gone.

Phryne spoke interestingly of shame. But I should like to introduce a small refinement into what she said. It seems to me that there are two kinds of shame: there is the shame of the body, which causes us to hide from the eyes of men, and to feel affronted by every unwanted glance in our direction. And there is the shame of the soul, which leads us to avoid the reproach of others, and to live our lives in justice and piety as the gods decree. And while the first shame is a mystery, along with all the other gifts of love, the second is clear and right and reasonable; for it does but tell us, as my brother says, to be what we would seem, and to live well and virtuously.

As for the first shame, who knows why we feel it and for what purpose? Like all the gifts of love, it comes to us without instructions, and sticks to us immovably, whether we will or no. Now when I awoke from what might have been an ordeal, had I been conscious enough to feel it, my case was precisely the opposite of that described by Phryne. She, if we are to believe her, felt no shame of the body, since her body had long since been conquered by desire; such shame as she felt was that of the soul – knowing that her reputation was destroyed for ever, and that henceforth she must either brazen out her misfortune or live a lie. I, however, felt no shame of the soul: on the contrary, I had done all that was expected of me, and in losing my maidenhead had merely brought to fruition the painless process of acquiring it. My reputation had suffered nothing, and, in the eyes of the world, I was all that I should be. My only shame was body shame, that mysterious legacy of forces that we do not understand. How easy, therefore, to apply myself to the task of defeating my body. I confess that I did not understand what Phryne said, concerning the unity of body and soul, and the incarnation of the 'I'. The matter seems to me far more simple. I maintain, as my brother does, that the rational being is quite distinct from her body, and can overcome her body in the contest between them, be the contest never so unequal. And in this victory of the soul over the body happiness lies. For some, overcoming the body means overcoming the body's desires: so it has ever been for my poor brother. For such as myself, it means overcoming the body's reluctance – defeating bodily shame, through the shame of the soul.

Nor was my task so difficult, ladies. For as I awoke to my new condition, I saw the eyes of my husband looking down on me with such an unexpected concern and tenderness that I felt at once that it was not he who had acted unjustly in seizing his right, but I in resisting him. And I resolved then and there, since it was honourable to do so and in any case I had no alternative, to do my utmost to love him, to welcome his embraces, and to cast away the shame that made me hesitate.

My efforts were gradually greeted with success, and although I do not recall any experience to equal those aphroditic sensations described by Phryne, I put this down more to the ebullience of her language than to any defect in myself. At least I can say this: that I learned to welcome my husband's embraces as the sign of his love and perfection, and that the thought of this love caused such reciprocal love in me that the barriers of shame were breached between us, and I rejoiced in his pleasure, hence pleasing myself.

At this the young Perictione put up her hand, begging Phryne for an audience, which was granted.

'OK, Mum,' said the girl, not a little agitated. 'So why did the bastard take up with that Syrian concubine, Cholcis or whatever her name was? Maybe he wanted something more than you being pleased at his pleasure. Maybe he wanted to be pleased at *your* pleasure too.'

'Perictione!' cried Potone with a gasp. 'Just you wait till we get home.'

'My dear ladies,' put in Phryne, 'I beg you to remember our rules. We are here to speak freely of every matter that seems relevant to our theme. Perictione is wrong to address such personal remarks to her mother, ignoring the company at large. But she does right, my dear Potone, to remind you of Cholcis. And this leads me to regret even more that dear Cholcis could not be with us tonight, on account of that General of hers.'

'You invited *her?*' gasped Potone, her cheeks pale with indignation.

'My dear Potone, it is only natural. Our common interest as women is surely of more importance, on such an evening, than our occasional disagreements over men.'

'Disagreements over men! Is that how you see it? Does it count for nothing that he is not just a man for me, but my lawful husband and the father of my children?'

'Come now,' said Phryne, 'descend from your high horse and answer the girl's question, which is surely of the greatest relevance to our theme.'

'Answer it?' repeated Potone with a sigh. 'Answer it? Ah, how I wish I could!'

And with that she began to weep, tears not of rage or jealousy, but of helpless sorrow. At once Perictione embraced her, saying, 'Mother, please forgive me. I don't know why I had to mention it. Only – only it hurt me too, just as much!' And mother and daughter mingled their tears and their kisses, as surely, to Arete's thinking, they were mingled at every hour of the day. At last, detaching herself and drying her eyes, Potone turned once more to the company.

Enough has been said, my dears, of men and their fickle love, and who am I to make sense of such a mystery? But perhaps there was good to be obtained, even from my husband's infidelity. For it was this that caused me to reflect again on the mystery of love and the need to overcome those passions of the body which afflict us so unsparingly, and among which, as Phryne has rightly said, none is more cruel than jealousy. So let me offer you now the fruits of my speculations. And although the boy, I mean girl, from Mantinea is a somewhat partial exponent of my brother's teachings, there is in what he says an important insight, which I beg in my own words to expound to you.

I first knew Aphrodite through bodily shame. I knew her again through jealousy. And these I believe are the 'dread gifts of the love-crowned goddess of Cyprus',[25] though if Phryne is to be believed, we women may be blessed by her with pleasure too. But in the heart of all these feelings lies a mystery. The Mantinean tries to solve it in one way, by saying that *eros* directs us beyond our bodily condition to the eternal world of the forms, and that this obscure metaphysical goal causes our confusion in the presence of beauty. Phryne proposes another solution – saying that we long to possess the individual, to unite with him in his flesh, and to be wholly one while yet being two. But I think you will agree, ladies, that these contradictory explanations are equally defective, and do but compound the mystery that they seek to clarify. Of the Mantinean I would ask: How can a mortal creature, loving another in the flesh, see through him to the purely intellectual and eternal? And how could this process, which discards the beloved in pursuit of something higher, be part of love? Of Phryne I would ask: how can two become one? And how can I possess the individual, of

---

[25] Bacchylides, poem no. 17, 9–10, in the Teubner text edited by Bruno Snell and Herwig Maehler, Leipzig, 1970. Some read ἄγνα δῶρα (holy gifts) rather than ἄηνα δῶρα (dread gifts). Potone does not agree with them.

whom nothing can be known except that he is, and from whom the only satisfactions that I obtain might equally be obtained from another? No, ladies, both those lines of enquiry are fraught with insuperable paradox, and we must look elsewhere for an answer to our question.

It seems to me that we are forever barred from saying what it is that we desire, when love has mastered us. Yet because we are rational, we strive to give a name to our desire, to say that it is this or that we want, and which justifies our striving. But the words we find are confused and contradictory: always they miss the peculiar quality of the feeling itself, to spiral away like smoke into abstractions. The reason is that it is not *we* who are desiring, but the force that masters us. And if we are to live well and reasonably, we should endeavour to understand this force, and why it chooses to work in this way through our bodies, in sovereign indifference to our rational souls. Having understood, we should then cease to strive against its great imperative; rather, we should accept its jurisdiction, lend ourselves to its purpose, and escape with minimum damage from the havoc that it otherwise may cause.

It needs but little thought, my dear ladies, to discover the aim of our enslaver – and Phryne too discovered it, only to cast it from her upon the altar of all-seeing Zeus. The thing which gripped my dear husband, and which clamped his body down on mine, intended you, dear Perictione. So too did the shame which had kept me for this moment, and the jealousy which prompted me to cling to my husband in my sorrow, to fight for his exclusive love, and to ensure for my child the continuing protection of a father. All these strange passions find their explanation here: for without them we should soon cease to bear and nurture our children, and the human race would fall prey to whatever stronger species could guarantee a future to its offspring.

And here I must take issue with a belief that the Mantinean and Phryne share: the belief that only rational beings are subject to the work of Aphrodite. True it is that only rational beings *interpret* her work in the strange ways we do, believing ourselves to be desiring another, and aiming purely at him. But if I am right, this is merely an illusion – one of the many illusions to which, as my mother used to say, reason itself is subject. The true desire of Aphrodite works in and through us, but is not ours. And we can see the goddess's mark throughout creation. Dog and horse, dove and swine, and all that crawls upon the earth, are subject to her yoke. And while male is drawn to female and female to male, the work of Aphrodite does not end with this but on the contrary begins there. For now arises a strange habit of sacrifice: first, to bring food to each other, and to fight on each other's behalf; then to bring food and shelter to the new-born, for whom they are ready to challenge the most dreadful of foes, even to the point of laying down their lives. The goal of love is sacrifice; the beneficiary of this sacrifice, however, is not me or the one I love, but the unborn creature who addresses us through our love with confused and supplicating gestures. This, my dear ladies, is the yoke of Aphrodite, that is laid over all the world.

It may happen, however, that reason, in its desire to master the world, damns up the channels through which Aphrodite flows, and diverts them in some strange direction. For reason is confused by this great force, misunderstanding its object, and often presenting, in the place of husband or wife, some rival image of the beloved. It is against this illusion of reason that the shame of the soul is directed, warning us to proceed no further down the path of temptation. And wise are those that heed the warning, even if they know no reason why.

It is this shame of the soul which tells the maid to wait upon her marriage. It also prompted my poor brother to invent the conception of '*eros* overcome' as we heard it expounded by the Mantinean. For you know, my dears – why should I not speak of it here, where everything may be said? – my brother was from the earliest age a thorough-going woofter,[26] and nothing would induce him to contemplate the female form, or to see in woman the beauty which spurs men to possess her. Such is the power and goodness of Aphrodite, however, that she resolved to use my brother's bewilderment for her own secret ends, causing him to wrestle with his base desires and at last to overcome them. His theory was his own emotional therapy, and by Zeus it worked! Moreover, what an inestimable gift to mankind will it prove! Posterity will surely spread my brother's renown, praising him and not the goddess who so wisely guided him, as generation after generation learns from his writings that the love of man for man is not to be

---

[26] κίναιδος: for a commentary on this word, see *Xanthippe's Republic*, note 7. The Turkish, interestingly, has *tikri* – 'fox' – suggesting that the translator, not finding κίναιδος in her dictionary, has assumed that Potone intended κίναδος, a Sicilian word meaning a fox (or metaphorically, a cheat). Assuming Potone really *did* mean κίναιδος she is being most unfair, for although Plato may have been attracted to boys, there is no suggestion that he would have dreamed of taking the passive role in any sexual encounter.

indulged but transcended. Believing this, the nascent woofter of the future will strive to unite with the eternal forms until, bored rigid by their inaccessibility, he will at last do the will of Aphrodite and take a wife.

So there, ladies, is my theory. The desires of Aphrodite are not ours but hers, and what she intends in them is not what we intend. Our own purpose remains a mystery, even to ourselves, while hers is sublime, orderly and forever transparent – the birth, the nurture, and the safeguard of – by Zeus! It's Castallax!

And with a gasp Potone staggered against the table, dropping the goblet which she had been lifting to her lips in honour of the goddess, and clutching at her neighbour's shoulder. All eyes turned from her pallid form to the inner doorway, where a small and dingy-looking old woman, dressed in a dirty tunic, was wiping her nose on the back of one hand. Her coarse features and greasy hair did not mask a certain cunning, though this was revealed more in her way of standing than in her face, which was maintained in a condition of deliberate blankness, like the face of a soldier awaiting commands.

'I thought I gave orders that we were not to be disturbed,' said Phryne.

'Dreadful sorry, your ladyship, only the door swung open in the wind.'[27]

'How come you were standing behind it?'

'It happened I was passing on the other side, your ladyship. And discovering the voice of Mistress Potone what was speechifying I couldn't help but listen to what she had to say. And I don't mind adding she's no mean orator, with a tongue in her head what would charm the stick off a one-legged beggar.'

Potone, who had somewhat recovered her composure, asked her hostess what Castallax was doing in the house.

'She's employed in the kitchen. In fact, she's in charge of it. I say, is there something wrong?'

---

[27] Castallax's speech exists only in the Turkish – though a few fragments of Greek have been preserved. According to Şule, the Turkish translator/embellisher has rendered the slave's discourse in the proletarian idiolect of old Istanbul, while the few fragments of Greek seem to be in a debased version of the Attic dialect, and not in the Spartan tongue familiar to us, for example, from the *Lysistrata* of Aristophanes. It could therefore be that the life's work of Professor Hope-Dingwood (see Preface) has been in vain (save, perhaps, for the damson jam).

Potone, who had turned slightly green, sat down and stared at her empty plate in alarm.

'No, no,' she said at last, 'I'm OK.'

'You don't look it. But tell me, my dear Potone, how you and Castallax became acquainted.'

'She was my nurse.'

'Your nurse!' cried Phryne. 'And that crafty devil Androcles sold her as a cook, saying she had been all her life in the profession and was worth her weight in gold!'

'Well,' said Potone, 'I don't doubt that she is no less a cook than she was a nurse.'

'That is for my guests to decide, I think,' said Phryne, at which several of the ladies raised their goblets and drank the health of Castallax, swearing that the feast had been fit for the gods, and urging Phryne to be lenient with the old woman and to allow her a bowl of wine. This the courtesan duly did, taking care, however, that Castallax, whose savoury odour was not to everybody's liking, should remain standing apart from the table.

'If I may once more make use of the *archousa*'s privilege,' Phryne went on, 'it would seem to me no bad thing if Castallax were to tell us her view of what has been said, and perhaps enjoy, for the last time in this life, the opportunity to correct her former mistress.'

'Hear! Hear!' cried the company with a burst of applause, and Castallax was persuaded to drink down her bowl and share her thoughts with them.

CASTALLAX'S SPEECH

Well, the old woman began, I don't rightly know as I have anythink useful to say to your worships. Only, before Mistress Potone comes too cocky there's a thing or two she needs reminding of, with all this highfalutin talk of sacrifice, and offspring, and rearing and nurturing and a whole lot else what to my way of thinking's a load of codswallop! Weren't *her* mum took her in hand when she was a little 'un, nor I warrant you were it *her* what saw young Perictione through them years of screaming and stinking and puking. Maybe she finds it needful to think of summink else when her man comes in to sweep the chimney;

but the summink else ain't children, and for the upper classes the caring after children don't begin in bed, nor at any time thereafter.

Potone would have bounded to her feet, had not her hostess peremptorily beckoned her to remain seated, saying 'the rules, my dear; the rules'. With a long hiss of indignation, Potone collapsed onto the couch and shielded her face with her hand.

And if you ask my opinion, the old nurse continued, Aphrodite don't care an obol about the bringing up of children, as is proved clear as crystal by Mistress Potone herself. For it's only them children like young Perictione here, what was conceived without Aphrodite's having much to do with it, what gets the real education. And the more the goddess has to do with it, the less chance the poor buggers have got. There's scarce a crossroads outside this Athens of ours what ain't littered with their little carkisses, and you can bet a thousand drachmas each of them is a victim of Aphrodite. And the more pleasure was had in the getting of them, the less obligation there is to give them a start. For a girl what obeys Aphrodite ain't going to wait for marriage before she stokes her fire, and what can she do nine months thereafter, save leave the thing by the roadside, like a piece of offal for the dogs?

And there's another reason too, for thinking that Aphrodite ain't much bothered about the future of the human species. Even when a girl is married, she can't be relied on to protect her little 'uns, specially if there be girls among them, what are as likely to be left out with the rubbadge as the boys of them what never wed.[28] And to my way of thinking, if Aphrodite is a goddess, she's a very contrary one, and none too good at what you'd call rational argumentification. Not only don't she take no care of the species what is designed to worship her; she is specially hard on the girls among them, even though it's the girls, as every woman knows – though course we never let on about it to the men – what feels the joys of Aphrodite most strong. Fact is, if I were her, I'd be more inclined, if exterminating there must be, to exterminate the men, the small respect they pay to my instructions – it being for most of them a in-and-out job, one two three, bang, the girl's

---

[28] A papyrus letter from the first century BC, found at Oxyrhynchus, and sent by a man to his wife, illustrates the easy disregard for human life with which fathers viewed their unwanted daughters: 'if you bear a child, and it is a girl, throw it away.' (*Select Papyri*, Loeb Edition, vol. I, p. 295.)

knocked up and on to the next one. Whereas, your worships, I venture there be few among us, Mistress Potone always excepted, what don't long for hours of kisses and what have you, and then the action staged good and proper to last a night – and even then, come morning, wanting more and different before the other man (supposing there's another man) comes home. And that's why I says, if Aphrodite is a goddess, she's a right contrary one, what destroys the sex as is most made for worshipping her.

However, I ain't to be accused of no impiety. So I says rather that she ain't no goddess at all, and that the thing we worship as Aphrodite comes straight to us from Zeus, on account of a blundering silly mistake what he made way back at the beginning. And if the slave here – Cleio, what I can't help remarking has had the privilege of enjoying your philosophical speeches even though the cook has been shut in the kitchen – was to fill my bowl, I don't mind giving your worships the drift of my meaning.

(Her bowl was filled and, having drained it, smacked her lips, wiped them with the back of her hand, and held out the bowl for more, Castallax resumed her discourse.)

In the beginning there was only one kind of human being. And Zeus designed her in every way most scrupefully so she would be content with herself and lacking for nothing. Therefore he made for each human being a companion what he put inside of her, to live there all tucked up and cosy and exclusively the possession of her what was wrapped around outside. The earth was fruitful and the gods was kind. And because no human had need of nothing outside herself except food and drink, what was always to hand, no human ever moved, nor had the use of arms and legs, these being quite superflutious. So it was that, in them happy days, the human shape was like a oblong box, with just a few bits sticking out here and there for eyes and ears and the like, so as our ancestors could study the beauty of the world and be content with their condition. Each human could talk to her heart's content to the one inside, and each lay in the place what Zeus had given her without lifting a finger, and without no finger to lift.

Then one day Zeus began worriting about the creature inside the box. For the gods, your worships, are like us. They can't help from looking at the things they've made and admiring them and saying to theirselves, what a stroke of genius it was, to make a thing like that. So he bored a hole in one end of the box, with the aim of looking inside and seeing how his creature was getting along in there. And this was his great blundering mistake, your worships. For all the time the creature had been shut in there, warm and cosy and protected, it had never crossed his mind to be outside. He had everything a human could reasonably want: food and drink and conversation, warmth and sleep and love. But now, looking out of that hole what Zeus had made, he catched sight of another world; and the light what shone in from there made his little hovel seem dreadful mean and dingy. From that day on his one ambition was to get out as fast as what he could.

Course it warn't easy. He had to heave and squeeze and contortulate hisself, till he was one long tube of human stuff. And this was how he got hisself arms and legs, the one for pulling, the other for pushing hisself out through that tunnel into the light. Anyhow, at last he done the job, and out he comes, a long tall tube-thing, with arms and legs, what landed in that world all fighting and thrashing. And this was to be the race of men, your worships, just as the box he had come from was to be the race of women.

But that there box was in a sorry state, with all her insides bashed and bruised, and a great emptiness where her only friend had been. And as she felt him emerging she tried to hold him back, as is only natural, and so pushed herself out to each side of the hole in the hope of trapping him. So she acquired a pair of legs and all – shorter and fatter nor his were, but legs all the same. And her middle caved in where he had emptied it, leaving the hips and the boobs like mountains on either side. And when she saw it warn't no good and her friend was leaving her, she was mad with grieving and out of her sides come two arms, reaching for him what was gone forever. And here we have the wherefore, your worships, why men and women are so different to look at, the man tall and slim like a tube, with arms what are always fighting and legs always running; the woman a kind of bashed-in box, with legs what refuse to run and arms what are fit only to hug and squeeze and cling to them little bits of love the gods allow for them.

Well now, once out of the box, the man run around in excitement, exploring this new world what he had come into, putting his head into this and his hand into that, and generally making of hisself the kind of nuisance as is familiar to your worships. And in the course of doing this, naturally he got lost, and couldn't find his way back to his box; and then he began grieving for the warmth and comfort of it, and fearing as he would be forever lost outside, which when all's said and done, your worships, is the main fear what men have. And because the woman couldn't move much as yet, she give up trying to follow him, and sat near by where he had left her, feeling sad and humilified and empty, like every woman feels when her man is gone.

In time the man comes across another woman, and turning her over in his hands and exploring around, he eventually comes to think that this is the box what he escaped from, only a bit changed by her experience as is only natural. He shouts for joy and clasps her in his arms; and then, as nature calls, he tries to crawl back into the hole from which he left. But of course, your worships, the woman ain't sure this is the rightful occupant of her lodgings, and ain't disposed at first to open the door. And when she gives way, thinking that a new companion is better than no companion at all, they discover a impediment, it being easier to squeeze out of a hole than into it. What a wailing and despairing there was then, your worships, and how pitiful our lot would have been, if Zeus hadn't looked down on us and with houndsight regretted his great blunder.

Seeing how matters stood, the father of the gods decided to give the man another limb, small enough to enter the hole what craved for him, but not so small it couldn't fill for a time the woman's aching emptiness. Good though this were, it were better for the man, what could have his dose of comfort, and then run off again, escaping her what had obliged him. And she could never keep up with him, what with him being so agile and childish and excited; so she was forced to let him wander wherever the fancy took him, until coming to rest again in the hole what he craved – only usually another hole. So the woman grieved the more, seeing her happiness so brief, and her emptiness thereafter ever greater. Until Zeus took pity on her, and decided to grant her all what she desired. And here we come, your worships, to the great stroke of genius what shows Zeus is first among the immortals and ever deserving of our obedience and praise. He fixed things up so whenever the man entered the woman and awoke in her all over again the old, old longing for love, she wouldn't thereafter suffer such pangs of emptiness, but a seed would be planted inside her, there to grow apace into a new companion. And all would of worked out wonderful and the old happiness brung back to womankind, but for one thing, which was this. What with the shoving and heaving and tearing, and the running and wailing and aggravating, the inside of the woman was all distortled and constriculated, and no longer big enough to hold another human what was fully growed. Only for nine months could her new guest remain there, after what he became too big for his lodgings, and must begin to crawl around and twist about, until stumbling at last on that fatal hole what Zeus had opened.

Zeus thought about this for some while, and was in two minds whether to start again or revise the whole arrangement. But at last he decided to let it be. And I'll tell you why, your worships. Although the new situation is far from satisfactory for us women, there being at best but nine months of happiness at a stretch, and thereafter toil and trouble and grieving, Zeus saw the way to solve another of his problems. For what with all this running and agitating, them men and women were getting wore out. Famines and diseases and wars was starting up everywhere, and Zeus was in a tight corner as to how to keep the population at a satisfactory level. And he seen the new arrangement answered his purpose better nor anythink else he could immediately think of, since new humans come into being constantly to replace the used-up ones. Only one thing was wanting, which was them as would look after these half-made little creatures, what crawled out of the women still unfinished and unable to fend for themselves. And thinking on this, your worships, he had another flash of aspiration. He planted in the hearts of certain women – them what was good enough and wise enough and full of pity, and what were capable of them sacrifices what Mistress Potone referred to – he planted in them the desire to take hold on these poor creatures, howsoever little they was thanked for it, and howsoever poor was the material what was given them, so as to shape them into respectable-looking humans.

So there you have the truth, your worships, as I see it. This desiring we say is Aphrodite's is not her doing at all. It is the work of Zeus the father, and his great mistake. And it's this causes us women to pass such long and empty hours, and to give way at last when some man tricks us into believing it's him what rightfully belongs inside. It's this explains the great joy and pleasure what fills us while he stops over there, and causes us to keep him fast inside as best we can, knowing full well that it won't be for long. And it's this causes the only true happiness we know – them nine months of contentment, when we're filled again with our dear companion, and can enjoy a faint little echo of them glorious days when we lived, quiet and happy and filled to the brim with love, as harmless boxes, each in her allotted place on earth.

After Castallax had thus spoken there was a great shout of applause from all the company save Potone, who was beginning to remark to her neighbour on Castallax's failings as a nurse, and the part she had played in perverting her brother's instincts. Then suddenly there was a violent knocking on the outer door, followed by a sharp altercation of female voices. The company fell silent, and Phryne, speaking to Castallax, said:

'Go and see who it is. And as a reward for your cooking – I will say nothing about your speech – you can assume the right to open the door or close it, according to whether the visitor seems to you to be suited to our company. And you too may sit with us, provided you obey the rule of secrecy, and provided that you stay a little way apart from the table, as is only fitting.'

Having swallowed more wine and wiped her mouth, Castallax did as she was bidden. But no sooner had she opened the door into the *aula* than she was swept off her feet by a dark-eyed woman, with slender Asiatic features, who stormed past her crying 'Phryne!' at the top of her voice. Then, seeing the assembled company, the newcomer stopped in her tracks.

'By Apollo,' she said. 'It's one of *those* evenings!'

'My dear Archeanassa,' said Phryne, 'the servants have been scouring the streets for days in the hope of finding you, and as luck would have it you have come uninvited. You are most welcome. But surely you must have a lover who keeps you under lock and key, since you have so entirely dropped out of circulation!'

'A lover!' replied Archeanassa with a scornful laugh. 'The more fool me! But don't let me disturb you. I'll come back tomorrow.'

So saying she turned as if to leave. But, rising from the table, Phryne detained her.

'My poor Archeanassa, seldom have I seen you so troubled. And since, as I guess, the cause of your trouble is love, I do beseech you to share it with us, since Aphrodite is the theme of our symposium, and has filled us with sympathy for her victims.'

The company responded with compassionate murmurs, begging the visitor to unburden herself, and in any case to sit down awhile, so that they might restore her composure.

'I couldn't possibly!' said Archeanassa, and she turned her great dark eyes, in the depths of which burned little fires of gold, upon the company, looking from one to the other most pitifully. She was not young, Arete said, but beautiful, with lyre-shaped lips, a clear brow and something touchingly naïve in her expression, as though she had lived her life as a girl, had been ever astonished by the world's dark perfidy, and never been granted the wisdom and the acquiescence which it is the good fortune of womanhood to acquire. As her eyes roamed the pitying faces, she slowly melted until, receiving the warm and peaceful smile of Xanthippe, she was at last overcome by her emotions. Bursting into tears, she buried her face in her hands.

'Come, my dear Archeanassa,' said Phryne, who wrapped her arm about the sobbing shoulders, 'lie here beside me at the table, where we can easily make a place for you. Surely you could do no better than to stay awhile with us, whose thoughts are turned to love.'

Archeanassa allowed herself to be comforted, and, leaning upon the arm of her hostess, she was guided at last to Phryne's couch.

'And now,' Phryne went on, 'what better sequel to the speech of Castallax than to invite our new guest to tell the woe that has befallen her, and to enjoy the consolation of philosophy.'

'Oh no, I couldn't!' said Archeanassa, as she dried her tears.

'Of course you could, my dear. You know the rules. Nothing travels beyond these walls. No harm can come from unburdening yourself, but only good. So tell us everything.'

'Everything? Would you really want to know everything?' asked Archeanassa, with sudden ferocity.

'Indeed,' Phryne replied, though she looked at her friend askance as though fearing some breach of her proprieties.

'Well then,' said Archeanassa, after a moment's thought, 'I *will* speak; and because I recognize here so many excellent ladies, including my dear friend Musea who was with me at Mytilene, I shall tell you all my troubles, and hope that you will not be shocked by what I say but on the contrary instructed by my example.'

At which all murmured their approval, and Phryne motioned to the servant to bring another goblet.

How grim, angry and vulnerable she seemed, Arete recounted, as she rose to speak. It was as though she faced the world as its accuser, one who had taken just so much from it, and could take no more. Indeed, there was something barbaric in her naïveté and, learning that the girl was from Colophon, Arete supposed her to be no member of the colony there, but an infiltrator from the Persian tribes. Yet her

Greek was perfect, and she held herself as only Greek women do, upright, hands at her sides, and eyes looking alertly before her.

ARCHEANASSA'S SPEECH

I do not know what has been said here, ladies, and were I to discourse in philosophical terms about Eros and Aphrodite I should doubtless repeat what you have already heard this evening. I run less risk of boring you, therefore, if I do as I promised, and speak not of love in the abstract, but of my own love and its grievous history. So let me begin at the beginning.

I fell in love at a tender age with a literary man, a great poet as I esteem him to be, in my home town of Colophon. His name is familiar to you, and if I confess now to my feelings for Antimachus this is because they can no longer damage him. Antimachus was older than me and already married. Since I could not be his wife, I chose instead – so great was my love for him – to become his hetaera. I did not regret it: every hour that I spent with him was a gift of heaven, and I enjoyed from him a love that was free, full and lyrical, such as a wife may never know. Indeed, if you wish to learn what he felt for me, you have only to consult his famous poem to Lyde – that being the name he chose for me, pretending to his wife (whose name was Sophia) that the poem was for her. (I should add that my name is neither Lyde nor Archeanassa, but Doris, though no man knows this save Antimachus.)

I understood, of course, that the hetaera's joys are short-lived, and when he left with his wife for Athens, forbidding me to follow him, I accepted my fate and called on the heavens to bless him. My grief was great, dear ladies, but I thanked the gods that Antimachus had left our dear Colophon before the King's Peace had enslaved it, and that his memories of our life together would be untainted by the image of his city's shame. I was forced to live, and finding a Persian protector, I settled as best I could in this new, subdued and all-but-lifeless Colophon, whose every ruined house and temple, whose every weed-filled avenue and dried-up fountain, still spoke to me of Antimachus, and of the love that we had known.

My protector died; I acquired another, and through prudence and skill in those arts by which we hetaerae are compelled to live, I secured my independence. I was not rich, but I could afford the company of a servant, could travel where I wished, and could set up house without a lover. And because I had not forgotten my dear Antimachus, and longed for news of him, I decided at last to sail secretly to Athens. I had no plans, ladies, save one: to conceal from Antimachus my presence in his adopted city. But I nurtured the hope that I might catch sight of him at public lectures, or hear him praised by others whose good fortune in speaking to him I could never share.

On arriving in Athens, therefore, I made a point of moving in literary circles, so as to hear his name, and the name of the beloved Lyde whom he had made so famous. I found myself besieged by admirers, from whom I at last chose two lovers – Isocrates, the sophist, who taught me rhetoric, and his handsome pupil Theopompus, to whom I taught desire.[29] Yet still my heart yearned for Antimachus, and no conversation was truly welcome to my ears in which he was not mentioned. Although I was obliged to assume a new name, and studiously to avoid every encounter with my darling, I felt as though I lived with him as his faithful friend and consort, following his fortunes as a mother follows the fortunes of her child, cherishing too his face and words, reflected in the faces and the words of his companions, who were my companions too.

In this way I lived for a year, dear ladies, enjoying my substitute for happiness, and taking comfort in the increasingly competent embraces of Theopompus, whom I was also helping to compose his far less competent books of history. And then a terrible thing happened – so terrible that I can hardly bring myself to relate it.

(Here Archeanassa bit her lip, and looked round at the company, who murmured their encouragement. After a moment, she continued in a trembling voice.)

[29] Isocrates' school of rhetoric rivalled the Academy in recruiting the brightest young talents. Nevertheless, it is clear that Plato's hatred of the rhetors and sophists had deeper origins than academic competition. Theopompus was born in Chios, from which island he came to Athens as one of Isocrates' many pupils. There again seems to be an anachronism in the story, Theopompus being only in his teens at the time of the symposium in Phryne's house. On the other hand Theopompus is said to have written furious diatribes against Plato, which the academicians no doubt felt duty bound to destroy. It is therefore possible (see below) that Archeanassa's wayward love-life caused the loss not only of the works of Antimachus, but of those of Theopompus too. Of his two most famous pupils, Isocrates said that Theopompus needed the curb, but Ephorus the spur. This tends to confirm Archeanassa's story.

I fell in love, dear ladies. All at once, and helplessly, so that overnight my Antimachus slipped from lover to father in my emotions, and my yearning for him ceased. No longer young, though in the prime of life, I was gripped by the passion of a girl: my senses bewildered, my mind obsessed, my body aching for these new embraces, my life beset by weariness. I shut my door to Theopompus, who raged against it fruitlessly, and I ceased to visit poor old Isocrates, who in any case had begun to bore me with his sententious speeches. Literary conversation struck me now as wholly vain, except when it touched upon my new love (which sometimes it did, for he too is a man of letters).

Greatest of shocks, however, was my inconstancy. I had lived as women of my profession must live, studying to enjoy the work of Aphrodite, but in my heart loyal to the gentle Antimachus, with whom, had the fates permitted, I would have spent my days. Indeed, it was the knowledge of this inner loyalty that enabled me to accept my life, to receive the embraces of my lovers and to stay in my heart aloof from them and pure. Now, without warning, I had slipped and fallen – I, the wise one of Colophon, who rivalled even dear Phryne in my mastery over love. All at once I was a ruined woman, dirtied by my past and fearing that I must surely suffer for it.

Nor was I wrong, dear ladies. Smitten, obsessed, consumed as I was, I ran after my love quite shamelessly; waiting for him on every corner, contriving to speak to him, forcing myself on his attention until at last he began to notice me. He was bothered at first, then flustered, and finally hooked. He began to search for me, and was visibly anxious until we were together. Little by little I placed my net around him, using every art and every power that was mine, until at last, having traced him to his lair and made an enticing show of resistance, I conquered him, and lay beneath his body. And what a disappointment, ladies! For, notwithstanding his years, he was unacquainted with love. And when, in my astonishment, I asked him whether he had sought the instruction of dear Phryne, he said, 'Phryne? Phryne? Who on earth is she?'

He was not slow to learn, however. And alas the first thing that he learned was jealousy. Perhaps because he was a newcomer to Aphrodite's joys, perhaps because he had no confidence in his own ability to provide them, he became obsessed with my former loves: Isocrates, for example, and then all the sophists of Athens, with most of whom my relations had been quite innocent. He would lie awake at

night crying 'Alas, that I came too late to save you: alas for me and you!'
I did not tell him of Antimachus, dear ladies, whose memory was still
precious to me; but somehow he found out, so relentless were his
researches. So that my first and most innocent love – my only love but
this one – was dragged before my eyes, anatomized and spat upon.

Now this jealousy over the past is a fruitless and terrible emotion,
ladies. How he made me suffer for it, so that I felt remorse for all
my loves, even for dear Antimachus, so much did he make his pre-
decessors seem like treasons to himself, and prostitutions of my body!

And the more jealous he became, ladies, the greater was his lust. He
would excite me to the highest pitch, and then, taking me to him as his
loving mistress, denounce me contemptuously as a whore. After a
week of that, a girl begins to lose her mind, and if I seem a trifle mad
tonight you will know the reason.

This treatment did not diminish my passion for him: on the
contrary. The more he abused me, the more I craved for his love, and
the more willing I was to succumb to his every whim in the act of it. I
followed him everywhere, tried without success to move into his
house, haunted his precincts, and even – most shameful – crept into
his study during his absence, simply to be where he had been and to
breathe his air. And I too became jealous. Surely, I said to myself,
he will seek to avenge himself by taking another mistress. Only such a
course could assuage him, as well I know. And no sooner had the
thought occurred to me than I noticed indeed how secretive he was,
how all his life save those lustful moments was hidden from me, and
that I had neither the power nor the right – so much had he persuaded
me of my unworthiness – to question him. In my anguish I kept secret
watch on him, hoping to catch a glimpse of my rival and to see my
suspicions confirmed. And, discovering nothing, save that he was
seldom home, I came to believe, not that he was faithful to me, but that
my rival was kept elsewhere.

At last, ladies, I took to sifting through the tablets and papyruses that
lay upon his table. I found nothing at first, and came to the conclusion
that the correspondence between them was kept in some secret place.
But then, today, the truth came finally to light – and the truth, dear
friends, is far more terrible than I had suspected. I discovered a poem,
addressed to my rival, which expresses no love for her, but only lust.
And I saw that, instead of inducing love in him, I had merely
precipitated a base desire for women, which would be satisfied neither

with me nor with her, but must drive him henceforth into untold extremities of destructive passion. Such is the shame that fate prepared for me, the moment my heart ceased to beat for Antimachus. I love a man as ever wife loved husband; he turns my love to lust, and practises this lust upon my rival!

And at this Archeanassa again began to weep, until Phryne, kissing her, bid her drink more wine and declare to the company the contents of her lover's poem. At first Archeanassa staunchly refused; after another goblet, however, she reluctantly agreed to summarize the offending document.

'It begins,' she said, 'by declaring that he does not love this other girl of his; and he goes on to reveal that this lack of love is the premise of his vast desire for her. Then he describes what they do together.'

'And what do they do together?' asked Phryne eagerly.

'All the usual things. But he gets to a certain point, and then . . .'

She faltered slightly and seemed to glance at something within her tunic.

'You've got it with you!' cried Phryne. 'Read it out! Come on!'

'Read it out!' cried the company, most of whom had by now taken more wine than was strictly good for them. Archeanassa hid her face in her hands and mutely protested; taking advantage of her confusion, Phryne snatched the papyrus from her tunic and began to read. As she did so, Archeanassa fell as though dead onto the couch and covered her face with her sleeve.

The Poem

You know I do not love you, for my love is far too rare;
And though I want your body, I have only lust to spare.
Yet every day, recalling it, I long to do again
The senseless act of pleasure, whose consequence is pain.
I come again to see you, where you wait for me alone
In your room of soft abundances, behind the curtains
drawn;
I step enthralled towards you, as you stand with lips apart,
I touch your thrilling body, feel the beating of your heart;
You lean your face towards me, press your cool lips to mine,
And place your gentle fingers in the hollow of my spine.

I kiss your eyes and brow, and play my tongue into your ear;
You do the same to me and then, all trembling as I steer
My hand beneath your robe to feel the crop of bosom there,
You fall against my body, press your thigh against my thigh,
Raise your neck for kisses, and receive them with a sigh!

I put my hand inside the band that holds your robe aloft,
And feel the hair that's growing there, so delicately soft,
While you with eager kisses press your tongue upon my lips
And reach within my *chiton* with exploring fingertips.
Then, finding what excites you, with a gasp of new desire,
You tenderly ignite in me the all-suffusing fire.
Soon we are unbanded, and our clothes are falling fast,
Until you stand before me in your nakedness at last.
Who knows what most delights me: the breasts that swell so
fair,
The full and burnished nipples which electrify the air;
The soft unfurrowed belly, the separated thighs;
The swelling lips between them where the fount of pleasure
lies!

Your tongue explores my body as you sink towards the
ground;
Your mouth slides all about me, till your trembling lips have
found
The emblem of my longing and the source of your delight,
Chief of my possessions, and your most cherished sight
Which – breathing sighs of rapture – you brush your mouth
along
Until you touch the crown of it with palpitating tongue.
You settle down and, panting fast, you spread your
moistened thighs,
Revealing coral lips to my entranced and greedy eyes;
Upon your flowing crevice then I launch the richest
shipment
Of titillating kisses, as you fondle my equipment:
Each plays the other's body, as musicians play the lyre,
Feasting eye and mouth upon the object of desire.
Satyronymphomania, Aristophanes might say –

At any rate, it needs a name, this tragi-comic play
With you the nymph of comedy, and I the tragic goat, as
On your crimson cheek I see the burning φῶς ἔρωτος.[30]

What follows you remember: like me you re-enact
The scenes of greedy passion when you study me erect,
And squeeze and kiss and sigh upon the fascinating part
Which points towards your nether lips and prizes them
                apart.
Most wonderful, however, when I lift you to the couch
And spread your legs asunder with a tantalizing touch;
When, all aglow in ecstasy, you watch my livid staff
And bite your lips with pleasure as it enters: first by half,
And then another inch, until at last it fills the place
Which opens to receive it, and you stare with blushing face,
Raise up your lovely haunches now, and roll your hips
                around,
And press yourself against me with a gentle moaning sound.
I thrust again, another inch, you watch me with surprise
That more of me should still intrude between your
                gleaming thighs!

So pleasure follows pleasure then, as one by one we try
The much-rehearsed suggestions of our eager fantasy:
You raise yourself above me and I lie upon the floor;
You spread along the tapestries, a victim of our war;
You turn upon your stomach, raise your buttocks in the air
And, reaching to my sceptre as it probes your maidenhair,

---

[30] Until reaching this line, I was in considerable doubt as to whether there ever had been a Greek version of Archeanassa's discourse. The Turkish reads thus:

Al yanağının üstünde yanıyor aşkın şulesi.

Şule (whose name means 'flame' and hence 'passion') saw only a reference to herself, a secret message of encouragement, perhaps, from her friend in Istanbul; it was therefore some while before I could return to the manuscript and confirm the hunch which had instantly occurred to me. It was apparent that the line is a direct translation of another, attributed to the early tragedian Phrynichus (whose works have not come down to us): λάμπει δ'ἐπὶ πορφυφέαις παρῃσι φῶς ἔρωτος. ('Upon those crimson cheeks there burns the flame of *eros*'.) I could not refrain from restoring two words of the original, as a tribute to the *aşkın şulesi* which I enjoyed that day.

You guide me to the passage where you moistly open wide
And groan with lustful pleasure as I enter deep inside;
Then thrusting ever faster as your fingers squeeze my sack
I feel the surging rhythm where it drums along your back;
I reach beneath your body now to seize your throbbing
breast
And 'yes,' you cry, 'yes, yes my love, just there, oh there is
best!'
For each desire that's ended, another steps behind,
Imperious as the last desire, and, like the last one, blind.

Well: now the scene is over, and we find some words at last;
I look on you in misery, regretting what has past.
You're hurt – how can I blame you? – and I am all remorse
Until I come again to you: and come I do, of course.

Phryne looked up at the assembled faces, upon all of whom, virgin and harlot, matron and hetaera, a hot flush was glowing.

'Well,' she said at last, clearing her throat. 'We had better have a drink. But before that, Archeanassa, you must tell us the identity of this literary lion, who has eaten up your heart. For we should all feel safer, if we knew how to avoid him.'

Archeanassa slowly lifted the tunic from her face, to reveal a livid countenance.

'Avoid him, ladies,' she cried. 'Avoid him like the Gorgon!'

'Willingly,' said Phryne, who seemed to Arete, nevertheless, to have some other design in mind. 'But we must first know who he is.'

At last, with an effort that visibly shook her, Archeanassa spat out the offender's name:

'Plato!'

Hearing which Lastheneia, who had sat upright and attentive throughout the recital, almost as though she were a student at a lecture, released a yelp of triumph:

'Plato the dramatist! So much for Phryne's victory. I think we know the name of Archeanassa's rival!'

'Plato the dramatist?' cried Archeanassa, 'that second-rate worm-eaten scumbag? What do you take me for? I mean Plato the philosopher!'

Upon which both Phryne and Lastheneia emitted the most piercing shrieks, and launched themselves, claws outstretched, towards the now fiery Archeanassa. For a moment there was pandemonium, as all the women rose to their feet, each remembering some score that she had to settle with another of the guests there. It was not until Castallax seized the *archousa*'s baton and violently rapped the table that there was a lull. Then Lastheneia, fainting into the arms of Arete, was carried back to her couch, while Archeanassa, whom Phryne had pinned to the floor in a wrestler's grip, panted out that there was no finer poet in all of Greece than Plato the dramatist – save only Antimachus perhaps, no, not even Antimachus – and that she envied the good fortune of any woman who could hold in her arms such a sublime concoction of beauty, intelligence, emotion and wit. At which Phryne released her, and all the ladies, dusting their tunics, tottered back to their places at the table. As the uproar died down, and the weeping dwindled to an occasional stifled sob, it was left to Xanthippe to restore the company's equilibrium, which she did with the following words.

XANTHIPPE'S SPEECH

My dear ladies, she said, a great amount of wine has been drunk, and a great many passions have been released among us. And because it is late, and because I have a hard day before me, I will not take much of your time. Nevertheless, there are certain things I must say before I leave this morning, and I see clearly why old Socks told me to come here. Where's that Cleio? Fill my goblet, if you don't mind.

First, let me say a few words to Archeanassa. Although I have met this Plato of yours only once, I think I know him rather better than you do. And lest you should consider me arrogant, I must add that I know him through conversations I had, some with my dear Socrates, and others with Perictione, mother of Potone here and Plato. I will not pass judgment on his poem, except to say that to my way of thinking, such matters should not be written about. However, I doubt that it is the work of Plato himself: the style reminds me a little of Phrynichus – though if it is indeed by him, all I can say is:

Onto the fire with this spittle-spattering reed,
This blabber-bawling enemy of rhythm, rhyme and feet![31]

From the metrical point of view, on the other hand, it recalls the work
of Plato the dramatist, who perhaps helps the philosopher to compose
when his thoughts turn to porn. I will say, none the less, that the
sentiments confirm what I know of Plato the philosopher, who has
from the earliest age found human relationships difficult to enter and
yet more difficult to sustain. He is impetuous in his admiration, and
therefore easily disappointed; affectionate, yet in awe of his own ideal
and frozen in the imagined presence of it. Above all, he is deeply
suspicious of woman, the arch-deceiver as he imagines her; he has
therefore continued to shield himself from the love for which he
hungers, lest – possessing it – he should be destroyed by the
knowledge of its imperfection. That, in my view, explains the poor
boy's theories of the erotic, as Lastheneia expounded them. It explains
his homosexuality, overcome at last, not by philosophy, for all that
Potone says, nor by any stupendous effort of self-denial, but by
Archeanassa here, whose triumph is the truest and greatest that any
woman could know. And this, my dear, explains his poem to you – for,
whether or not Plato the dramatist had a hand in writing it, it is
addressed to you, as surely as was the *Lyde* of Antimachus. As for this
rival, I doubt that you have one, outside your own jealous imaginings.
Unless your rival be Plato himself.

And here, my dear Archeanassa, is how I prove the point. The
attitude of the poet is throughout defensive. He wishes to emphasize
that he is not committed to this woman whom he desires. And to
reinforce the point he makes of his desire a barrier to love, stressing its
bodily aspect, hoping that the soul of the other will not shine through,

---

[31] Further proof that there was once a Greek original of Archeanassa's speech.
Xanthippe is quoting Pratinas, whose *Hyporcheme*, or dance-song, from which these
lines are taken, was directed against Phrynichus. (The song is preserved by
Athenaeus, *Deipnosophistae*, 14, 617b.) The evidence suggests that Pratinas was
writing at the end of the fifth century BC – see Hugh Lloyd-Jones, *Academic Papers*,
vol. I, Oxford, 1990, pp. 225–37 – a conjecture confirmed by Xanthippe's reference.
   Xanthippe is steering close to social disaster; for *phryne* means 'toad' and as Phryne
would doubtless know, Pratinas goes on to make mock of Phrynichus, playing on his
name, as a 'little toad'. On the other hand, given Xanthippe's revulsion towards the
extremes of sensuality practised by Phryne and Archeanassa, it could be argued that
this condensed allusion to Phryne's more repulsive side has a certain artful delicacy.

and the question of love will not be answered, because it remains unasked. He puts the trappings of Aphrodite in the centre of his vision, and displays himself and the woman as actors in a tragi-comic play. It is as though the woman, in order to be fit for his embraces, must first be reduced to her sex, and therefore, in a sense, to nothing. The object of his desire is not a presence, but an absence. And if I were to choose an expression with which to summarize poor Plato's vision of the erotic, I should call it 'the desire and pursuit of the hole'.[32] For it is by this means that he seeks to divorce the act of love from the love that is its motive.

Notice, however, that he does not succeed. The word 'love' breaks through at last, the barrier is pierced, and the soul of the woman shines across in all its vividness. She uses the word as it should be used, expressing in her desire the outward movement of her tender feeling. The poet is led by the very path of lust he treads, to the love that keeps it open. And that is the reason why he promises to visit her again: he hopes to reach the point of confession, to respond as she responds, to utter the words 'my love' as she does, in the very heat of his desire.

Now this, my dear Archeanassa, is as near as Plato could possibly come to a woman, and you would do well to accept the fact, recognizing the great service you do to him and to all mankind, in acquainting the philosopher with your true emotion. That you can cure him of his self-obsession I doubt. And I fear you must suffer for a year or so his dreadful jealousy. But his jealousy too has a comforting side, and gives my final reason for believing the poem to be addressed, my dear, to you. For consider the nature of Plato's jealousy, as you described it. Surely such a jealousy, which focuses severely on the other's body, is the counterpart of the desire expressed in this poem.

---

[32] τῆς τρύπης τῇ ἐπιθυμίᾳ καὶ διώξει. Cf. Plato, *Symposium*, 192E–193A: τοῦ ὅλου οὖν τῇ ἐπιθυμίᾳ καὶ διώξει ἔρως ὄνομα: 'The desire and pursuit of the whole is called *eros*.' Fr. Rolfe, Baron Corvo, in the book which takes its name from this sentence, attributes the thought to Plato. It is uttered, however, by Aristophanes, whose 'whole' is a primal unity, distinguished from that proposed by Castallax largely by being spherical rather than box-like. (The sphere, on the other hand, is Plato's unmistakable hallmark.) As for the influence of Xanthippe on Baron Corvo (or of Baron Corvo on Xanthippe) see H. P. de Selby, 'Holism: its causes and cures', *Epithumia*, XXII, 1983, pp. 108–582. It is possible, too, that a Xanthippic influence should be discerned, in the philosophical books about 'holism' attributed to Jan Smuts. (See again H. P. de Selby, 'Smut and Smuts', *Epithumia*, XXIII, 1984, pp. 5–17.)

Potone and Phryne have shown, in their most interesting speeches, the close connection between jealousy and *eros*. These two emotions focus on a single object, perceiving him as an individual, and endeavouring to grasp him as he is. Hence the character of a man's love is exactly displayed in the mirror of his jealousy. And what is the counterpart of Plato's jealousy, if not the lust described in Plato's poem? Therefore, my dear Archeanassa, take comfort in the fact that you have no rival, and that Plato the dramatist – I mean Plato the philosopher – feels for you and you alone, the thing that he would fain deny is love.

Which brings me to Lastheneia, whose spirit, I fear, is thunder-struck by wine.[33] You should reflect that the love you praised in your speech is one that you may yet obtain from the man who is its object. There is no way that Plato's lust for Archeanassa can possibly impede that higher feeling. Therefore, dear Lastheneia, follow your master's precepts, study to be wise and noble and austere, and he may yet love your soul even if he prefers – as any man in his senses *would* prefer – the body of Archeanassa.

But now, my dears, I hope I may be permitted a few philosophical reflections upon our theme. And I shall begin by remarking on a strange fact, as it seems to me. We are assembled to discuss the power of Aphrodite, and of Eros, her son. And yet our speeches have constantly veered away from the general to the particular, focusing, indeed, on the individual man who is the object of our affections. Funnily enough, the man is usually called Plato. And although Plato the dramatist is presumably distinct from Plato the philosopher, it was not, come to think of it, always so. I remember Perictione telling me they were once inseparably joined by Eros and consecrated their spiritual marriage by taking a common name. Be that as it may, my dears, there is no greater proof of the superiority of women in the matter of love, than our habit of returning to the individual who is its object. And I most heartily agree with Phryne, that the mystery of love lies here: its thought, its desire, and its ambition are inextricably linked with that which is most real and least describable, the individual himself. It is the individual who appears incarnate before us and whom we wish to hold in the flesh; what we can hold in the mind is no individual at all, but at best the incomplete idea of him.

---

[33] The interesting phrase οἴνῳ συγκεραινωθέις φρένας comes from Archilochus: Fr. 120, in I. Tarditi, *Archilochus*, Rome, 1968.

Alas, however, from this mystery stem all our woes: shame and humiliation, jealousy, and the dreadful knowledge that the object of our love is irreplaceable, so that we either love for ever, or love not at all. The one who loves risks everything, and, once betrayed, must either do as Phryne did, burying her innocence, or drift in bewilderment like Archeanassa. And the one who does not love is destined for so grim a solitude, that she had better never have been born. Therefore, dear ladies, it behoves us to discipline the force of Aphrodite, so as to live with it in harmony. And to my way of thinking we do a great wrong when we seek, as Potone seeks, for a right and wrong in love, by looking elsewhere than love itself. Of course it is the human race, and not the individual, that has the greatest interest in Aphrodite. But it is the individual who must think and act, and who is judged accordingly. She therefore has no knowledge in these matters, no certainty in her acts and feelings, until she discovers how her happiness is bound up with her desire. Who would, with foresight, embrace the life of Archeanassa, or suffer the humiliations described by Castallax?

To my way of thinking, ladies, we should distinguish the social function of our emotions, from the benefit and harm that come to us in feeling them. Perhaps it will not come amiss, even in so distinguished a company, if I reflect on this matter. Indeed, I do so the more willingly, in that Potone reminded me of a conversation I once had with my dear husband, concerning honour and shame: the shame of the soul which she so carefully distinguished from the shame of the body. We were discussing military matters, and reminiscing about his campaigns. In his last years he took a lively interest in strategy, developing theory upon theory as to why we lost the war with Sparta. Now as a matter of fact old Socks had a sneaking admiration for Sparta; still has in a way. And often he would return in his thinking to the great days, when we and the Spartans fought side by side for Hellas against the Persians. To his thinking the decisive engagements were not those which ended in victory, but those in which, through honourable defeat, our army prepared itself for sacrifice. This explains, he argued, the importance of Thermopylae. For although the Spartans who defended the pass were overrun, Thermopylae spelled the end to Persian ambition. All Hellas was moved by the tale of this defeat, which inspired a desire in our youth to be worthy of those heroes who obediently and without a murmur had laid down their lives for others. Henceforth Greece was formidable to Persia, and there arose in the Aegean the balance of power that is the foundation of peace.[34]

'But what,' Socrates asked, 'could possibly have motivated the Spartan heroes?'

'Well,' I answered, 'I doubt they had much choice.'

'My dear Xanthippe,' he continued, 'you have not fought in battle, else would you realize that there is always a choice, and a most pressing one. You can stand or flee, face the enemy or turn your back to him. And it is this which determines the outcome of the war.'

'I meant that their upbringing left them with little choice, so great is the shame that the Spartans attach to cowardice. Was it not their poet (their only poet, apart from Cleitagora, to my way of thinking) who said:

It is a fair death, fighting in the front of battle
For the cause of country like the brave to fall;
But to flee his city, his fields of corn and cattle,
And beg! – among man's sorrows, this is worst of all.[35]

'Now you are nearer to the matter, my dear Xanthippe,' he said. 'For this shame that prompts the Spartans even to throw away their lives rather than encounter it: what kind of motive do you suppose it to be?'

'What do you mean, Socrates?'

'I mean, does the Spartan hoplite wish to avoid the reproaches of others, for example?'

---

[34] The concept of a 'balance of power' may have been, as Xanthippe implies, a Socratic (or at any rate Xanthippic) invention. But it is more often attributed to the fourth-century statesman Callistratus. See Werner Jaeger, *Paideia, The Ideals of Greek Culture*, vol. III, Oxford, 1944, p. 26.

[35] Tyrtaeus of Sparta, late seventh century BC: Fr. 10, 1–4, in M. I. West, *Iambi et elegi graeci*, II, Oxford, 1972. I give the translation by F. L. Lucas, *Greek Poetry for Everyman*, London, 1951, p. 235. Tyrtaeus may deserve Xanthippe's description of him as Sparta's only poet apart from Cleitagora (although it is strange that she should fail to mention Alcman); however, Tyrtaeus was probably a native of Aphidnae in Attica, for all his Spartan sentiments. As for Cleitagora, her dates are uncertain; she is mentioned by Aristophanes (*Wasps*, 1245, *Lysistrata*, 1237), being identified as a Spartan poetess, writer of drinking songs, by the scholiast on the second of those lines.

According to Lycurgus, the Attic orator: 'whenever the Spartans take the field under arms, every man has by law to be summoned to the King's tent to hear Tyrtaeus' verses, this being the surest way of making him willing to die for his country.' (*Against Leocrates*, 107.)

'Indeed he does,' I answered.

'But he could do that well enough by escaping from the battle and giving out that he is dead.'

'True, Socks. But his new life, as Tyrtaeus says, would not be very amusing.'

'You think not? Suppose he learned Persian, sold a few military secrets, and settled down, pampered and prosperous, in the flesh-pots of Mesopotamia.'

'All the same,' I said, 'his soul would not be at rest. For he would remember his comrades and the fatherland groaning in slavery.'

'That's more like it, Xanthippe. So it is not the reproaches of others that he fears, but the reproaches of himself?'

'True, Socrates.'

'But a man may reproach himself for many things: for missing a great performance in the theatre; for eating a rotten oyster; for not remembering to take the lentils off the boil. Yet such mistakes do not summon shame in us, nor do we blush to confess them.'

'Indeed, Socrates,' I said; 'and from that we must conclude that the self-reproach of shame is a very special kind of emotion.'

'And what, my dear Xanthippe, do you consider to be the object of this emotion? What is the thought that motivates and focuses our shame?'

Here Phryne stood up, still a little flushed from her wrestling match, and interrupted the speaker.

'Most respected Xanthippe,' she said; 'I beg to suggest that Socrates did not use that language, which belongs to more recent discussions, such as you have been having with Aristotle, and I with Plato – the dramatist, I mean.'

'You may be right, my dear,' the old lady replied; 'but I am entitled to invent my own husband. Besides, when the person you love is dead, he remains present inside you, and you enter a blissful state not unlike the one described by Castallax. Your intimacy is so complete, that the whole of your past can be made and re-made to your common satisfaction. And as I look for words to express my thoughts, behold, no sooner have I discovered them, than they are seized by the Socrates within, who hands them back in delight to his living predecessor. Thus it is that the past becomes present in me, and the present past. Indeed, a great gift is granted to the one whose beloved is dead: she is released from time, just as he is.'

Phryne, impressed by Xanthippe's answer, proposed that the company pour a libation to Socrates; having done which they all drank again deeply from their goblets, with the exception of Lastheneia, who was being sick in a distant corner, and who therefore missed the best part of Xanthippe's speech. (Not that she was in a condition to absorb it.)

So here, dear ladies, Xanthippe went on, is my answer to Socrates.

'The object of shame,' I said, 'is your own dishonour, and shame comes about when a rational being, studying her conduct, sees it as another would, and is filled with disgust.'

'Excellent, my dear Xanthippe,' he said. 'So if we are to understand shame, we must first understand honour?'

'Indeed,' I answered, 'and I think I can make a first step in that direction.'

'And what is that?'

'I would distinguish two kinds of motive: those whose aim is the gaining of pleasure or the avoidance of pain; and those whose aim is honour.'

'And what is the difference between these motives, Xanthippe?'

'The first may be balanced against a motive that conflicts with it. Suppose that by turning left I acquire an amphora of wine, by turning right a box of dried sardines. The question whether to turn left or right is a matter of calculation. Which do I prefer, the wine or the sardines; and by how much? But when my motive is honour, such calculations have no meaning. When a woman is told, go left and you will be whipped, go right and you will be given a thousand drachmas, and also condemned to lie with Diogenes, she will not reckon the pleasure and the pain. It would be dishonourable to lie with Diogenes; therefore she has no alternative, save whipping. If she lies with Diogenes none the less, it is not because she has calculated that this would be to her advantage. It is because she has been *overcome* by desires that do not bear the stamp of her approval, and which silence her reasoning powers – desires like greed and terror. The motive of honour is immune to calculation: it cannot be qualified, but only overcome, and its overcoming is our undoing. It tells us that this deed is impossible, that here all calculation stops. And in telling us this, it fills our life with order: for it offers us a final reason, an end in itself. That, my dear Socrates, is my account of the two motives.'

'Excellent, Xanthippe,' he replied, 'and very much to our purpose. For now we may understand the Spartans at Thermopylae. They were motivated by honour, I think you will agree. And honour commanded that they stand and die. No calculation could recommend such a course. Indeed, from the point of view of your first kind of motive, the pursuit of honour seems quite irrational. For the calculating person, death is the supreme evil, the end of every pleasure; and those who are slaves to calculation could never consider such a course as the Spartan heroes took, until their lives are filled with unbearable pain, when death itself is cowardice.'

'You speak wisely, Socks,' I said; 'and this is yet another way in which reason is in conflict with itself.'

'What do you mean?'

'I mean . . .'

Here Phryne again interrupted the speaker.

'I am most reluctant,' she said, 'to make a fuss, but it does seem to me that there is too much agreement in this dialogue. It is not in the least like your conversations with Socrates, as dear Aeschines used to report them.'

'Is it not?' answered Xanthippe sweetly. 'Then either Aeschines was wrong, or the past has changed sufficiently to make him so. True, I remember some disagreements. But since my husband died we have been on the best of terms, and I can recall none of the details. In any case . . .'

'Sorry,' said Phryne, who again sat down.

'In any case, the truly reasonable person,' I went on, 'is the one who pursues honour, and who is therefore prepared to set aside all calculation, so as to die when honour requires it.'

'How so?' he asked.

'This is how I see it. You will admit, I suppose, that the motive of honour is useful to the society that instils it?'

'Naturally. For what else explains the triumph of the Greeks in general, and of Sparta in particular, during those years of strife and adversity? A society without honour must soon fall prey to chance, tempting its neighbours to pillage and enslave it.'

'But perhaps,' I said, 'something similar is true of the individual life. And here is my reason, Socrates. A rational being will do whatever brings her happiness. But happiness is not a matter of pleasure only; it

260

involves self-esteem, self-harmony, a self-welcoming of one's acts and character. In short, it is given only to the person whose motives are acceptable to herself. Now the honourable action could not conceivably be justified by rational calculation, since it is a kind of defiance of the calculating spirit. But for all that, the *motive* of honour is an immovable part of happiness, and a needed possession of the rational being. Her reason may tell her to acquire the motive, therefore, even if the motive tells her not to reason.'

'Well,' he said, 'I should like to see a proof of the point.'

'So should I,' was my reply. 'But is not friendship a part of happiness?'

'I strongly suspect that it is,' he said.

'And is not honour a part of friendship?'

'You may be right.'

'So there, or somewhere there, is the argument. For I do not say that the Spartans were made happy by Thermopylae. But, being happy before that dread encounter, they needs must have acquired the motive which compelled them to enter it, and so to die.'

And with that we returned to our discussion of strategy.

Now I recall this conversation, ladies, since it forms the background to the thoughts that have occurred to me during our symposium. For what a sea of unhappiness has been spread before us by Phryne, with her story of Peleus; by Potone, recalling her husband's infidelity, and by poor Archeanassa, for whom the very act of love has become the most exquisite spiritual torment, while remaining the greatest of pleasures! It seems, my dear ladies, that the erotic emotions touch far more nearly on our happiness than we may like to suppose. And when we say, without knowing why, that certain desires are bad and others good, we do not mean to refer to their consequences only, but to the desires themselves.

The pleasures of eating and drinking, ladies, contain no judgment on themselves. But the pleasures of Aphrodite are otherwise. I cannot experience them without asking whether they be right or wrong, and without hoping for the divine permission, on which my safety depends. And perhaps nothing more clearly prompts this thought, than the poem addressed to Archaenassa. This poem is the record of an unhappy pleasure: a pleasure obtained in the teeth of shame. And you see how the poor man is in the grip of it, enslaved, burdened, reduced to staring at his own sensations, like Narcissus beside the pool. And were it not for the love of Archeanassa – which he acknowledges in that one sad line – he would fall into his pleasure and drown there, his personality overcome at last by his obsession with the body.

This leads me to another thought, ladies. Decorum is no adjunct to the work of Aphrodite, but part of the work itself. Without decorum, our desire is destructive of love, and therefore of the personality of the lover. The indecorous lover enters the temple of the goddess in chains, enslaved by his lust, neither acknowledging the freedom of the other, nor enjoying a freedom of his own. His desires are at war with the ethical life, since they cause the body to loom ever larger in his thoughts, until it has cancelled the soul that lives in it.

Now Potone may be right, that the shame of the body serves the interest of the species, by prompting us to do what is best for future generations. But in my view shame also serves the interest of the individual, by causing her to put self-interest aside, to rule against degrading pleasures, and to live in the light of her own self-approval. It is the call of honour amid the temptations of the flesh.

Let me conclude, dear friends, with a fragment of my own story, since I have received from Aphrodite only the greatest happiness, and never known the sorrows that have been described around this table. I was eighteen when Socks came to ask my father for my hand in marriage, he being newly widowed and still unable to tie his own sandals or distinguish a lentil from a haricot. I knew the joys of Aphrodite only in imagination, and my desire was to experience them at last with the man I loved, and in the act of loving him. When my father came to tell me that Socrates was thirty years my senior, and lacked every apparent attraction, being neither handsome nor well-connected nor wealthy, I told him to jump off the cliff at Sunium and leave me to my weaving. But when he added that he was also brave and wise and just beyond anyone he had met, I at last agreed to examine my intended's *curriculum vitae*. And discovering that he was a tramp and a layabout, who spent his days in conversation and fancied himself a philosopher, I consented to meet the ogre. And behold, no sooner had I come into the room, where he was pacing nervously up and down, muttering to himself and wiping his filthy great hands on his sweat-covered tunic, than I laughed at my foolishness and thought what a lovable buffoon this was my father had picked up in the Agora. And by the time Socrates had opened his mouth, ladies, and revealed that he was not a buffoon at all, but a passable literary critic with a cranky side-line in politics, I was head over heels in love. I wanted to close those ever-moving lips with a kiss. But since this was not allowed, I resorted instead to argument, and proved to him, who was nervously spouting Homer and banging on about the manly ideals of the old Ionic culture, that Homer was in fact a woman, and that the true heroine of the *Iliad* is Andromache, just as Penelope, as all of you know, is the central character of the *Odyssey*. He liked this so much, my dears, that he stole a march on convention, and treated me then and there to the kiss I coveted. We never looked back, and in all our days together the work of Aphrodite remained one with our constant dialogue. When he died, there was no question of my losing him. For we were joined eternally, and our marriage was merely the public recognition of our indestructible bond. Between us there was neither shame nor jealousy, but only the comfortable sense of mutual responsibility and mutual love.

And although I am full of vices, dear ladies, being mean, hasty and often afraid, I know that one part of me at least is virtuous, the part that Aphrodite gave. That part was schooled to respond to my beloved, and to none but him. And when it responded, it was fully and faithfully, without a trace of shame. That is what I mean by chastity: not the frigid refusal advocated by Pythagoras, but the fullness of desire, towards the right object, on the right occasion, and in the right degree. If we care for our children's happiness, it is such a habit of desire that we must plant in them, shielding them as much from the plight of Archeanassa, as from the perverted pleasures that have hardened the heart of Plato the dramatist – or was it Plato the philosopher? If these chaste desires find their goal in marriage, it is not for the sake of future generations, but for the sake of Aphrodite herself, from whose pleasures, rightly felt and duly ordered, a temple of safety arises.

But now, ladies, lest you think I have cast aspersions on your great profession, let me retreat a little from my moralizing. Our happiness on earth cannot be guaranteed, but only rendered more probable, by the education of our passions. And so great is the force of Aphrodite that even our best attempts to govern it may meet with failure. Therefore we do well to hesitate before we condemn another's pleasure. Rather than reprove the imagined criminal, we should reflect on the many ways in which the soul may lift itself from its earthly prison, and the many avenues, even in the most sordid pit of human appetite, to the higher world of love. Therefore let us keep before our minds the vision of Lastheneia, not because it is true, but because it reminds us of the mystery of our condition, and holds a light through all our darkest passages. For even in the worst predicament there is yet a remedy, which is the divine path of renunciation, leading us high above this petty world, to see it in the mirror of eternity. That, my dear ladies, was what old Socks was saying in the prison, when we sang together that wonderful song by Stesichorus; you know – the one that goes[36] . . . hello, what's that smell?

Looking round the table in alarm, Arete saw that many of the company were wrinkling their noses and murmuring against poor Castallax, who was promptly ordered to the kitchen. But the smell remained, and the rosy light of morning, which was stealing across the courtyard in search of sleepless miscreants, fell upon Xanthippe's face like an accusing finger, lighting with the colour of shame those pale old features, and causing another light to dawn in her soul.

'The anchovies!' she shrieked.

And bounding from the table to the place where they had been stowed, she prized open the box, beginning to sort through the fishes in search of those that were rotting. Soon she had made a most obnoxious pile of flesh upon the marble.

'Sorry about this, ladies, but I won't be a moment.'

Scraping up the stinking fish with a bowl, she dropped it into the cringing hands of Cleio, who ran shrieking from the room. The old lady took the box beneath her arm and walked hastily to the door where, turning to the company, she made the following farewell:

'I shall have to sell these before the first boat-loads come up from the Piraeus. I will therefore take leave of you, my dears, and bid you praise the goddess, queen of well-built Cyprus,[37] for whose sake we have been assembled. But as for whether she is best honoured in marriage, or in the excitement of a secret liaison, or in the hopeless passion of the forlorn hetaera, I leave it for you to judge. The wise woman is the one who seeks to love where love is granted. The unwise woman is she who falls for Plato the self-dramatist, and who finds that

---

[36] Ammianus Marcellinus (*History*, xxi, 4) confirms the story that Socrates spent some of his last hours learning a song by Stesichorus; he does not add that it was Xanthippe who taught him.

[37] Homeric *Hymn to Aphrodite*, 292.

the other whom she loves recognizes no other, but only the universal, which is but a pompous name for the self.'

'Well,' said Phryne, when Xanthippe had left, 'and not a word of thanks for the wine! But come, ladies, and do you also come to the table, dear Lastheneia, so that we may cease to study how best to live with this thing called Plato, and attend instead to our immortal souls. For in the vast calm of the breathing universe, how small is the troubled corner filled by man!'

And she sighed wearily, as did all the ladies save Perictione, who clapped her hands for the flute girl and welcomed the morning with a dance.

'Such, my dear Phrasiclea, were the speeches at Phryne's symposium, as Arete recounted them. And now the sun is declining and we too must leave our hospitable table if we are to reach your aunt before nightfall.'

'Indeed you are right, Damareta,' I said, and thanked her with a kiss for entertaining me.

'And is it true, as I have heard,' she asked, 'that your aunt has a son, who lives with her and practises the art of poetry?'

'Indeed she has,' I said, 'and a most charming fellow too.'

'Then let us go quickly,' said she, 'and on the way I shall tell you another story of Xanthippe.'

'Which story?'

'Did you not know that it was she who wrote that brilliant parody of Euripides called *The Sophists*, which Plato the dramatist had the impertinence to claim as his?'

'I don't believe it!'

'You don't believe it?' she said. 'Then listen to my story.'

And with a laugh she jumped before me into the chariot.

FINIS

Phryne's Symposium
and the Characters Portrayed in It

It is difficult to assign a consistent dramatic date to Phryne's symposium, though we might hazard 360 BC, when Plato was in his sixties and Xanthippe well over seventy. (It should be remembered that the symposium was an established literary form in fourth-century Athens, with several instances, besides those of Plato and Xenophon, still extant: see J. Martin, *Symposium: Geschichte einer literarischen Form*, Paderborn, 1931, and Oswyn Murray, ed., *Sympotica*, Oxford, 1990.) Certain of the *dramatis personae* are mentioned elsewhere in the classical sources, and I briefly summarize here what I have been able to discover about them:

PHRASICLEA: a stone inscription, discovered in Cyrene, and dating from the fourth century BC, forbade sexual congress during the hours of daylight. Recent excavations have uncovered a tablet, inscribed with the names of those condemned for breaking this law: a certain Phrasiclea heads the list. See H. P. de Selby 'Libyan Libertines', *Epithumia* XXVI, 1987, pp. 46–89.

ARETE: daughter of Aristippus, pupil of Socrates, and mother of Aristippus 'the mother-taught'. Aristippus was a hedonist, notorious for his pleasure-loving way of life (see, for example, Xenophon, *Memorabilia*, 2.1; St Augustine, *Civ. Dei*, 18, 41a). For a while, much to Plato's annoyance, Aristippus was court philosopher to Dionysius I of Sicily. He returned in later life to Cyrene, where, as one scholarly tradition has it, he founded the Cyrenaic school of philosophical hedonism. A rival tradition credits Aristippus the younger with this great achievement, of founding a school of which posterity knows next to nothing. (Though see the attempts at reconstruction by G. Giannantoni, *I Cirenaici*, Florence, 1958.) A further tradition, weighing all the evidence, and judiciously assessing the entire controversy, concludes that we cannot know whether the Cyrenaic school was founded by Aristippus *grand-père* or Aristippus *petit-fils* (see, e.g. E. Mannebach, *Aristippi et Cyrenaicorum fragmenta*, Leiden, 1961, p. 88.) The self-evident fact is that the school was founded by Arete: why else was the epithet 'mother-taught' (μητροδίδακτος) applied to her son, stupid ass though he no doubt was? Some sources claim that Plato visited Cyrene in his wanderings: though surely it was neither Aristippus nor Arete who attracted him. (See W. K. C. Guthrie, *A History of Greek Philosophy*, Cambridge, 1971, vol. III, pp. 14–16.)

ARISTIPPUS: see above, under Arete.

LASTHENEIA OF MANTINEA: referred to also by Diogenes Laertius, as one of two female pupils at Plato's Academy, at least one of whom was in the habit of wearing men's clothes. (Diogenes Laertius, III, 46.) Lastheneia is mentioned in another ancient source: the papyrus fragment from Oxyrhynchus, *P. Oxy.* 3656, which suggests that her behaviour at Phryne's symposium was far from typical. (See Mary Lefkowitz, *Women in Greek Myth*, London, 1986, p. 144.)

XANTHIPPE: see *Xanthippe's Republic* and *Xanthippe's Laws*, which are the most authoritative extant records of this intriguing character.

PHRYNE: famous courtesan of the fourth century BC, said to hail from Thespiae in Boeotia, where a statue of her existed, made by her lover Praxiteles. (See Pausanias, *Description of Greece*, 9, xxvii, 3.) The sculptor is also said to have taken Phryne as a model for his famous statue of Aphrodite in the temple at Cnidus – a statue so full of erotic power that at least one youth came to grief, if pseudo-Lucian is to be believed, through attempting to have intercourse with it (see Pseudo-Lucian, *Erotes*, 15, 16). Yet another statue of Phryne, this one gilded, could be seen at Delphi. According to Pausanias (10, xv, 1) this statue was dedicated by Phryne herself, although others say that it was a gift to the god from her admirers. There is even a Hellenistic portrait of Phryne in bronze, to be seen to this day in the museum at Corfu.

However attractive she may have been in marble, gilt or bronze, however, Phryne was yet more impressive in the flesh. On one occasion she was defended in court by her lover Hypereides, pupil of Isocrates, and author of a polemic against Demosthenes. In order to clinch the argument, he arranged for Phryne to bare her breasts at the climax of his speech. With this conclusive refutation of all conceivable criticism, she was acquitted. (The story exists in two versions: Pseudo-

Plutarch, *Hypereides*, 849E; Athenaeus, 13, 591E.) The precise charge against Phryne is not certain: though like Socrates she was arraigned under the general accusation of 'impiety'. It could well be that her usurpation of the masculine institution of the symposium came at last to the attention of the authorities, thus leading to her prosecution.

It is perhaps churlish to point out that Phryne is unlikely to have been the lover of Praxiteles and Hypereides and also a sexually active woman during the last days of Xanthippe. This is one of several anachronisms in *Phryne's Symposium* which detract, to my mind, from its value as a historical document. Of course, it is always possible that Phryne had a predecessor of the same name.

POTONE: Diogenes Laertius confirms that Plato had a sister of this name (III, 4). He also recounts that Potone was mother of Speusippus, who was to succeed Plato as head of the Academy in 347 BC, and who travelled with Plato on his last visit to Sicily. Other ancient sources reveal that Potone's husband was called Eurymedon; none, so far as I can discover, makes mention of a daughter to the marriage.

PERICTIONE: on Perictione the elder, see *Perictione's Parmenides*. I have been unable to discover any other reference to Perictione the younger, apart from that in Pamphila's *Memorabilia* (76, iii), which mentions a Xanthippic dialogue between Perictione and Archeanassa, set in Colophon.

CASTALLAX: mentioned also in *Perictione's Parmenides*, which seems to confirm both Castallax's unpopularity with the children of Perictione's household, and the fact of her unpleasant smell.

ARCHEANASSA of COLOPHON: mentioned in the famous poem attributed to Plato (see preface to this edition), and also by Pamphila, *Memorabilia*, 76, iii (see above, under Perictione). It is worth pointing out that another version of Plato's poem exists, which some scholars suppose to be a fictitious grave-inscription by the Alexandrian Asclepiades, the first two words ('Αρχέανασσαν ἔχω) really meaning 'I contain Archeanassa', and being spoken by her tomb. If this view (defended by A. S. F. Gow and Denys Page, *Hellenistic Epigrams*, pp. 88 and 144–5) were true, then the poem must have been remodelled at a later date, in order to give credence to the story that Plato picked up a girl on holiday in Colophon. Rather than pursue these preposterous speculations, however, I refer the reader to Sosipatra's discussion of the disputed third line of Plato's poem in her *Discourse on Amatory Verse*, 102A – a source unaccountably overlooked by Gow and Page. (See also H. P. de Selby, 'Page upon Page', *Epithumia*, XIII, 1975, pp. 457–2764.)

PLATO the DRAMATIST, generally known as Plato Comoedius: ancient sources attribute twenty-eight comedies to this writer, who was probably also the inventor of 'tragi-comedy', as well as a leading exponent (in the second part of his long literary career) of the Middle Comedy. Ancient critics commented on his elegance, and also on his obsession with erotic matters, which he would often treat in a scurrilous way. His dates are not precisely known, but he was certainly an established writer by the time of the Lenaean competition referred to in *Perictione's Parmenides*. He must therefore have been older than Plato the philosopher; and it is certainly anachronistic to suppose that he could have been the lover of Phryne. Nevertheless, oblique references in *Perictione's Parmenides* seem to confirm the theory (suggested here by Xanthippe) that the two Platos were once lovers, a fact that has something to do with the mystery of their common name. There are 269 fragments of Plato's work in Kock, *Fragmenta comicorum graeci*, from which we learn that there was indeed, among the plays attributed to Plato, a parody of Euripides, entitled *The Sophists*.

Index

compiled by H. P. de Selby.

Alexander, Bill, theatre producer, 10

alienation, affliction of self-proclaimed aliens, 96–8

Anscombe, G.E.M., philosopher, enjoys claret, 153, 164

Arnold, Matthew, inspector of schools, 54

Atatürk, Kemal, soldier and statesman, liked women and drink, 176

Austen, Jane, averse to music (cf. Kant (qv), Samuel Johnson and Evelyn Waugh) and to strong drink (contrast Johnson and Waugh), 200

Beauchet, Ludovic, classical scholar, 156n

beauty, self-abusing concept in aesthetics, 50, 68–9, 196, 197f, 221

Benecke, E.F.M., romantic scholar, related to Mendelssohn, 180

Bentham, Jeremy, jurist, philosopher and moral *ingénu*, 256, 259f

Bernal, Martin, author of *Black Athena*, 7

Bloom, Allan, humanist and scholar, now dead, 21, 67

Bloom, Harold, tripe as trope, 16, 191–2

Bloom, Leopold, see Flower, Henry

Bonhoeffer, Dietrich, German priest and martyr, 145f

Bradley, A.C., Shakespeare critic, did not sin with Elinor Glyn, let alone on a tiger-skin, 52

Bradley, F.H., philosopher, brother of A.C., perhaps did, 47

Brentano, Franz, founder of Austrian philosophy, 258

Buber, Martin, Jewish theologian, philosopher and rhapsode, 164

Burke, Edmund, posthumous convert to conservatism, 26f, 36, 89f, 142f

Calame, Claude, classical scholar and dancing master, 66n

Carroll, Lewis (pseud), set to music by David del Tredici, 68

Cavafy, Constantine, re-inventor of Alexandria, 2

Cave, The, allegory with many meanings, 24–5, 26ff, 148–9

Cellini, Benvenuto, top people's cutler, killed a man in the *piazzetta del Biscione*, 56

censorship, the ship that's always at sea, 21

chastity, form of temperance, 263

citizenship, perennial mystery, 33–4, 36

civil society, understood when lost, 33–4, 128–44, 157

Clark, Sir Kenneth, good on the

Gothic Revival and the Nude, later Lord Clark of Civilisation, 56

Clausewitz, Karl von, strategist, always misapplied, 256–7

Cohn, Norman, American social historian, scourge of chiliasm, 89–90

common law, God's gift to the English, 133–5, 137

constitution, a mistake when written down, 115f

Croce, Benedetto, Neapolitan philosopher, adored shellfish, 34–5, 52

dancing, a disappearing art, 66f, 69–71

Dante Alighieri, Italian poet, views on erotic literature, 177

Darwin, Charles, pigeon fancier, 159f, 167

Davies, M., classical scholar, 228n

death, imminent prospect an incentive to most worthwhile endeavour, 147f, 167, 168, 180

decorum, lost virtue of architecture, 262

democracy, creator of Margaret Thatcher, 14, 20

de Selby, H.P., creation of Flann O'Brien, 18n, 175n, 195n, 254n, 267, 270, 272

desire, a state of mind, 78–9, 80f, 195

desire, sexual, rare among philosophers, 82f, 194f, 218–222, 232–3, 253f

'Derrida, Jacques', always *entre guillemets*, 7, 16, 25

Dicey, Albert Venn, jurist and historian, 137f

Dillon, John, classical scholar, 156n

Dilthey, Wilhelm, neo-Kantian philosopher, 150–4, 165–6

Disraeli, Benjamin, Earl of Beaconsfield, author of *Tancred*, 86, 89

Dodds, E.R., encounter with bedmaker, 122

Douglas, Norman, hedonist, knew everyone, 1f

Durkheim, Emile, sociologist, son of a rabbi, 87–90, 146, 167

Durrell, Lawrence, failed diplomat, 2

Edmonds, J.M., failed classical scholar, 66n

education, the pursuit of irrelevance, 31–5, 50f, 131, 140, 170, 188–9, 214, 215, 237, 263

Eliot, T.S., admired F.H. Bradley (qv), 60

emotion, state of mind, 153f, 165

equality, disconsolate chimera, 20f, 38, 118–9

equity, available to all who come with clean hands, 139

eternity, the destiny of all, whatever the state of their hands, 168–9, 197–8, 200, 258, 259

family, from Latin, *famulus*, a slave, 34–6, 97f, 120–1, 139–40, 171–2

Feuerbach, Ludwig, Young Hegelian philosopher, 89, 92

Fichte, J.G., posited by Fichte, 163

fidelity, achieved by photographs, 193, 194, 199, 231–3, 246

Field, G.C., classical scholar, 198n

Finley, Sir Moses, classical scholar, 156n

Flower, Henry, see Bloom, Leopold

Foucault, Michel, corrupter of the youth, 7, 15

Fourier, F.M.C., utopian social reformer, 46, 64, 81, 90, 92, 95

freedom, metaphysical, a conundrum, 153f, 162, 163–5, 168

Freeman, Kenneth, classical scholar, never complained, 119, 180

Frege, Gottlob, upset by Russell (qv), 70, 80

Freud, Sigmund, attended lectures by Brentano (qv), 47f, 70, 93–4

gardening, popular response to socialism (qv), 106

Giannantoni, G., classical scholar, 267

Gierke, Otto von, German jurist, somewhat *völkisch*, 156

Goethe, J.W.F. von, supported Fichte (qv), 180

Goodman, Nelson, nominalist philosopher, uninfluenced by Fichte, 70–1, 151

Gould, John, classical scholar, 12n

Gow, A.S.F., classical scholar, with suspicious connections, 269f

Griswold, Charles, American philosopher, disturbed by Plato's bed, 15f, 101–2

Guthrie, W.K.C., ancient historian – in fact dead, 155n, 268

happiness, obtained by Xanthippe, 260–3

Havel, Václav, Central European hero, widely acknowledged, 157

Hayek, Friedrich von, Central European hero, widely

unacknowledged, 92, 129–40, 144

Hegel, G.W.F., died of cholera, 28–9, 35–6, 82, 89, 90–2, 143–4, 146, 156–7, 220

Heidegger, Martin, prestidigitator, 43, 62, 91n

Henderson, Jeffrey, American classical scholar, 54n

Hind, Egyptian archaeologist, 3–7, 118

Holford-Strevens, Leofranc, classical scholar with remarkable name, 8

homosexuality, no longer a badge of sophistication, 25n, 82, 234, 253

honour, interesting name for a girl, 141–2, 256–62

Hope-Dingwood, Littleton, another remarkable name, 175–6, 235n

Horkheimer, Max, low-calorie (*nähwertarm*) frankfurter, 217

Horsfall, Bernard, distinguished actor and motorcyclist, 10

Hume, David, successful diplomat, 89

Husserl, Edmund, a transcendental ego, 36, 162, 163

imagination, the path from fantasy to reality, 166

imitation, the path to virtue (qv), and hence the sincerest form of flattery, 36, 50

individuality, not possessed by cucumbers, 34–6, 164–6, 168, 197, 220–2, 232–3, 255f

infanticide, a man's right to choose, 215, 237

Jaeger, Werner, German classical scholar, liked horses, 257

Jackson, Michael, a graven image, 108

jealousy, impossible to express in music, 220f, 225, 232f, 246f, 254f

Jefferson, Thomas, owned slaves, 22

Jefferies, Richard, exponent of decision theory, 259

Jones, Ernest, hagiographer, 57ff

Jowett, Benjamin, Master of Balliol, 73n

Just, Roger, classical scholar, 12n, 201n

justice, possible to express in music, 130, 135–9, 148–9, 154–5, 207, 223, 229–31

Kant, Immanuel, disliked music, 88ff, 154–5, 162–7, 221–2

Kierkegaard, Søren, the erotic in music, 18, 25, 36, 72

Klein, Melanie, emphatic believer in original sin, 81–2, 90

knowledge, philosophy's most tedious concept, reputedly co-extensive with the intellectual acquisitions of Jowett (qv), 16f, 22, 104–5, 112–14, 122

Kock, T., German classical scholar, 181, 270

Laplace, Pierre Simon, Marquis de, hypothetical French scientist, not needed by God, 160

language, mine meta than yours, 88, 113

law, unreliable in warm climates, 33, 114–17, 120f, 124–9, 137–9, 144f, 155, 158

Leavis, F.R., hostile to classical scholars, 18, 53, 210

Lenin, V.I., (pseud.), once had a city named after him, 31–9, 157

Lefkowitz, Mary, American classical scholar, 268

legislation, usually a mistake, 137–40

Leigh-Fermor, Patrick, conscience of the Mediterranean, 1f

Lloyd-Jones, Sir Hugh, classical scholar, married to Mary Lefkowitz (qv), 253

Lobel, Edgar, killjoy, 66

Locke, John, disciple of Gassendi, 161

Loti, Pierre, French writer, made love in a fez, 176

love, absent from the works of Lukács and Sartre (qqv), 34–6, 106f, 110, 142, 165, 193, 194–9, 231, 233, 246f, 254f, 262–3

love, Aristophanic, 236–41

love, Platonic, not what it seems, 195–8, 234–5, 255, 263–4

Love, Patti, distinguished actress, not in alphabetical order, 10

Lucas, F.L., poet and translator, hostile to Leavis (qv), 257

Ludwig, Walter, German classical scholar, 7 (unless it was Snell (qv)), 21n

Lukács, György, cultural commissar, 15, 36–9, 258

lust, also absent from the works of Lukács (qv), 219f, 248–51, 254

Lynch, J.N., classical scholar, 156n

Machler, Herwig, German classical scholar, 232n

McTaggart, J.M., refuses to lie down, 71, 73–4

Mannebach, F., German classical scholar, 268

Mao-Tse-Tung, admired by Sartre (qv), 31–2

market, place of celebration, 45, 129–33, 157

marriage, not always a mistake, 262f

Martin, J., classical scholar, 267

Marx, Karl, essential reading, 15, 89, 91–2, 118, 157

Marxism, distinguishes essence from appearance, 36–9

masks, show essence as appearance, 54–5, 152, 155, 161–2

mathematics, the study of essence, 76–7, 93–5, 112, 121

medicine, the restoration of appearances, 124–5

Merleau-Ponty, Maurice, encounter with elephant, 222

Milton, John, marriage sometimes a mistake nevertheless, 153

Moltmann, Jürgen, German theologian, 87f

music, pop, see pop music

music, real, disliked by Kant and Jane Austen (qqv), 67

natural law, still believable, 128–40

Nietzsche, Friedrich, no longer believable, 22, 57–8, 122

Noh, the art of veiled negation, 54–5

Notopoulos, J.A., classical scholar, 51n

Nussbaum, Martha, why so aggressive, 253

Oakeshott, Michael, why so gentle, 27–8, 142–4

original sin, known among the Japanese?, 87, 91–2

Orwell, George (pseud.), prophet, 38

Page, Sir Denys, classical scholar, averse to noise, 269f

Peirce, C.S., American philosopher, amazed by moths, 70

personality, in which poetry, law, morality and religion conspire, 155–6, 161–2, 207, 262

pictures, forbidden by Muhammad, 150–2, 158, 161, 166

poetry, Ar: *ash'ar*, from root *sha'ara*, to know; derivative *sha'aara*, goats, 17–18, 36, 53–9, 86, 141f, 168f, 179–81, 252

Polanyi, Michael, Hungarian philosopher and scientist, to be sharply distinguished from his brother Karl, 90, 144

police, secret, encouraged by Karl, reviled by Michael, 123–4, 130, 134

pop music, approved by neither Polanyi, 21, 67, 107–8, 109n, 121f

Popper, Sir Karl, approved by Michael, 36–9

prayer, disapproved by Karl, 167, 215, 217

price, Karl's erroneous theory of, 129f, 132, 136f, 186–7

property, why the brothers fought, 38, 117f

prostitution, widespread in Hungary, 184, 186–7, 215, 263

Proust, Marcel, never visited Hungary, 253

Quine, W.V., American philosopher, no reference found

rape, oleaginous crop, much cultivated by the Red Army, 207

rationality, distinct from rationalism, especially that of the Red Army, 32–3, 64, 68–9, 80f 83f, 88, 90–2, 113, 121, 140ff, 153–8, 161, 163–6, 197–9, 220f, 233f, 259f

Rawls, John, American philosopher, said to be partial to the xylophone, 139

reason, ability to survive *delirium tremens*, see: rationality

religion, *tantum potuit suadere malorum*, 84–90, 122f, 145f, 158–9, 166–9

responsibility, not to quote from Lucretius without translating, 153–5, 164–5

rhetoric, useful in bed, 193, 198n, 245

Rilke, Rainer Maria, the only begetter, 158–9, 166–7

Robespierre, Robespierre, lost his head, 37

Rolfe, Frederick, 'Baron Corvo', lost his bearings, 254n

Rousseau, Jean-Jacques, inventor of Newspeak, 38

rule of law, known through its absence, 115–16

rules, a mystery, 97–8, 127, 139

Russell, Bertrand, Earl Russell, saw through Lenin (qv), 70, 80, 91n

St Just, L. de, French revolutionary, 31, 37

Sarambus, wine merchant, 118

Sartre, Jean-Pol-Pot, 79, 91n, 220, 222

scandal, distinguished from knowledge, 104–5, 122, 191, 207

Schaps, David M., classical scholar, 208n

Schelling, F.W.J. von, posited by Fichte (qv), 92

Schiller, Friedrich, supported Fichte (qv), 126, 141–2

Schleiermacher, F.D.E., interpreter of Plato, who proved the impossibility of interpretation, 52

Schopenhauer, Arthur, kept a revolver by his bed, 230, 232–5

Schubert, Franz, spurred on by death (qv), 180

Schüler, Charlotte, vanished scholar, 5

science, also spurred on by death (qv), 150, 159–62, 165

sculpture, condemned by Muhammad, 55–6, 223, 268

sentimentality, the ruin of Arab politics, 18

Shakespeare, William, on the form of the second-best bed, 20, 57–63, 74

shame, gift of the gods, 223, 230, 256–62

Shoemaker, Sydney, American philosopher, no friend to cobblers, 162f

Simmel, Georg, German sociologist, may have known Charlotte Schüler (qv), 184, 186–7, 217

Smautf, no reference found

Smith, Adam, relations with butcher and baker, 129–40, 144, 145f

Smuts, Jan, easily removed from memory by means of patent solvent 'PC', 254

Snell, Bruno, German classical scholar, 7 (unless it was Ludwig (qv)), 232n socialism, not much fun, 20, 118–20, 140 (in education), 144

soul, a mistake of grammar, 86, 147–9, 152–4, 161, 162–6, 198–9, 265

Spinoza, Benedict, liked beer, 115

state, including Spinoza's theory of, 14, 23ff, 36–9, 114–40, 143–4

Stendhal (pseud.), French novelist, 210–11

Strauss, Leo, his amazing influence compared with David, Johann (elder), Johann (younger), and Richard, 25

Strawson, Sir Peter, admiration for Marvell's Horatian Ode, 164

Stucchi, Sandro, Italian archaeologist, 183n

Şule, Turkish dragoman, 177, 250n

Surtees, R.S., lost voice of England, 208

Tarditi, I., Italian classical scholar, 255n

Tarski, Alfred, his disturbing theorem not mentioned, 72, 150

Tönnies, Ferdinand, German sociologist, 135

Troyes, Chrétien de, still relevant, 63

truth, self-effacing concept of metaphysics, 22, 36, 50, 63, 86f, 113, 150, 168, 193, 222

universals, exemplified by

cucumbers, 17f, 24f, 195, 197–8, 200, 221, 232–3, 265

value, self-defeating concept of ethics, 75–8, 140–3, 166, 261–3

virtue, whether possible in women, 33–4, 75, 88, 116–18, 129f, 141, 144, 187, 219f, 221f, 256–63

Wagner, Richard, use of triads, 63

weaving, Penelope's art, 107, 113, 114–17, 120f, 142

Weber, Max, spoilsport, 158

Weinribb, E., American jurist, 135

West, Martin, I., classical scholar, 57n, 257n

White, Donald, American archaeologist, 183n

Wiggins, David, philosopher of substance, 88

Wilamowitz-Moellendorf, Ulrich von, hostile to Nietzsche (qv), 156

Wilde, Oscar, inconceivable in Arabic, 57, 72, 165

Winkler, J.J., American classical scholar, overrated by Martha Nussbaum (qv), 25n

Wittgenstein, Ludwig, encounter with Leavis (qv), 88, 150f, 162, 164

Yeats, W.B., last champion of beauty (qv), 70

Zimmern, Alfred, classical scholar, enjoyed apricots, 201n